Академия наук
СССР

National
Academy of Sciences
of the USA

АНГЛО-РУССКИЙ
И
РУССКО-АНГЛИЙСКИЙ
СЛОВАРИ МАТЕМАТИЧЕСКИХ ТЕРМИНОВ

ENGLISH-RUSSIAN
AND
RUSSIAN-ENGLISH
DICTIONARIES OF MATHEMATICAL TERMS

RUSSIAN-ENGLISH DICTIONARY

OF THE

MATHEMATICAL SCIENCES

by

A. J. LOHWATER

WITH THE COLLABORATION OF

S. H. GOULD

Under the joint auspices of

THE NATIONAL ACADEMY OF SCIENCES OF THE USA
THE ACADEMY OF SCIENCES OF THE USSR
THE AMERICAN MATHEMATICAL SOCIETY

Published by

THE AMERICAN MATHEMATICAL SOCIETY

Providence, Rhode Island

1961

The author and publisher acknowledge Grants NSF-G6771 and NSF-G7136
made by the National Science Foundation
in connection with the preparation of this volume.

Printed in the United States of America

Library of Congress Catalog Card Number 61-15685

МАТЕМАТИЧЕСКИЙ ИНСТИТУТ им. В.А. СТЕКЛОВА
АКАДЕМИИ НАУК СССР

АНГЛО-РУССКИЙ СЛОВАРЬ МАТЕМАТИЧЕСКИХ ТЕРМИНОВ

ИЗДАТЕЛЬСТВО ИНОСТРАННОЙ ЛИТЕРАТУРЫ
МОСКВА, 1961 г.

CONTENTS

FOREWORD

In June and July of 1956 Professor N. E. Steenrod of Princeton University and the author comprised the American delegation to the Third All-Union Congress of Soviet Mathematicians held in Moscow. In the friendly atmosphere which prevailed at that Congress, it was natural that questions of exchange and contact between mathematicians should be discussed. Among the ideas brought up there, the question of joint collaboration on Russian-English and English-Russian scientific dictionaries seemed to hold the most promise of tangible results to the American scientific community. Following an exchange of letters between Detlev Bronk, President of the National Academy of Sciences of the U.S.A., and A. N. Nesmeyanov, President of the Soviet Academy of Sciences, committees of mathematicians were appointed to represent the two academies. The Soviet committee consisted of P. S. Alexandrov (Chairman), I. R. Shafarievich, M. M. Postnikov, A. F. Leontiev and A. A. Dezin, while the American committee consisted of S. H. Gould, A. J. Lohwater and G. I. Rainich. Later the Soviet committee was augmented by the appointment of L. N. Bolshiev, S. M. Nikolskii, E. D. Solomentsev, V. S. Vladimirov and L. D. Kudryavtsev, who acted as executive vice-chairman.

On 10 September 1958 representatives of the two committees met in the Steklov Institute in Moscow to discuss the preparation of the dictionary. At this meeting essential agreement was reached on the areas of coverage, the means of communication and collaboration between the two committees, and the eventual publication of the dictionary. The Russian-English half of the dictionary would be published in the United States by the American Mathematical Society while the publication of the English-Russian half would be undertaken by the Soviet Academy of Sciences. The guiding principle in the preparation of the dictionary was that a person using the dictionary would be able to read virtually any publication reviewed either in *Referativnii Zhurnal Matematika* or in *Mathematical Reviews* without the aid of any other dictionary. It was agreed that before publication the manuscripts of the two parts of the dictionary would be exchanged and commentary made on each by the committee of the other side. By January 1960 the compilation of both parts of the dictionary had been completed and the manuscripts had been exchanged for mutual criticism. The work of incorporating Soviet suggestions for improvement in the American part of the dictionary was completed ten months later, in November.

The present volume is intended for use in reading papers and books at any level in mathematics and theoretical physics, and a short grammar of mathematical Russian precedes the vocabulary of the dictionary. Since there is no clear dividing line between 'pure' mathematics and 'applied' mathematics, no effort was made during the compilation to limit the vocabulary to 'more desirable' areas of mathematics, and the vocabulary carries a useful, but not necessarily complete, coverage of the following branches of theoretical physics:

Astrophysics	Hydrodynamics
Atomic spectra	Information theory
Biophysics	Magnetism
Celestial mechanics	Molecular spectra
Classical mechanics	Particle accelerators
Computer science	Physical optics
Cosmic ray theory	Plasticity
Electromagnetic theory	Quantum mechanics
Electron optics	Solid state physics
Geometrical optics	Sound and accoustics
Heat and thermodynamics	Statistical mechanics

It is suggested that a scientist wishing to learn Russian should obtain a Russian publication in his field where the subject matter is already familiar to him, so that no serious question of the scientific content will arise. At first he will have trouble with passages in italics, especially in mathematical works, where the statements of definitions and theorems are usually italicized. Consequently, almost all phrases and illustrative sentences in the grammar have been written a second time in italic type so that the reader may become familiar with it.

The author wishes to express his gratitude to S. H. Gould, Executive Editor of *Mathematical Reviews*, for his invaluable assistance at every stage of the preparation of the dictionary; his contributions range from critical examinations of the grammar and vocabulary and correction of galley sheets to the establishment of the working relation between the National Academy of Sciences and the American Mathematical Society on the one hand and the Soviet Academy of Sciences on the other hand. In addition, the author is grateful to Irmgaarde Braunsteins and Laszlo Kiraly for their assistance in preparing a preliminary draft of the manuscript, and also to Mychajlo Ciapa, Ben Dushnik, Victor Halich, Patricia Van Loon, Victor Streeter and Andrew Zakala, as well as to Marjorie Lohwater, who typed the grammar and made many helpful suggestions in its preparation. The author also wishes to express his gratitude to Professor A. I. Markushevich, the Russian First Deputy Minister of Education, who, on a visit to this country, inspected the project, making helpful suggestions and verifying many idiomatic expressions. Grateful acknowledgment is made to the Guggenheim Foundation, the National Science Foundation and the Office of Air Force Research, for their support of various aspects of the dictionary project.

The author is particularly grateful to Mrs. Olive J. Alexander to whose patient editing the final form of this Dictionary owes a great deal.

It is the intention of the author and of the American Mathematical Society to keep this dictionary up-to-date. Despite the efforts of both the American and the Soviet committees, a certain number of errors and misprints is virtually inevitable in the first edition of an undertaking of this size, and the author will appreciate being informed of such errors and of desirable additions. New words, *together with a reference to where the words are used*, should be sent to the author in care of the Society.

PREFACE TO THE SOVIET EDITION

Mathematics has always been the cornerstone of the exact sciences as well as of engineering, and in recent years its importance has increased to an extraordinary degree: Completely new fields of technology have arisen, and in those areas of science where mathematics has been applicable from the outset, especially in physics and mechanics, new fields of mathematics have come to be applied, fields for which no applications had been dreamed of even as recently as a few years ago. The face of mathematics itself has been completely changed, for it is characteristic of mathematics that it generates new scientific directions and formulates great new areas of research; here it suffices only to mention information theory, modern computational mathematics, the theory of automation, etc. In addition, mathematics has come to have important applications in areas where it had never before been used to any significant degree; in biology, in economics, and in linguistics.

It is not surprising then that there has been an unusual growth in the number of mathematicians working in all categories as well as in the number of mathematical papers of every possible character and direction. As a result, the number of mathematical terms in use has been increased many times over.

In order to keep up with the literature as well as to maintain scientific contact between mathematicians of different countries who are publishing in their own languages, special dictionaries of mathematical terms have become a necessity. The highest priority has been accorded to a unified English-Russian and Russian-English mathematical dictionary, which is now placed before the reader.

This is the first dictionary of its kind; it is intended to serve everyone connected directly or indirectly with mathematics. Basically, the dictionary gives translations from one language to the other of mathematical terms in all areas of modern mathematics. Whenever an equivalent term has not yet been established in the other language, an event not seldom encountered, the dictionary gives a short description of the term.

In the spring of 1958 the President of the National Academy of Sciences of the U.S.A., Detlov Bronk, proposed in a letter to A. N. Nesmeyanov, President of the Academy of Sciences of the U.S.S.R., a joint edition of an English-Russian and Russian-English mathematical dictionary. As a result of subsequent negotiations between the two academies an agreement was reached concerning collaboration on the dictionary. Soviet and American dictionary committees were appointed for the organization of the undertaking, and a joint conference was held in Moscow on September 10, 1958 in the Mathematical Institute of the Soviet Academy of Sciences to discuss plans for work on the dictionary. Dr. S. H. Gould and Prof. A. J. Lohwater were the Americans present for this conference; the Soviet committee was represented by Academician P. S. Alexandrov (Chairman), Academician I. N. Vekua, Corresponding Member I. R. Shafarievich, Prof. L. D. Kudryavtsev, Prof. A. F. Leontiev, Prof. S. M. Nikolskii, Prof. M. M.

Postnikov, Dr. V. S. Vladimirov, and Kandidat A. A. Dezin. At the conference, it was agreed specifically that work on the English-Russian half of the dictionary would be carried out in the Soviet Union while the work on the Russian-English half would be carried out in the United States. Both parties came to an agreement concerning mutual assistance during the course of the work on the dictionary.

Initially we compiled word-lists (i.e., translations of English terms into Russian) in the following fields of mathematics (names of the compilers are given in parentheses):

1. General and elementary terms (E. D. Solomentsev and E. G. Schulheifer).
2. Mathematical logic (G. N. Povarov).
3. Theory of numbers (V. K. Belov).
4. Algebra (E. G. Schulheifer).
5. Topology and theory of sets (V. K. Belov).
6. Analysis (M. S. Agronovich and E. D. Solomentsev).
7. Theory of functions of a real variable (E. D. Solomentsev).
8. Theory of functions of a complex variable (K. S. Szilard).
9. Probability and statistics (D. I. Golenko).
10. Linear programming and the theory of games (D. I. Golenko).
11. Geometry (G. I. Kruchkovich).
12. Algebraic geometry (V. K. Belov).
13. Numerical methods (D. I. Golenko).
14. Computers (G. N. Povarov).
15. Cybernetics (G. N. Povarov).
16. Mathematical economics (D. I. Golenko).
17. Astronomy and geophysics (E. D. Solomentsev).
18. Mechanics (G. M. Ilicheva).

The Editorial Board of the English-Russian half of the dictionary consisted of the following members of the Steklov Institute of the Soviet Academy: Academician P. S. Alexandrov (Chairman), Kandidat L. N. Bolshiev, Prof. L. D. Kudryavtsev (Vice-Chairman), Prof. A. F. Leontiev, Prof. S. M. Nikolskii, Prof. M. M. Postnikov, Kandidat E. D. Solomentsev, Corr. Member I. R. Shafarievich; the members of the Editorial Board took an active part in editing both the word-lists and the final draft of the Dictionary, while L. D. Kudryavtsev carried out the responsibilities of executive director of the work on the English-Russian part of the dictionary.

During the entire course of the work, a regular liaison and a constant exchange of information were maintained between Soviet and American specialists working on the dictionary. Much invaluable information was received from Dr. S. H. Gould and Prof. A. J. Lohwater (who directed the compilation in the United States). The word-lists which we compiled were sent to the United States for examination by Prof. Lohwater who returned to us a detailed critique. We express to Prof. Lohwater our deep gratitude for his extensive work on our word-lists, an effort which was of substantial help to us and which served to increase the quality of our Dictionary. For our part we received from Prof. Lohwater a preliminary draft of the Russian-English part of the Dictionary and returned to him our critique, which was made by L. D. Kudryavtsev, Yu. K. Solntsev, and E. D. Solomentsev.

The extensive and responsible task of combining our word-lists from the various fields of mathematics into a single dictionary and of drawing up the final draft of the

English-Russian dictionary was carried out by E. D. Solomentsev. To the terminology in the fields mentioned above we added a number of terms frequently used in physics as well as a number of words which, while not mathematical in any strict sense of the word, are frequently encountered in the mathematical literature. The phonetic transcription (which was adapted from V. K. Müller's *English-Russian Dictionary*, 7th Edition, Moscow, 1960 and *Webster's New International Dictionary of the English Language*, 2nd Edition, 1950) was written by O. G. Tarasova and edited by H. A. Mastalygina. A short grammatical sketch was written by H. A. Mastalygina. The publication of the manuscript was undertaken by the Foreign Languages Publishing House in Moscow.

In conclusion it must be pointed out that the project of publishing an English-Russian and Russian-English mathematical dictionary is the first project ever completed by the joint action of Soviet and American mathematicians. It is our hope that a subsequent development of such cooperation and joint activities between Soviet and American colleagues will contribute to the further growth of world science, to an improvement of mutual understanding and to friendship between the peoples of our countries.

Moscow, 1961 P. S. ALEXANDROV

A SHORT GRAMMAR OF THE RUSSIAN LANGUAGE

§ 1. INTRODUCTION AND ALPHABET

Like any inflected Indo-European language, the Russian language is studied by means of an analysis of the declension of nouns and adjectives and the conjugation of verbs, together with their use in conjunction with prepositions, connectives, etc. The first obstacle which the beginner encounters, however, is the problem of the alphabet. Once the alphabet has been learned, the study of Russian becomes relatively simple, certainly no more difficult than the study of German. The Russian, or Cyrillic, alphabet is an interesting combination of Roman, Greek and Hebrew characters; following the Bolshevik Revolution, the orthography was revised and modernized, and, in the alphabet given immediately below, the older characters are listed for the convenience of those readers who must make occasional references to the pre-Revolution literature. Since the italicized alphabet is used in places of such critical interest as the statements of theorems, etc., almost all phrases and sentences are duplicated in italics in the grammatical sketch so that the reader will become accustomed to reading italicized printing.

No universal agreement has been reached on the transliteration of the Russian alphabet, and the three most commonly used systems of transliteration are given in the table below. System I is that used by the Library of Congress and is the most commonly used system for non-technical literature in the United States. System II is the system used in the *Mathematical Reviews*, while System III is a German system which is frequently encountered in mathematical literature.

THE ALPHABET

PRINTED	ITALICS	SOUND	TRANSLITERATION I	II	III
А а	*А а*	ah (f*a*ther)	a	a	a
Б б	*Б б*	b (*b*ed)	b	b	b
В в	*В в*	v (*v*igor)	v	v	w
Г г	*Г г*	g (*g*o)	g	g	g
Д д	*Д д, g*	d (*d*o)	d	d	d
Е е	*Е е*	yeh (*ye*t)	ye, e	e	je
Ё ё[1]	*Ё ё*[1]	yo (*yo*lk)	ye, e	ë	jo
Ж ж	*Ж ж*	zh (plea*s*ure)	zh	ž	sh

PRINTED	ITALICS	SOUND	TRANSLITERATION I	II	III
З з	*З з*	z (zigzag)	z	z	s
И и	*И и*	ee (feet)	i	i	i
Й й	*Й й*	y (to*y*)	y	ĭ	j
(I i)[2]	*I i*	ee (feet)			
К к	*К к*	k (*k*ing)	k	k	k
Л л	*Л л*	l (ba*ll*)	l	l	l
М м	*М м*	m (*m*an)	m	m	m
Н н	*Н н*	n (*n*ose)	n	n	n
О о	*О о*	o (sort)	o	o	o
П п	*П п*	p (*p*in)	p	p	p
Р р	*Р р*	r (*r*ing, trilled)	r	r	r
С с	*С с*	s (*s*un)	s	s	s (ss)
Т т	*Т т*	t (*t*ime)	t	t	t
У у	*У у*	oo (poor)	u	u	u
Ф ф	*Ф ф*	f (*f*ig)	f	f	f
Х х	*Х х*	kh (like *ch* in German *ach*)	kh	h	ch
Ц ц	*Ц ц*	ts (tar*ts*)	ts	c	z
Ч ч	*Ч ч*	ch (mu*ch*)	ch	č	tsch
Ш ш	*Ш ш*	sh (*sh*op)	sh	š	sch
Щ щ	*Щ щ*	shch (lu*sh* *ch*erry)	shch	šč	stsch
Ъ ъ[3]	*Ъ ъ*	(silent)	″	″	′
Ы ы	*Ы ы*	i or e (*i*t, w*e*)	y	y	y
Ь ь	*Ь ь*	(silent)	′	′	j
(Ѣ ѣ)[4]	*Ѣ ѣ*	ye (*ye*t)			
Э э[5]	*Э э*	e (t*e*n)	e	è	e
Ю ю	*Ю ю*	yu (*you*)	yu	yu	ju
Я я	*Я я*	ya (*ya*rd)	ya	ya	ja
(Ѳ ѳ)[6]	*Ѳ ѳ*	f (*f*at)			
(Ѵ ѵ)[7]	*Ѵ ѵ*	ee (m*ee*t)			

1. Usually written as е although the pronunciation of ё is retained.
2. Replaced by и in the post-Revolution orthography.
3. Used only as a separation mark after certain consonants; sometimes replaced by the symbols ′ or ″ in the middle of words, and dropped altogether when used at the end of a word in the old orthography.
4. Replaced by е in the post-Revolution orthography.
5. Retained in the post-Revolution orthography, but replaced by е in certain words.
6. Replaced by ф in the post-Revolution orthography.
7. Replaced by и in the post-Revolution orthography.

§ 2. THE NOUN

As in most inflected languages, such as German, nouns have three genders, masculine (*m.*), feminine (*f.*), and neuter (*n.*), but since there is no article (*the*, *a*, *an*) in Russian, the gender of a given Russian noun is determined by the noun itself. There are six cases in the declension of nouns, indicated and abbreviated as follows:

Nominative case	Nom.
Genitive case	Gen.
Dative case	Dat.
Accusative case	Acc.
Instrumental case	Instr.
Prepositional case	Prep.

The nouns will be classified into groups within each of the genders with full declensions of nouns typical of the specific classification. With Russian, as with any language, it would be expecting too much to hope that everything be regular, and declensions of the important exceptional cases will also be given. Exceptional parts of declensions which are peculiar to individual words are given in the vocabulary of the dictionary.

2.1. The Masculine Nouns

There are five general classifications of masculine nouns, those ending in:
1°. Every consonant except those in 4°;
2°. -й, but not falling in 5°;
3°. -ь;
4°. -ж, -ш, -ч, -щ.
5°. -й and formed from an adjective.

The declensions of these classifications are exemplified in the following tables.

1°. Masculine Nouns ending in a Consonant

	Singular	*Plural*
Nom.	интеграл (integral)	интегралы
Gen.	интеграла	интегралов
Dat.	интегралу	интегралам
Acc.	интеграл*	интегралы*
Instr.	интегралом	интегралами
Prep.	интеграле	интегралах

Note. The nominative and accusative plurals of nouns ending in -г, -к, or -х is -и instead of -ы.

	Singular	*Plural*
Nom.	ранг (class, rank)	ранги
Gen.	ранга	рангов
Dat.	рангу	рангам
Acc.	ранг	ранги
Instr.	рангом	рангами
Prep.	ранге	рангах

Note. The instrumental singular and genitive plural of some nouns ending in -ц may change to -ем and -ев respectively whenever the accent is not on the last syllable; thus, for месяц (month, moon) месяцем and месяцев (instead of месяцом and месяцов respectively). But for близнец (twin, one of a pair of twins; близнецы pl., prime pair), the instrumental singular is близнецом and the genitive plural is близнецов.

* Whenever a masculine noun denotes an animate object, the accusative case coincides with the ordinary genitive.

2°. **Masculine Nouns ending in -й** (which have not been formed from adjectives)

	Singular	*Plural*
Nom.	случай (case, event)	случаи
Gen.	случая	случаев
Dat.	случаю	случаям
Acc.	случай	случаи
Instr.	случаем	лусчаями
Prep.	случае	случаях

Note. A few words ending in -ий, *but not in the form of an adjective being used as a noun*, have the ending -ии in the prepositional singular instead of -ие, e.g. критерий (criterion, test) becomes критер**ии** in the prepositional singular.

3°. **Masculine Nouns ending in -ь**

	Singular	*Plural*
Nom.	делитель (divisor)	делители
Gen.	делителя	делителей
Dat.	делителю	делителям
Acc.	делитель	делители
Instr.	делителем	делителями
Prep.	делителе	делителях

4°. **Masculine Nouns ending in -ж, -ч, -ш -щ**

	Singular	*Plural*
Nom.	выигрыш (payoff)	выигрыши
Gen.	выигрыша	выигрышей
Dat.	выигрышу	выигрышам
Acc.	выигрыш	выигрыши
Instr.	выигрышем (-ом)[1]	выигрышами
Prep.	выигрыше	выигрышах

1. The ending -ом instead of -ем whenever the accent is on the last syllable, e.g. Nom. этаж (step, stage), Instr. sing. этажом.

5°. **Masculine Nouns ending in -ый, -ой or -ий.** Nouns falling into this category usually consist of proper names and adjectives which are no longer accompanied by the nouns which they used to modify. In both cases, the declension is the same as that of an adjective (cf. § 3).

	Singular	*Plural*
Nom.	подынтегральный[1] (integrand)	подынтегральные
Gen.	подынтегрального	подынтегральных
Dat.	подынтегральному	подынтегральным
Acc.	подынтегральный	подынтегральные
Instr.	подынтегральным	подынтегральными
Prep.	подынтегральном	подынтегральных

1. The compilation of the dictionary uncovered some relatively rare instances where this noun was treated as the neuter подынтегральное, indicating only that the author had in mind a neuter noun which was being modified by подынтегральный. One important variant of подынтегральный is подинтегральный, which is listed separately in the dictionary; the variant is peculiar to non-Russian Soviet authors who are unaware of the change of и- to ы- whenever the prefix ends in -д.

Note. Variations on the endings arising from the last consonant in the noun are discussed in the section (§ 3) devoted to the adjective.

The declension of proper names. The declension of proper names varies according to the form of the name; many proper names have been formed from adjectives, e.g. surnames ending in -ский, while a surname ending in -ов may be considered as a short form of an adjective ending in -овый, which has the declension given below. In the tables below, the declensions describe a wide class of Russian surnames; only the singular is given.

Ending	-ов	-ев	-вич	-ский
Nom.	Александров (Alexandrov)	Кудрявцев (Kudryavtsev)	Шафаревич (Shafarevich)	Белинский (Belinskii)
Gen.	Александрова	Кудрявцева	Шафаревича	Белинского
Dat.	Александрову	Кудрявцеву	Шафаревичу	Белинскому
Acc.	Александрова	Кудрявцева	Шафаревича	Белинского
Instr.	Александровым	Кудрявцевым	Шафаревичем	Белинским
Prep.	Александрове	Кудрявцеве	Шафаревиче	Белинском

Note. Some surnames, both foreign and Soviet, are not declined at all in Russian.

2.2. The Feminine Nouns

There are five principal categories of feminine nouns, those ending in

1°. -а;
2°. -я preceded by a consonant;
3°. -ия;
4°. -ь;
5°. -ая and formed from an adjective.

Typical declensions are given in the following tables:

1°. Feminine Nouns ending in -a

	Singular	*Plural*
Nom.	сторона (side)	стороны
Gen.	стороны	сторон
Dat.	стороне	сторонам
Acc.	сторону	стороны
Instr.	стороной	сторонами
Prep.	стороне	сторонах

Note. If a feminine noun denotes something animate, the accusative plural takes the same form as the genitive plural.

If the nominative singular ending -а is preceded by г, к, х, ж, ш, ч or щ, the ending -ы in the preceding table becomes -и, while if -а is preceded by ж, ш, ч, щ or ц, the instrumental singular ending -ой becomes -ей. Thus

	Singular	*Plural*
Nom.	перестановка (permutation)	перестановки
Gen.	перестановки	перестановок
Dat.	перестановке	перестановкам
Acc.	перестановку	перестановки
Instr.	перестановкой	перестановками
Prep.	перестановке	перестановках

	Singular	*Plural*
Nom.	задача (problem)	задачи
Gen.	задачи	задач
Dat.	задаче	задачам
Acc.	задачу	задачи
Instr.	задачей	задачами
Prep.	задаче	задачах

Note. Feminine nouns in this category in which the ending -ка is preceded by a consonant will generally have the ending -ок or -ек in the genitive plural. Thus перестановок from перестановка above, ошибок from ошибка (error), точек from точка (point), ячеек from ячейка (cell), etc. More generally, the note following 2° is also applicable here.

2°. Feminine Nouns ending in -я preceded by a Consonant

	Singular	*Plural*
Nom.	потеря (loss)	потери
Gen.	потери	потерь
Dat.	потере	потерям
Acc.	потерю	потери
Instr.	потерей	потерями
Prep.	потере	потерях

Note. If the ending -я is preceded by two consonants, an о or е appears between them in the genitive plural, e.g. земля (earth) becomes земель.

3°. Feminine Nouns ending in -ия. Feminine nouns in this category are often of non-Russian origin; the following is quite typical:

	Singular	*Plural*
Nom.	функция (function)	функции
Gen.	функции	функций
Dat.	функции	функциям
Acc.	функцию	функции
Instr.	функцей	функциями
Prep.	функции	функциях

4°. **Feminine Nouns ending in -ь.** Certain masculine nouns ending in -ь have already been encountered (cf. 2.1, 3°), but all nouns ending in -сть with the exception of гость (guest) are feminine.

	Singular	*Plural*
Nom.	часть (part)	части
Gen.	части	частей
Dat.	части	частям
Acc.	часть	части
Instr.	частью	частями
Prep.	части	частях

	Singular	*Plural*
Nom.	приводимость (reducibility)	приводимости
Gen.	приводимости	приводимостей
Dat.	приводимости	приводимостям
Acc.	приводимость	приводимости
Instr.	приводимостью	приводимостями
Prep.	приводимости	приводимостях

Note. If the ending -ь is preceded by ж, ш, ч, щ, the endings -ям, -ями, -ях are replaced by the endings -ам, -ами and -ах respectively. The following table is typical.

	Singular	*Plural*
Nom.	вещь (thing)	вещи
Gen.	вещи	вещей
Dat.	вещи	вещам
Acc.	вещь	вещи
Instr.	вещью	вещами
Prep.	вещи	вещах

5°. **Feminine Nouns formed from Adjectives.** Nouns of this type are declined like adjectives (cf. § 3). The most common nouns end in -ая:

	Singular	*Plural*
Nom.	постоянная (constant)	постоянные
Gen.	постоянной	постоянных
Dat.	постоянной	постоянным
Acc.	постоянную	постоянные
Instr.	постоянной	постоянными
Prep.	постоянной	постоянных

Note. A few nouns end in -яя, but the declension is deferred until § 3.

2.3. The Neuter Nouns

There are five general classes of neuter nouns, ending in

1°. -о;
2°. -ие;
3°. -е, preceded by a consonant;
4°. -мя;
5°. -ое and -ее.

Case 2° consists primarily of nouns formed from verbs by adding the ending -ие to some form of the verb, case 4° consists of no more than ten or twelve words in the entire language of which only two (время *time* and имя *name*) are of importance in mathematics and physics, while case 5° consists largely of adjectives used in the neuter case as nouns.

1°. Neuter Nouns ending in -о

	Singular	*Plural*
Nom.	место (place, locus)	места
Gen.	места	мест
Dat.	месту	местам
Acc.	место	места
Instr.	местом	местами
Prep.	месте	местах

Note. If the ending -о is preceded by two different consonants, these consonants are frequently separated by о or е in the genitive plural. For example, ядро (kernel) has ядер as genitive plural.

Note. The ending -ство is used to form abstract collective neuter nouns from simpler nouns and adjectives; a typical declension is given in the following table:

	Singular	*Plural*
Nom.	множество (set)	множества
Gen.	множества	множеств
Dat.	множеству	множествам
Acc.	множество	множества
Instr.	множеством	множествами
Prep.	множестве	множествах

2°. Neuter Nouns ending in -ие

	Singular	*Plural*
Nom.	отображение (mapping)	отображения
Gen.	отображения	отображений
Dat.	отображению	отображениям
Acc.	отображение	отображения
Instr.	отображением	отображениями
Prep.	отображении	отображениях

3°. **Neuter Nouns ending in -е.** The principal nouns in this class end in -ле or -ре; the case of neuter nouns ending in -ее and formed from adjectives is given in 5°.

	Singular	*Plural*
Nom.	поле (field)	поля
Gen.	поля	полей
Dat.	полю	полям
Acc.	поле	поля
Instr.	полем	полями
Prep.	поле	полях

4°. **Neuter Nouns ending in -мя.** The two important words in this class, время (time) and имя (name), are given here in full.

	Singular	*Plural*	*Singular*	*Plural*
Nom.	время	времена	имя	имена
Gen.	времени	времен	имени	имен
Dat.	времени	временам	имени	именам
Acc.	время	времена	имя	имена
Instr.	временем	временами	именем	именами
Prep.	времени	временах	имени	именах

5°. **Neuter Nouns ending in -ое and -ее.** This class is comprised primarily of adjectives used in the neuter case as nouns. The declension is identical to that of the corresponding adjective.

	Singular	*Plural*
Nom.	делимое (dividend)	делимые
Gen.	делимого	делимых
Dat.	делимому	делимым
Acc.	делимое	делимые
Instr.	делимым	делимыми
Prep.	делимом	делимых

	Singular	*Plural*
Nom.	среднее (mean, average)	средние
Gen.	среднего	средних
Dat.	среднему	средним
Acc.	среднее	средние
Instr.	средним	средними
Prep.	среднем	средних

§ 3. THE ADJECTIVE

The role of the adjective is the same in Russian as in other western inflected languages and will be described here in the following manner. The regular declensions for the three genders are listed together with the important variations. Rules for the formation of the comparative and superlative degrees are given, followed by a description of the formation of adjectives from other parts of speech.

3.1. The Long Form of the Adjective

Russian adjectives admit a long form and a short form, the latter appearing mostly in the role of a predicate. As expected, adjectives take the same gender, case, and number as the nouns they modify, except in certain cases which will be described below.

The normal form of the adjective is given by its masculine singular nominative, and there are two primary classifications, the first consisting of adjectives ending in -ый, with the variations -ой and -ий not preceded by н, the second consisting of adjectives ending in -ний.

1°. **Adjectives ending in -ый or -ой, and -ий not preceded by н.** The ending -ой is used instead of -ый or -ий whenever the accent is on the last syllable, while the ending -ий appears when preceded by г, к, х, ж, ш, ч, or щ. Thus массовый (mass) but круговой (circular), хороший (good) but большой (large), ложный (false) but двойной (double, dual, binary).

	Masc. sing.	*Fem. sing.*	*Neut. sing.*
Nom.	ложный	ложная	ложное
Gen.	ложного	ложной	ложного
Dat.	ложному	ложной	ложному
Acc.	ложный	ложную	ложное
Instr.	ложным	ложной	ложным
Prep.	ложном	ложной	ложном
Nom.	двойной	двойная	двойное
Gen.	двойного	двойной	двойного
Dat.	двойному	двойной	двойному
Acc.	двойной	двойную	двойное
Instr.	двойным	двойной	двойным
Prep.	двойном	двойной	двойном
Nom.	хороший	хорошая	хорошее
Gen.	хорошего	хорошей	хорошего
Dat.	хорошему	хорошей	хорошему
Acc.	хороший	хорошую	хорошее
Instr.	хорошим	хорошей	хорошим
Prep.	хорошем	хорошей	хорошем

The plural is the same for all three genders.

	Plural (all genders)		
Nom.	ложные	двойные	хорошие
Gen.	ложных	двойных	хороших
Dat.	ложным	двойным	хорошим
Acc.	ложные	двойные	хорошие
Instr.	ложными	двойными	хорошими
Prep.	ложных	двойных	хороших

2°. **Adjectives ending in -ний.** Adjectives in this class are quite regular, and the example given in the table below, внутренний (inner, interior, intrinsic), is typical.

	Singular			Plural
	Masc.	*Fem.*	*Neut.*	*(all genders)*
Nom.	внутренний	внутренняя	внутреннее	внутренние
Gen.	внутреннего	внутренней	внутреннего	внутренних
Dat.	внутреннему	внутренней	внутреннему	внутренним
Acc.	внутренний	внутреннюю	внутреннее	внутренние
Instr.	внутренним	внутренней	внутренним	внутренними
Prep.	внутреннем	внутренней	внутреннем	внутренних

Note. Whenever an adjective modifies an animate noun, the masculine singular and plural accusative is replaced by the corresponding genitive.

3.2. The Short Form of an Adjective

The formation of the short form of adjectives encountered in 3.1 is achieved essentially by dropping the ending and using the stem alone as the masculine singular. The feminine, neuter and plural nominatives are then obtained by adding the endings -а, -о, -ы respectively. The following table is based on the adjective дуговой (arc).

	Long form	*Short form*
Masculine	дуговой	дугов
Feminine	дуговая	дугова
Neuter	дуговое	дугово
Plural	дуговые	дуговы

Note. Whenever the dropping of the ending in the masculine nominative singular gives rise to a stem ending in two consonants, е or о is inserted; the vowel е or о is usually dropped in the feminine, neuter, and plural forms: интересный (interesting): интересен, интересна, интересно, интересны; ясный (clear, explicit): ясен, ясна, ясно, ясны; легкий (easy, light): легок, легка, легко, легки.

In a non-predicative form, the short form of an adjective appears only in connection with certain adjectives which have been formed from proper names. Thus, the short form of the adjective эрмитовый (Hermite, Hermitian) is эрмитов and has the following declension:

	Masc.	*Fem.*	*Neut.*	*Plural*
Nom.	эрмитов	эрмитова	эрмитово	эрмитовы
Gen.	эрмитова	эрмитовой	эрмитова	эрмитовых
Dat.	эрмитову	эрмитовой	эрмитову	эрмитовым
Acc.	эрмитов	эрмитову	эрмитово	эрмитовы
Instr.	эрмитовым	эрмитовой	эрмитовым	эрмитовыми
Prep.	эрмитовом	эрмитовой	эрмитовом	эрмитовых

In this dictionary the past passive participles, as well as other participles, are listed as adjectives since they are declined like adjectives and must agree in gender, number and case with the nouns they modify. Such participles have short forms which are formed according to the rules formulated above, and we note here that their use as predicates may also mean that they may be translated in terms of the passive voice of the verb (cf. 5.4, 3°). Note that, if the participle ends in -нный, one н is dropped.

Long form	*Short form*
полученный (obtained, received)	получен, получена, получено, получены
данный (given)	дан, дана, дано, даны
открытый (opened, open)	открыт, открыта, открыто, открыты
насыщенный (saturated)	насыщен, насыщена, насыщено, насыщены
интегрируемый (integrable)	интегрируем[1], интегрируема, интегрируемо интегрируемы

1. It must be pointed out that the masculine singular of short forms of adjectives ending in -мый often coincides with the first person plural in the verb conjugations (cf. 5.2); this form, regarded as the present indicative, can also mean "we integrate", and only the context of the Russian can clarify the form.

3.3. The Comparative and Superlative Degrees of Adjectives

The simplest method of forming the comparative degree is to place the words более (more) or менее (less) in front of the adjective, thus более трудный = *more difficult* and менее трудный = *less difficult*. The words более and менее are not inflected, but the adjective under comparison agrees with the noun it modifies in gender, number and case, for example

Более ранняя теорема Белинского

Более ранняя теорема Белинского

An earlier theorem of Belinskii

В более узком смысле

В более узком смысле

In a narrower sense.

The comparative is also formed by adding -ее to the stem of an adjective, and, when the stem ends in ж, ч, ш, щ, by adding -е to a modified stem of the adjective. Thus сильный (strong) becomes сильнее (stronger), while легкий (easy) becomes легче (easier). This form of the comparative is not inflected and is the same for all genders and numbers. The English word "than" can be rendered by the genitive case whenever nouns, pronouns or adjectives are being compared, or by чем followed by the nominative, for example

Неравенство (11) слабее неравенства (12)

Неравенство (11) *слабее неравенства* (12)

The inequality (11) is weaker than the inequality (12)

Теорема 1 лучше, чем теорема 2

Теорема 1 лучше, чем теорема 2

Theorem 1 is better than Theorem 2.

The superlative may also be formed in more than one way, the first way being the addition of the inflected word самый in front of the adjective to be modified; thus, for the word трудный (difficult),

самый трудный,	*masculine singular*
самая трудная,	*feminine singular*
самое трудное,	*neuter singular*
самые трудные,	*plural, all genders.*

A second way of forming the superlative is to allow the uninflected word наиболее to precede the adjective in question; just as более corresponds to the English "more" in the comparative degree, the word наиболее plays the role of the word "most" in the superlative. The words более and наиболее may also be used to form the comparative and superlative degrees of adverbs by placing более or наиболее before the usual form of the adverb.

A third way of forming the superlative consists of adding the ending -ейший to the stem of the adjective; the resulting superlative is then declined like any adjective ending in -ший. If the stem ends in one of ж, ш, ч, щ, then -ейший is replaced by -айший; moreover, the superlative of an adjective ending in -кий preceded by o is formed by replacing -кий by -чайший. Thus the superlative of новый (new) is новейший, the superlative of важный (important) is важнейший, while the superlative of высокий (high) is высочайший. A number of irregular comparatives and superlatives is given in the following table.

Positive	*Comparative*	*Superlative*
близкий (near)	ближе	ближайший
большой (large)	больше	наибольший
высокий (high)	выше	высочайший, высший
далекий (far)	дальше	дальнейший
короткий (short)	короче	кратчайший
краткий (short)	кратче	кратчайший
легкий (easy)	легче	легчайший
маленький (small)	меньше	наименьший
низкий (low)	ниже	низший, нижайший
плохой (bad, poor)	хуже	худший
поздний (late)	позже, позднее	позднейший
простой (simple)	проще	простейший
узкий (narrow)	уже	
хороший (good)	лучше, лучший	лучший, наилучший

Note. The superlatives of some adjectives can not be formed by means of regular endings, and some adjectives have special forms which may be comparative or superlative, the meaning usually being clear from the context.

Superlatives of some adjectives are formed by adding to the comparative the prefix наи-, e.g. наибольший (the largest), наименьший (the smallest), etc. Sometimes the prefix наи-, when appearing with an adjective already in the superlative degree, serves to emphasize that degree, e.g. наилучший (the very best).

The superlative may also be formed by the comparative followed by the genitive singular всего (of all) or by the genitive plural всех (of all), e.g. проще всех других (simpler than all others, i.e. the simplest of all).

§ 4. THE PRONOUN

The declensions of the various pronouns are given in the tables below; examples of the use of pronouns will be made in § 5.

4.1. The Personal Pronouns

Singular

Nom.	я (I)	ты (you)[1]	он (he, it)	она (she, it)	оно (it)
Gen.	меня	тебя	его (него)[2]	ее (нее)[2]	его (него)[2]
Dat.	мне	тебе	ему (нему)	ей (ней)	ему (нему)
Acc.	меня	тебя	его (него)	ее (нее)	его (него)
Instr.	мной	тобой	им (ним)	ею (нею)	им (ним)
Prep.	мне	тебе	нем	ней	нем

Plural

Nom.	мы (we)	вы (you)	они (they)
Gen.	нас	вас	их (них)[2]
Dat.	нам	вам	им (ним)
Acc.	нас	вас	их (них)
Instr.	нами	вами	ими (ними)
Prep.	нас	вас	них

1. Familiar form; never used in scientific writing.
2. Third person personal pronouns (both singular and plural) always prefix н- when used after prepositions.

Personal possessive pronouns: First person

	Masc.	*Fem.*	*Neut.*	*Plural*
Nom.	мой (my, mine)	моя	мое	мои
Gen.	моего	моей	моего	моих
Dat.	моему	моей	моему	моим
Acc.	мой	мою	мое	мои
Instr.	моим	моей	моим	моими
Prep.	моем	моей	моем	моих
Nom.	наш (our)	наша	наше	наши
Gen.	нашего	нашей	нашего	наших
Dat.	нашему	нашей	нашему	нашим
Acc.	наш	нашу	наше	наши
Instr.	нашим	нашей	нашим	нашими
Prep.	нашем	нашей	нашем	наших

Note. Whenever the modified noun is animate, the genitive case is used in place of the accusative in the masculine, neuter and plural.

The possessive pronoun твой corresponding to ты is declined like мой, while the possessive pronoun ваш corresponding to вы is declined like наш. The possessive pronouns corresponding to он, она, оно, они are его, ее, его, их, respectively, and are not declined, for example

Теория групп и ее применение

Теория групп и ее применение

Group theory and its application.

4.2. The Interrogative Pronouns кто and что

All genders (singular and plural)

Nom.	кто (who)	что (what)
Gen.	кого	чего
Dat.	кому	чему
Acc.	кого	что
Instr.	кем	чем
Prep.	ком	чем

The interrogative possessives какой (what, what kind of), который (which, what) are declined like the adjectives of 3.1, while что gives rise to the interrogative possessive чей, which appears sufficiently frequently in the mathematical literature to warrant its declension here.

	Singular			*Plural*
	Masc.	*Fem.*	*Neut.*	*(all genders)*
Nom.	чей (whose, of which)	чья	чье	чьи
Gen.	чьего	чьей	чьего	чьих
Dat.	чьему	чьей	чьему	чьим
Acc.	чей	чью	чье	чьи
Instr.	чьим	чьей	чьим	чьими
Prep.	чьем	чьей	чьем	чьих

4.3. Demonstrative Pronouns

	Singular			*Plural*
	Masc.	*Fem.*	*Neut.*	*(all genders)*
Nom.	этот (this)	эта	это	эти
Gen.	этого	этой	этого	этих
Dat.	этому	этой	этому	этим
Acc.	этот	эту	это	эти
Instr.	этим	этой	этим	этими
Prep.	этом	этой	этом	этих
Nom.	тот (that)	та	то	те
Gen.	того	той	того	тех
Dat.	тому	той	тому	тем
Acc.	тот	ту	то	те
Instr.	тем	той	тем	теми
Prep.	том	той	том	тех

The word такой (such, so) is declined like какой (cf. 3.1) and the reflexive pronoun себя (myself, yourself etc.) follows the declension of тебя and agrees with its noun in case, but is declined only in the singular.

4.4. Miscellaneous

The so-called negative pronouns никто (no one, nobody) and ничто (nothing) are declined like кто and что respectively; in combination with prepositions, they are customarily divided by the preposition into ни followed by the appropriate form of кто or что.

The declensions of весь (all, all of, whole) and сам (same, the same, self) are given in the following tables.

		Singular		*Plural*
	Masc.	*Fem.*	*Neut.*	*(all genders)*
Nom.	весь	вся	все	все
Gen.	всего	всей	всего	всех
Dat.	всему	всей	всему	всем
Acc.	весь	всю	все	все
Instr.	всем	всей	всем	всеми
Prep.	всем	всей	всем	всех
Nom.	сам	сама	само	сами
Gen.	самого	самой	самого	самих
Dat.	самому	самой	самому	самим
Acc.	сам	самое	само	сами
Instr.	самим	самой	самим	самими
Prep.	самом	самой	самом	самих

§ 5. THE VERB

The first principal difference between Russian and the more "western" languages appears in the analysis of the Russian verb, where notion of "aspect" is encountered. The Russian writer is more concerned with the completion or non-completion of the act described by the verb than with the fine distinction between such tenses as the perfect and pluperfect. Consequently, Russian verbs are divided into two important categories, the *imperfective aspect* and the *perfective aspect*, the first of which is used to indicate that the action has not been completed, but is continuous or recurring, while the second, or perfective, aspect is used to indicate that the action has been, or will be, completed, or that there has been, or will be, a definite result. Verbs in the perfective aspect have no present tense and are properly used only in the past or future.

Almost every verb has an imperfective infinitive and a perfective infinitive, and, in accordance with tradition, the verbs in this dictionary are given in terms of the imperfective infinitive followed by the perfective infinitive in parentheses. In many cases, there is a separate entry for the perfective infinitive, particularly if it differs substantially from the imperfective.

Before an analysis of the various classifications of verbs is undertaken, it is desirable to examine the manner in which the English verb "to be" is handled in Russian.

5.1. The Verb "to be"

The sense of the English verb "to be" may be expressed in several ways in Russian. In short sentences, or in parts of sentences, where there can be no confusion, the verb form is either omitted entirely,

Предложение P эквивалентно Q

Предложение P *эквивалентно* Q

Proposition P is equivalent to Q

or is replaced by a dash (—),

Если E — некоторое множество точек комплексной плоскости, . . .

Если E — *некоторое множество точек комплексной плоскости*, . . .

If E is a point set of the complex plane, . . .

Пространство R_n^* гомеоморфно $R \times S_{n-1}$

Пространство R_n^* *гомеоморфно* $R \times S_{n-1}$

The space R_n^* is homeomorphic to $R \times S_{n-1}$

Пусть I — замкнутый куб в R^n

Пусть I — *замкнутый куб в* R^n

Let I be a closed cube in R^n.

Sometimes one uses the present tense of the verb быть (to be), which is the Russian verb whose form, and in many cases whose usage, most closely resembles the verb "to be" in English; the present tense is есть in the singular and often in the plural and суть in the plural only. Often есть is used in conjunction with one or both of the methods illustrated by the examples above, for example

Граница этой области есть окружность K_r, где r — постоянная

Граница этой области есть окружность K_r, *где* r — *постоянная*

The frontier of this domain is the circle K_r, where r is a constant

Матрицы суть спиновые матрицы Паули

Матрицы суть спиновые матрицы Паули

The matrices are the Pauli spin matrices

Note. The phrase то есть (abbreviated т. е.) is the same as the English *that is* (abbreviated i.e.).

The conjugation of быть is given in the following table:

Infinitive. быть, to be (cf. 5.6, 4°.)

Present Indicative. он (она, оно) есть (sing.), he is, etc. они суть (plur.), they are.

Note. Forms for first and second person are rarely used, except in grammar books.

PAST INDICATIVE		FUTURE INDICATIVE	
я был	I was	я буду	I shall (be)
ты был	you were	ты буешь	you will (be)
он был	he (it) was	он будет	he (it) will (be)
опа была	shc (it) was	она будет	she (it) will (be)
оно было	it was	оно будет	it will (be)
мы были	we were	мы будем	we shall (be)
вы были	you were	вы будете	you will (be)
они были	they were	они будут	they will (be)

The past indicative and future indicative are used in the same way as есть and суть except that they can never be omitted; it frequently happens, however, that the predicate is in the instrumental case with the past and future indicative, for example

Если α алгебраическая величина относительно Σ, а Σ алгебраическое поле относительно Δ, то α будет алгебраическим[1] относительно Δ

Если α алгебраическая величина относительно Σ, а Σ алгебраическое поле относительно Δ, то α будет алгебраическим относительно Δ

If α is algebraic with respect to Σ, and Σ is algebraic with respect to Δ, then α will be algebraic with respect to Δ.

1. Note the instrumental case here.

In addition to being used in a similar way to express the simple future of the verb "to be", the future indicative of быть may be used with the infinitive of any imperfective verb to express the simple future of that verb:

Мы будем называть функцию $f(z)$ непрерывной, если . . .

Мы будем называть функцию $f(z)$ непрерывной, если . . .

We shall call a function $f(z)$ continuous if . . .

(*or*, A function $f(z)$ will be called continuous, if . . .)

Тогда потенциал будет равен ϕ

Тогда потенциал будет равен ϕ

Then the potential will be equal to ϕ.

Since the complete omission of a verb meaning "to be" can lead to confusion in a more complex sentence, some sort of verb is needed; the most common way of handling such a verb in Russian, particularly in an involved sentence, is by the use of the words является and являются, which are the third person singular and plural, respectively, of the infinitive являться (which is sometimes used in the sense of "appears to be" or "reveals itself to be"); the reflexive ending -ся, which becomes -сь after vowels, will be discussed below. The predicate following является and являются is always in the instrumental case, as the following examples show.

1°. Такая функция существует и является единственной
Такая функция существует и является единственной
Such a function exists and is unique.

2°. Точка w является образом точки z
Точка w *является образом точки* z
The point w is the image of the point z.

3°. F является продолжением f
F *является продолжением* f
F is a continuation of f.

4°. Единственными изоморфизмами топологической группы T в себя являются тождественное отображение и симметрия $x \to -x$
Единственными изоморфизмами топологической группы T *в себя являются тождественное отображение и симметрия* $x \to -x$
The only isomorphisms of the topological group T into itself are the identity map and the symmetry $x \to -x$.

5°. Вероятность P будет являться абстрактной копией эмпирической частоты
Вероятность P *будет являться абстрактной копией эмпирической частоты*
The probability P will be an abstract counterpart of the empirical frequency ratio.

5.2. Verb Conjugations

Russian verbs are ordinarily classified into two principal conjugations according to the form of the second and third person in the present indicative. Generally speaking, this classification by endings may be described as follows:

	CONJUGATION I		CONJUGATION II	
	Singular	*Plural*	*Singular*	*Plural*
1st Person	-ю (-у)	-ем	-ю (-у)	-им
2nd Person	-ешь	-ете	-ишь	-ите
3rd Person	-ет	-ют (-ут)	-ит	-ят

Within each conjugation there are several categories, and, while no effort has been made to achieve completeness in such a classification, the tables below give a representative cross-section of the types usually encountered in reading.

As will be seen in the conjugations below, there is no general rule for the formation of the perfective from the imperfective, although in certain cases the perfective infinitive will be dictated by the form of the imperfective infinitive. The perfective is often formed from the imperfective by altering the ending of the infinitive, and this may or may not change the verb from Conjugation I to Conjugation II, or vice versa; sometimes the perfective is formed by adding a prefix to the imperfective, leaving the perfective in the same conjugation as the imperfective.

The tables of verb conjugations below are constructed in the following way. The imperfective verb is given in the same manner as in the dictionary, with its perfective in parentheses, followed by its meaning. The imperfective is then conjugated in the present, past and future. The two imperative forms are then given, along with the conditional or subjunctive (which consists of the simple past tense followed by the particle бы which indicates the subjunctive) followed by the participles and the so-called adverbial participle, sometimes referred to as the gerundive. The various participles are listed separately in the dictionary as adjectives, since they are declined and agree in case, number and gender with the word modified. The adverbial participle is never declined and is capable of various translations into English as the examples at the end of this section show.

Conjugation I. делать (сделать) *v.*, make, do

1. Imperfective[1]

PRESENT INDICATIVE

я делаю	I am doing	мы делаем	we are doing
ты делаешь	you are doing	вы делаете	you are doing
он делает	he (it) is doing		
она делает	she (it) is doing	они делают	they are doing
оно делает	it is doing		

PAST INDICATIVE

я делал	I was doing	мы делали	we were doing
ты делал	you were doing	вы делали	you were doing
он делал	he (it) was doing		
она делала	she (it) was doing	они делали	they were doing
оно делало	it was doing		

FUTURE INDICATIVE

я буду делать	I shall do	мы будем делать	we shall do
ты будешь делать	you will do	вы будете делать	you will do
он будет делать	he (it) will do		
она будет делать	she (it) will do	они будут делать	they will do
оно будет делать	it will do		

CONDITIONAL (SUBJUNCTIVE)

я делал бы	мы делали бы
ты делал бы	вы делали бы
он делал бы	
она делала бы	они делали бы
оно делало бы	

Imperative. делай (*sing.*), делайте (*pl.*), do! make!

Participles

	Active		*Passive**	
Present	делающий	doing, making	делаемый	being made, being done
Past	делавший	(who was) doing, (who was) making	деланный	made

Adverbial participle. делая[2] doing, making, if we make, etc.

* There is another method of forming passive participles, namely the addition of the passive or reflexive suffix -ся to the active participle; this method is omitted from these tables, and the reader is referred to §5.3 below.

2. Perfective[1] (no present indicative)

PAST INDICATIVE

я сделал	I did	мы сделали	we did
ты сделал	you did	вы сделали	you did
он сделал	he (it) did		
она сделала	she (it) did	они сделали	they did
оно сделало	it did		

FUTURE INDICATIVE

я сделаю	I shall do	мы сделаем	we shall do
ты сделаешь	you will do	вы сделаете	you will do
он сделает	he (it) will do		
она сделает	she (it) will do	они сделают	they will do
оно сделает	it will do		

CONDITIONAL (SUBJUNCTIVE)

я сделал бы	мы сделали бы
ты сделал бы	вы сделали бы
он сделал бы	
она сделала бы	они сделали бы
оно сделало бы	

Imperative. сделай (sing.), сделайте (pl.)

Past Participles (no present participles).

Active сделавший having done, having made

Passive сделанный done, made, having been done

Adverbial Participle сделав[2] (сделавши) having done, having made

1. The principal difference between the imperfective and perfective must be emphasized: the latter implies a completion of the action. For this reason, there is no present tense of the perfective, although the form of the future perfective corresponds to that of the present imperfective. Very often the perfective future may be rendered quite accurately in translation by means of the present indicative in English.

2. Adverbial participles are never declined, and the translation varies according to the context, as the examples in 5.4 indicate.

Conjugation II. строить (построить) *v.*, construct, build

1. Imperfective

PRESENT INDICATIVE

я строю I construct, etc.	мы строим
ты строишь	вы строите
он (она, оно) строит	они строят

PAST INDICATIVE

я (ты, он) строил, она строила, оно строило, мы (вы, они) строили

FUTURE INDICATIVE

я буду строить, ты будешь строить, etc.

CONDITIONAL (SUBJUNCTIVE)

я (ты, он) строил бы, она строила бы, оно строило бы, мы (вы, они) строили бы

Imperative. строй (sing.), стройте (pl.)

Participles

	Active		*Passive*	
Present	строящий	constructing	(none in use)[1]	
Past	строивший	(which was) constructing	строенный	constructed, under construction

Adverbial Participle. строя constructing, if we construct

2. Perfective (no present indicative)

PAST INDICATIVE

я (ты, он) построил, она построила, оно построило, мы (вы, они) построили
I (have) constructed, etc.

FUTURE INDICATIVE

я построю I shall construct, etc.	мы построим
ты построишь	вы построите
он / она / оно } построит	они построят

CONDITIONAL (SUBJUNCTIVE)

я (ты, он) построил бы, она построила бы, etc.

Imperative. построй (sing.), постройте (pl.)

Past Participles. построивший (Act.) (which) constructed
построенный (Pass.) constructed

Adverbial Participle. построив (построивши) having constructed

1. Some of the participles which can conceivably be formed do not always exist in practice; in most cases the meaning of the verb being conjugated precludes the existence of the form. The missing participle here would ordinarily be строимый, but, according to authoritative Soviet references, the form does not exist in current usage, nor did the form строимый appear in any of the literature from which the vocabulary of this dictionary was compiled.

A number of verbs admit various changes in stem during conjugation. No attempt will be made here to classify such changes, but the verb conjugations given below contain some of the more "regular" changes in stem. The differences between imperfective and perfective are given in the dictionary.

Conjugation II. приводить (привести) *v.*, reduce, cite

1. Imperfective

PRESENT INDICATIVE

я привожу I reduce, etc.	мы приводим
ты приводишь	вы приводите
он / она / оно } приводит	они приводят

PAST INDICATIVE

я (ты, он) приводил, она приводила, оно приводило, мы (вы, они) приводили

FUTURE INDICATIVE

я буду приводить, ты будешь приводить, etc.

CONDITIONAL (SUBJUNCTIVE)

я (ты, он) приводил бы, она приводила бы, etc.

Imperative. приводи (sing.), приводите (pl.)

Participles

	Active		*Passive*	
Present	приводящий	reducing	приводимый	(being) reduced, reducible[1]
Past	приводивший	(which was) reducing	(not used)	

Adverbial Participle. приводя reducing, if we reduce

2. Perfective (no present indicative)

PAST INDICATIVE

я (ты, он) привел, она привела, оно привело, мы (вы, они) привели

FUTURE INDICATIVE

я приведу	мы приведем
ты приведешь	вы приведете
он / она / оно } приведет	они приведут

CONDITIONAL (SUBJUNCTIVE)

я (ты, он) привел бы, она привела бы, etc.

Participles. (no present participles)

Past. приведший (Active), приведенный (Passive)

Adverbial Participle. приведя (привевши)

1. One important use of this participle, in addition to its ordinary meaning as a passive participle, is to indicate a passive capability. Thus, the adjective "capable of being reduced" or "reducible" arises in this connection.

разлагать[1] **(разложить)** *v.*, decompose, rearrange, expand, factor, etc.[2]

1. Imperfective

PRESENT INDICATIVE

я разлагаю I expand, etc.	мы разлагаем
ты разлагаешь	вы разлагаете
он / она / оно } разлагает	они разлагают

PAST INDICATIVE

я (ты, он) разлагал, она разлагала, etc.

FUTURE INDICATIVE

я буду разлагать, etc.

CONDITIONAL (SUBJUNCTIVE)

я разлагал бы, etc.

Imperative. разлагай (sing.), разлагайте (pl.)

Participles

	Active	*Passive*
Present	разлагающий factoring	разлагаемый (being) factored
Past	(not regularly used)[3]	(not regularly used)[3]

Adverbial Participle. разлагая factoring

2. Perfective (no present indicative)

FUTURE INDICATIVE

я разложу I shall factor, (I factor) etc.	мы разложим
ты разложишь	вы разложите
он / она / оно } разложит	они разложат

PAST INDICATIVE

я (ты, он) разложил, она разложила, etc.

CONDITIONAL (SUBJUNCTIVE)

я разложил бы, etc.

Imperative. разложи (sing.), разложите (pl.)

Participles

Passive, present разложимый[4]

Active, past разложивший (who has) factored, (which has) factored

Passive, past разложенный factored

Adverbial Participle. разложив (разложивши) having factored

1. Note that the imperfective is Conjugation I, while the perfective is Conjugation II.

2. This verb has more meanings than indicated here; a more complete set of meanings is given in the dictionary.

3. The missing forms here are easy to construct; the endings are the same as those for делать in the table above.

4. Even though present participles are not usually formed from the perfective, the meaning of a certain verb may be such that a *verbal adjective* exists, having the form of a perfective present participle. If one wishes to insist, as is usually done, on the grammatical rule that perfective verbs have no present passive participles, then such apparent exceptions as разложимый must simply be given some other name, such as "verbal adjective". This change of name is the more natural because such forms almost never have any other meaning than that of passive *capability*, in this instance, the capability of being factored, i.e. factorable.

выполнять (выполить) *v.* fulfil, satisfy, accomplish, etc.

1. Imperfective

PRESENT INDICATIVE

я выполняю I fulfill, etc.	мы выполняем
ты выполняешь	вы выполняете
он, она, оно выполняет	они выполняют

PAST INDICATIVE

я (ты, он) выполнял, она выполняла, etc.

FUTURE INDICATIVE

я буду выполнять, etc.

CONDITIONAL (SUBJUNCTIVE)

я выполнял бы, etc.

Imperative. выполняй (sing.), выполняйте (pl.)

Participles

	Active	*Passive*
Present	выполняющий fulfilling	выполняемый (being) fulfilled
Past	(not in use)	(not in use)

Adverbial Participle. выполняя fulfilling, satisfying

2. Perfective (no present indicative)

PAST INDICATIVE

я выполнил, он выполнил, она выполнила, etc.

FUTURE INDICATIVE

я выполню I (shall) fulfill, etc.	мы выполним
ты выполнишь	вы выполните
он / она / оно } выполнит	они выполнят

CONDITIONAL (SUBJUNCTIVE)

я (ты, он) выполнил бы, etc.

Imperative. выполни (sing.), выполните (pl.)

Participles

Present passive выполнимый[1]

Past active выполнивший (which) fulfilled

Past passive выполненный fulfilled

Adverbial Participle. выполнив (выполнивши) having fulfilled

1. Another "verbal adjective" meaning here *realizable*, *practicable*, *feasible*

доказывать (доказать) *v.*, prove, demonstrate, show

1. Imperfective

PRESENT INDICATIVE

я доказываю	мы доказываем
ты доказываешь	вы доказываете
он / она / оно } доказывает	они доказывают

PAST INDICATIVE

я (ты, он) доказывал, etc.

FUTURE INDICATIVE

я буду доказывать, etc.

CONDITIONAL (SUBJUNCTIVE)

я доказывал бы, etc.

Imperative. (not in use)[1]

Participles

	Active	*Passive*
Present	доказывающий proving	доказываемый (which is) being proved
Past	(none in use)	(none in use)

Adverbial Participle. доказывая proving

2. Perfective (no present tense)

PAST INDICATIVE

я (ты, он) доказал, она доказала, etc.

FUTURE INDICATIVE

я докажу	мы докажем
ты докажешь	вы докажете
он / она / оно } докажет	они докажут

CONDITIONAL (SUBJUNCTIVE)

я (ты, он) доказал бы, etc.

Imperative. докажи (sing.), докажить, доказать[2] (pl.)

Participles

Present passive	доказуемый demonstrable, provable[3]
Past active	доказавший (who has, which has) proved
Past passive	доказанный proved, proven

Adverbial Participle. доказав (доказавши) having proved

1. The meaning of the verb requires a perfective aspect in the imperative mood.
2. The infinitive may also be used to express the imperative of a Russian verb and is frequently used with доказать.
3. Another verbal adjective.

Some verbs have the same form in the imperfective and perfective; this is generally true of verbs which are brought into Russian from another language and which end in -ировать, for example

дифференцировать, differentiate
интегрировать, integrate

The latter example is conjugated below and is typical of such verbs.[1]

PRESENT INDICATIVE

я интегрирую	мы интегрируем
ты интегрируешь	вы интегрируете
он / она / оно } интегрирует	они интегрируют

PAST INDICATIVE

я (ты, он) интегрировал, она интегрировала, etc.

FUTURE INDICATIVE

я буду интегрировать, etc.

CONDITIONAL (SUBJUNCTIVE)

я (ты, он) интегрировал бы, etc.

Imperative. интегрируй (sing.), интегрируйте (pl.)

Participles

	Active		*Passive*	
Present	интегрирующий	integrating	интегрируемый	(being) integrated, integrable
Past	интегрировавший	(having) integrated	интегрированный	integrated

Adverbial Participles

Present интегрируя integrating, if we integrate

Past интегрировав[2] (интегрировавши) having integrated

1. Whenever the use of the perfective aspect must be emphasized, another perfective is often formed by prefixing про- or с- to verbs of this type.

2. Although интегрировать is perfective as well as imperfective, the form проинтегрировав appears more frequently than the form listed above. проинтегрированный is also used as a past passive participle.

5.3. Reflexive and Passive Forms of Verbs

The reflexive pronoun себя (oneself), which was encountered in § 4, is contracted and appears as a suffix -ся to many verbs; some verbs never appear without this suffix, while for other verbs, the suffix is added to modify or change the meaning of the verb. The usual method of expressing the passive voice in Russian is to add the suffix -ся, although other forms already encountered may be rendered into English by means of the passive voice. Since the passive voice in Russian may be formed by means of the suffix -ся, the dictionary does not, in general, list separately the passive forms; for example, from the entry отображать (отобразить), *v., map, etc.*, one may form the passive отображаться (отобразиться), *v., to be mapped, etc.* The addition of the suffix -ся may make the verb reflexive in the pure sense, e.g. ограничивать, *to limit, to restrict* with the reflexive ending becomes ограничиваться, *to limit oneself* (*to*), *to restrict oneself* (*to*), but, because of the use of the suffix -ся to indicate the passive voice, the verb ограничиваться may also be translated *to be limited* (*by*), *to be restricted* (*by*); in such cases, the context of the Russian sentence determines how the verb is to be rendered into English. On the other hand, many Russian verbs are reflexive in form but without a non-reflexive form e.g. уславливаться (perf. условиться), *to stipulate.* In other instances, a non-reflexive form exists but is irrelevant to the technical literature.

The conjugation of a verb with the reflexive ending is achieved by the usual conjugation of the verb without the ending and then adding the ending -ся; the reflexive ending -ся is replaced by -сь after almost all verb forms ending in a vowel, the important exception being the adjectival participle forms where -ся is used with *all forms.*

касаться (коснуться) *v.*, be tangent to, touch, concern

1. Imperfective

PRESENT INDICATIVE

я касаюсь	мы касаемся
ты касаешься	вы касаетесь
он, она, оно } касается	они касаются

PAST INDICATIVE

я (ты, он) касался, она касалась, оно касалось, мы (вы, они) касались

FUTURE INDICATIVE

я буду касаться, etc.

Participles. касающийся (pres.), касавшийся (past)

(There are no passive participles.)

Adverbial Participle. касаясь

2. Perfective

FUTURE INDICATIVE

я коснусь	мы коснемся
ты коснешься	вы коснетесь
он, она, оно } коснется	они коснутся

PAST INDICATIVE

я (ты, он) коснулся, она коснулась, оно коснулось, мы (вы, они) коснулись

CONDITIONAL (SUBJUNCTIVE)

я (ты, он) коснулся бы, она коснулась бы, . . .

Participles. коснувшийся

Note that the ending -ся is used without exception in the declension of participles, e.g. сходящийся (converging, convergent) which arises from сходиться (to converge):

	Masc.	*Fem.*	*Neut.*	*Plural*
Nom.	сходящийся	сходящаяся	сходящееся	сходящиеся
Gen.	сходящегося	сходящейся	сходящегося	сходящихся
Dat.	сходящемуся	сходящейся	сходящемуся	сходящимся
Acc.	сходящийся	сходящуюся	сходящееся	сходящиеся
Instr.	сходящимся	сходящейся	сходящимся	сходящимися
Prep.	сходящемся	сходящейся	сходящемся	сходящихся

5.4. Some Comments on the Translation of Verb Forms

The difference in the sense of the imperfective and perfective can be emphasized by exhibiting both aspects of the same verb in one sentence. (It is recommended that each word in the sentence be looked up in the dictionary, and its form be determined from the appropriate section of §§ 2–5; superscripts refer to the comments immediately following the translation.)

(1) Прежде чем[1] **доказывать**[2], что все собственные значения матрицы A удовлетворяют[3] уравнению (4), мы **докажем**[4], что если $h(\lambda)$ — общий наибольший делитель[5] элементов присоединенной к $A-\lambda I$ матрицы[6], то[7] $\phi(\lambda) = h(\lambda)\psi(\lambda)$.

Прежде чем доказывать, что все собственные значения матрицы A *удовлетворяют уравнению* (4), *мы докажем, что если* $h(\lambda)$ — *общий наибольший делитель элементов присоединенной к* $A-\lambda I$ *матрицы, то* $\phi(\lambda) = h(\lambda)\psi(\lambda)$.

Before we go on to prove (or, Before we prove) that all the eigenvalues of the matrix A satisfy equation (4), we shall prove that if $h(\lambda)$ is the highest common divisor of the elements of the matrix (which is) adjoint to $A-\lambda I$, then $\phi(\lambda) = h(\lambda)\psi(\lambda)$.

1. Under the entry прежде appears the phrase прежде чем as a conjunction, meaning *before*, which is usually followed by an infinitive.
2. The infinitive here can be rendered in many ways, the simplest and most usual way being "Before proving that . . ."; the less common English expression in the translation has been used to emphasize the use of the imperfective aspect which must be explicit in Russian.
3. Imperfective infinitive is удовлетворять; the conjugation is like выполнять in the tables above.
4. Perfective form доказать from the imperfective infinitive доказывать (cf. tables above). Although докажем is first person plural, future indicative, the translation "we prove" is as correct as "we shall prove", since the two renderings are fully equivalent in the context of the sentence.
5. The expression общий наибольший делитель will be found listed in the dictionary after each of the three words in the phrase, since a literal rendering with the same word-order could conceivably lead to confusion, particularly since общий has other meanings.
6. The phrase присоединенной к $A-\lambda I$ матрицы is literally "of the adjoint to $A-\lambda I$ matrix" and is somewhat reminiscent of a construction in German. Note that the – between A and λI cannot be misinterpreted as a substitute for the verb *to be*, since Soviet mathematical writers are quite careful not to use the dash or hyphen for the verb *to be* whenever there is any possibility of confusion.
7. The word то is the conjunction *then*, not the demonstrative pronoun of § 4.3.

(2) Для каждой строго возрастающей[1] последовательности σ индексов множество A_σ открыто[2] в $L_{n+1,\ p+1}$ и насыщено[2] по $\Delta_{n,\ p}$; поэтому его[3] канонический образ C_σ в $P_{n,\ p}$ является[4] открытым[4] множеством[4], гомеоморфным фактормножеству множества A_σ по отношению[5] эквивалентности[5] θ_σ, индуцируемому[6] в A_σ отношением $\Delta_{n,\ p}$.

Для каждой строго возрастающей последовательности σ *индексов множество* A_σ *открыто в* $L_{n+1,\ p+1}$ *и насыщено по* $\Delta_{n,\ p}$; *поэтому его канонический образ* C_σ *в* $P_{n,\ p}$ *является открытым множеством, гомеоморфным фактормножеству множества* A_σ *по отношению эквивалентности* θ_σ, *индуцируемому в* A_σ *отношением* $\Delta_{n,\ p}$.

For every strictly increasing sequence of indices σ, the set A_σ is open in $L_{n+1,\ p+1}$ and saturated for $\Delta_{n,\ p}$; hence its canonical image C_σ in $P_{n,\ p}$ is an open set (which is)[7] homeomorphic to the quotient of the set A_σ by the equivalence relation θ_σ induced in A_σ by the relation $\Delta_{n,\ p}$.

1. Present participle, having the form of an adjective (cf. 5.2); this form is listed as an adjective in the dictionary.
2. Short form, neuter, of открытый (open) indicates a predicative use with the verb "to be" omitted; note the short form, neuter, of насыщенный (saturated), cf. 3.2.
3. Note that его is not declined, even though it is linked to образ; cf. 4.1.
4. The verb являться (to be) is followed by the instrumental case.
5. отношение эквивалентности (lit. *relation of equivalence*) is the usual way of expressing the English phrase *equivalence relation*. In Russian, the noun "equivalence" cannot be used as an adjective without adding an adjectival ending. It is quite possible to form the adjective эквивалентностный (equivalence, pert. to an equivalence) and write эквивалентностное отношение (equivalence relation), but it lacks one essential ingredient: it is not the idiomatic expression for "equivalence relation" in Russian.
6. This is the present passive participle индуцируемый of индуцировать (to induce) and has a second meaning "inducible"; both meanings are given in the dictionary.
7. This phrase in parentheses may or may not be inserted, at the discretion of the translator.

(3) Если областью[1], в которой задана[2] начальная температура $t(x, y, z)$, является все[3] пространство, то[4] решение может быть[5] записано[5] в замкнутой форме.

Если областью, в которой задана начальная температура $t(x, y, z)$, *является все пространство, то решение может быть записано в замкнутой форме.*

If the domain, in which the initial temperature $t(x, y, z)$, is prescribed, is the whole space, then the solution can be written in closed form.

1. Instrumental case (cf. 2.2, 4°) with являться (to be).
2. Short form, feminine, of заданный; a predicative use is indicated here, and the passive participle gives the passive sense to the translation (cf. 3.2).
3. все is an adjective, and its synonyms often give a smoother translation than "all".
4. The conjunction "then" rather than the neuter of тот.
5. The same use of the passive participle as in 2.; the link-verb быть must be used here following может. Note also that может быть as a phrase has the meaning "perhaps", but that the context rules out this possibility. See also 5.5. below.

(4) Для того чтобы[1] этот процесс имел[2] смысл, необходимо[3], чтобы[4] он давал[4] единственный результат.

Для того чтобы этот процесс имел смысл, необходимо, чтобы он давал единственный результат.

In order that this process have meaning, it is necessary that it give a unique result.

1. для того чтобы is the usual phrase "in order that", and the verb to follow is always subjunctive or conditional.
2. The conditional or subjunctive mood of иметь (to have); the particle бы has been attached to the что (that) in the clause.
3. Note the short form and the implied predicative.
4. The conditional of давать (to give) is давал бы, and the particle бы usually combines with что.

(5) Повторяя[1] это рассуждение, мы получим[2] тот же[3] результат для функции $f_n(x)$.

Повторяя это рассуждение, мы получим тот же результат для функции $f_n(x)$.

By repeating this argument, we obtain the same result for the function $f_n(x)$.

1. Adverbial participle of повторять (to repeat); the translation of повторяя could have been rendered by "Repeating" or "If we repeat", to suit the taste of the translator.
2. Perfective form, and the future "we shall obtain" has the same sense, in the context, as "we obtain".
3. Note the pair тот же under тот or under же in the dictionary.

(6) Распределение, задаваемое[1] функцей[2] плотности[2] $s_n(x)$ или функцей[2] распределения[2] $S_n(x)$ известно под названием *распределения Стьюдента* или *t-распределения*; оно было впервые использовано[3] в одной важной статистической проблеме В. Госсетом, писавшим[4] под псевдонимом «Стьюдент» (Student)[5].

Распределение, задаваемое функцей плотности $s_n(x)$ *или функцей распределения* $S_n(x)$ *известно под названием* распределения Стьюдента *или* t-распределения; *оно было впервые использовано в одной важной статистической проблеме В. Госсетом, писавшим под псевдонимом «Стьюдент» (Student).*

The distribution defined by the frequency function $s_n(x)$ or the distribution function $S_n(x)$ is known under the name of *Student's distribution* or the *t-distribution*; it was first used in an important statistical problem by W. Gosset, writing under the pseudonym of "Student".

1. Present passive participle задаваемый of задавать (to define, etc.)
2. Cf. note 5 under example 2° of this section.
3. Short form of the participle использованный; with было the verb is passive.
4. The past active participle писавший of писать (to write); it may also be rendered as "who wrote" or "who was writing", the latter expressing literally the imperfective aspect of the verb.
5. Whenever a Western surname is introduced into Russian for the first time, the original spelling in the Roman alphabet often follows the transliteration into Russian.

(7) Примеры § 1 показывают, что ряд может быть сходящимся,[1] не будучи[2] абсолютно сходящимся[1].

Примеры § 1 показывают, что ряд может быть сходящимся, не будучи абсолютно сходящимся.

The examples of § 1 show that a series can be convergent without being absolutely convergent.

1. Instrumental case of the predicate following the simple past or simple future of быть (cf. 5.1).
2. Adverbial participle of быть (cf. 5.6, 4°).

5.5. Some Special Verbs

A number of auxiliary verbs and forms, such as *must*, *can*, etc., will be treated in this section. Since such words can modify the meaning of a sentence extensively, the form and usage of such words will be discussed in some detail.

1°. **должен (must).** This word is used like a short adjective and is generally followed by the infinitive.

Singular		*Plural*
я должен	I must, etc.	мы должны
ты должен		вы должны
он должен }		
она должна }		они должны
оно должно }		

e.g. Должны быть удовлетворены граничные условия

Должны быть удовлетворены граничные условия

The boundary conditions must be satisfied.

Note that Должны agrees with условия and that the passive participle, short form, when combined with быть is equivalent to the present passive.

2°. **нужно (must, ought), нельзя (must not, cannot)** are not declined and are followed by the infinitive.

(1) Чтобы представить уравнение в номографической форме, нужно сначала найти эквивалентный детерминант.

Чтобы представить уравнение в номографической форме, нужно сначала найти эквивалентный детерминант.

To represent an equation nomographically (*lit.* in nomographic form), we must first find an equivalent determinant.

(2) Если скоростью частицы нельзя пренебречь по сравнению со скоростью света c или энергией ее нельзя пренебречь по сравнению с энергией покоящейся массы, то необходимо пользоваться формулой $\lambda_D = \ldots$

Если скоростью частицы нельзя пренебречь по сравнению со скоростью света с или энергией ее нельзя пренебречь по сравнению с энергией покоящейся массы, то необходимо пользоваться формулой $\lambda_D = \ldots$

If the velocity of the particle is not negligible compared to the velocity of light, c, or if the energy is not negligible compared to the rest mass energy, then it is necessary to use the formula $\lambda_D =\ldots$. (Literally, If one must not, or cannot, neglect the velocity of the particle in comparison to the velocity of light, c, or if one must not neglect the energy, etc.)

Note. In the scientific literature, the meaning of нельзя shifts from "must not" to "cannot" or "it is impossible", for example.

(3) Теорему Абеля[1] нельзя распространить на пути, касательные к единичной окружности.

Теорему Абеля нельзя распространить на пути, касательные к единичной окружности.

It is not possible to extend Abel's theorem to paths which are tangent to the unit circle.

1. Nominative: Абель.

Note. The English words "must", "ought to", and "should" may also be rendered by следует followed by the infinitive; the past is следовало бы (should have, ought to have), for example

(4) Следует быть осторожным при использовании этой формулы.

Следует быть осторожным при использовании этой формулы.

One must be careful in using this formula.

(5) Вам следовало бы исключить сначала A, затем B.

Вам следовало бы исключить сначала A, *затем* B.

You should have eliminated A first, and then B.

N.B. следует may also have its usual meaning "follows", for example

Из (2) следует, что . . .

Из (2) *следует, что* . . .

It follows from (2) that . . .

3°. **можно (may, can, be possible)** is not declined and is followed by the infinitive.

(1) Используя интеграл Фурье[1], можно сконструировать сферические или цилиндрические волны из плоских волн.

Используя интеграл Фурье, можно сконструировать сферические или цилиндрические волны из плоских волн.

By using the Fourier integral, it is possible to construct spherical or cylindrical waves out of plane waves.
Or, more freely,
If we use the Fourier integral, we may construct spherical or cylindrical waves out of plane waves.

1. Used here in the genitive, but Фурье is not declined.

(2) Самодуальному тензору $G^{\rho\sigma}$ можно сопоставить симметрический спинор второго ранга g_{rs}.

Самодуальному тензору $G^{\rho\sigma}$ можно сопоставить симметрический спинор второго ранга g_{rs}.

With a self-dual tensor $G^{\rho\sigma}$ one can associate a symmetric spinor g_{rs} of rank two. (*Or*: It is possible to associate with a self-dual tensor $G^{\rho\sigma}$ a symmetric spinor g_{rs} of rank two.)

(3) Для заданного ε можно найти такое[1] δ, что[1] $|I_1| < \varepsilon/3$ для всех значений n; фиксировав[2] это значение δ, можно найти такое[3] $n_0 = n_0(\delta)$, что[3] $|I_2| < \varepsilon/3$ и $|I_3| < \varepsilon/3$ при $n > n_0$.

Для заданного ε можно найти такое δ, что $|I_1| < \varepsilon/3$ для всех значений n; фиксировав это значение δ, можно найти такое $n_0 = n_0(\delta)$, что $|I_2| < \varepsilon/3$ и $|I_3| < \varepsilon/3$ при $n > n_0$.

For given ε, we can find δ such that $|I_1| < \varepsilon/3$ for all values of n; having fixed δ, we can find $n_0 = n_0(\delta)$ such that $|I_2| < \varepsilon/3$ and $|I_3| < \varepsilon/3$ for $n > n_0$.

1. Literally, "such a δ that"; this is the usual Russian construction.
2. Adverbial participle; note that фиксировать is both perfective and imperfective.
3. Same comment as in note 1.

4°. The verb мочь (can, be able to, may)

PRESENT INDICATIVE

я могу	I can, etc.	мы можем
ты можешь		вы можете
он, она, оно } может		они могут

PAST INDICATIVE

я (ты, он) мог, она могла, оно могло, они (мы, вы) могли

Present Participle. могущий, capable of, able to.

Past Participle. могший, (which, who) could.

The perfective is смочь, and the conjugation is the same as мочь. One example of he use of мочь was given in 5.4 (3°).

(1) Может показаться, что такое явление трудно объяснить

Может показаться, что такое явление трудно объяснить

This phenomenon may seem difficult to explain.

(2) Если мы можем располагать большим числом точных наблюдений, . . .

Если мы можем располагать большим числом точных наблюдений, . . .

If we could have at our disposal a large number of precise observations, . . .

(3) Видоизменения центральной предельной теоремы могут все же показать, что распределение приближенно нормально.

Видоизменения центральной предельной теоремы могут все же показать, что распределение приближенно нормально.

Modifications of the central limit theorem may still show that the distribution is approximately normal.

(4) Если мы интегрируем функцую $(1 + x^2)^{-1}$ от 0 до ∞, мы сможем определить значение π.

Если мы интегрируем функцую $(1 + x^2)^{-1}$ *от* 0 *до* ∞, *мы сможем определить значение* π.

If we integrate the function $(1 + x^2)^{-1}$ from 0 to ∞, we shall be able to determine the value of π.

(5) Ответ на этот вопрос может дать ключ ко всей проблеме.

Ответ на этот вопрос может дать ключ ко всей проблеме.

The answer to this question may give the key to the whole problem.

5.6. Some Irregular Verbs

Some common verbs, which have certain irregularities, are given in the list below. The conjugations are given in a form which, while abbreviated, indicates the nature of the singularities. Missing forms, such as the conditional, future, etc., may be constructed by the rules given earlier.

(1) брать (взять, cf. (3) below), take

Present. беру, берешь, берет, берем, берете, берут

Past. брал, брала, брало, брали

Participles. берущий (pres.), бравший (past)

Adverbial Participle. беря.

(2) вести, lead, conduct

Present. веду, ведешь, ведет, ведем, ведете, ведут

Past. вел, вела, вело, вели

Participles, Active. ведущий (pres.), ведший (past)
Passive. ведомый (pres.), веденный (past)

Adverbial Participle. ведя.

(3) взять (perf. of брать, cf. (1) above), take

Future. возьму, возьмешь, возьмет, возьмем, возьмете, возьмут

Past. взял, взяла, взяло, взяли

Participles, Past. взявший (active), взятый (pass.)
Adverbial Participle. взяв.

(4) быть (cf. 5.1 for other forms), to be
Participles, Active. бывший (past), будущий (future)
Adverbial Participle. будучи

(5) давать (дать, cf. (6) below), give
Present. даю, даешь, дает, даем, даете, дают
Past. давал, давала, давало, давали
Participles. дававший (past act.), даваемый (pres. pass.)
Adverbial Participles. давая

(6) дать (perf. of давать, cf. (5) above), give
Future. дам, дашь, даст, дадим, дадите, дадут
Past. дал, дала, дало, дали
Participles, Past. давший (act.), данный (pass.)
Adverbial Participle. дав (давши)

(7) ехать (идти, cf. (8) below), go (ride)
Present. еду, едешь, едет, едем, едете, едут
Past. ехал, ехала, ехало, ехали
Participles, Active. едущий (pres.), ехавший (past)

(8) идти (from ехать), go
Present. иду, идешь, идет, идем, идете, идут
Past. шел, шла, шло, шли
Participles, Active. идущий (pres.), шедший (past)
Adverbial Participle. идя

(9) нести (понести), bear, carry
Present. несу, несешь, несет, несем, несете, несут
Past. нес, несла, несло, несли
Participles, Active. несущий (pres.), несший (past)
Passive. несомый (pres.), несенный (past)

(10) открыть (perf. of открывать), open, discover
Future. открою, откроешь, откроет, откроем, откроете, откроют
Past. открыл, открыла, открыло, открыли

Participles, Past. открывший (act.), открытый (pass.)
Adverbial Participle. открыв

(11) пойти (perf. of идти and ехать) go, begin
Future. пойду, пойдешь, пойдет, пойдем, пойдете, пойдут
Past. пошел, пошла, пошло, пошли
Participle, Active. пошедший
Adverbial Participle. пойдя

(12) понять (perf. of понимать), understand
Future. пойму, поймешь, поймет, поймем, поймете, поймут
Past. понял, поняла, поняло, поняли
Participles, Past. понявший (act.), понятый (pass.)
Adverbial Participle. поняв.

§ 6. PREPOSITIONS AND THEIR USE

Some prepositions have been encountered in the illustrative sentences in § 5, although no explicit mention has been made of their use. As the previous sample sentences have already shown, the use of the preposition in Russian is not essentially different from its use in, say, German, in the sense that the case of the noun modified by the preposition depends on the preposition, and, whenever a preposition governs more than one case, on the particular meaning of the preposition.

Since Russian is more highly inflected than the other international scientific languages, it is possible to introduce certain forms of nouns and verbs which serve in the capacity of prepositions, for example, the instrumental case кругом of круг (circle) is used as a preposition governing the genitive case and meaning "around", while the adverbial participle кончая of the verb кончать (to end) is used as a preposition governing the instrumental case and meaning "until".

The meanings of many of the common English prepositions are already embodied in the case endings of the Russian nouns and pronouns; the most obvious instance is, of course, the implicit rendering of the preposition "of" by the genitive case, the preposition "by" with the instrumental, e.g. примененный автором (applied by the author), etc. The table below gives some of the more commonly used Russian prepositions and the corresponding cases together with some typical phrases; for the sake of brevity, the repetition of the phrase in italics has been omitted. As can be seen from the illustrations, various prepositions may be used interchangeably.

Preposition	*Case*	*Illustration*
без (безо)[1] without	Gen.	без потери общности without loss of generality; без кратных точек without multiple points

Preposition	*Case*	*Illustration*
благодаря[2] due to, because of	Dat.	благодаря применению новых методов because of the application of new methods; благодаря сферической симметрии потенциала V because of the spherical symmetry of the potential V
в (во) in, into, at, on, to	Acc.	множество A переходит в множество B the set A goes into a set B;
	Prep.	в точке z_0 at the point z_0; почти во всех точках множества E at almost all points of the set E; в результате as a result; в 1952 г. in 1952
вблизи near, in the vicinity of	Gen.	поле сконцентрируется вблизи экваториальной плоскости the field is concentrated near the equatorial plane; Если $f(z)$ ограничена вблизи особых точек, . . . If $f(z)$ is bounded in the vicinity of the singular points, . . .
вдоль along, down, via, around	Gen.	интеграл взятый вдоль единичной окружности the integral taken around the unit circle; интеграл взят вдоль контура C the integral is taken along the contour C; вдоль соответствующих сторон along the corresponding sides
включая including, inclusive of	Acc.	включая бесконечно удаленную точку including the point at infinity
вместо instead of, in place of	Gen.	вместо обычных функций instead of the usual functions
вне outside, exterior to	Gen.	вне единичной окружности outside the unit circle, exterior to the unit circle

Preposition	*Case*	*Illustration*
внутри inside, interior to, on compact subsets of	Gen.	внутри области D interior to the domain D; равномерно сходится внутри области D converges uniformly on compact subsets of the domain D
внутрь in, into, inside	Prep.	где $\partial/\partial n$ — производная по нормали, направленной внутрь области where $\partial/\partial n$ is the normal derivative directed into the domain
вокруг around, about	Gen.	Интеграл взят вокруг эллипса E The integral is taken around the ellipse E; вращение вокруг точки $w = 0$ a rotation about the point $w = 0$
для for	Gen.	для всех n for all n; для того чтобы in order that
до to, up to, until, with respect to	Gen.	мы интегрируем от точки z_1 до точки z_2 we integrate from the point z_1 to the point z_2; расстояние до изображения distance to the image (i.e., image distance); приведены выражения только до членов третьего порядка expressions are given only up to the third order; дополнение A до полного пространства the complement of A with respect to the whole space
за for, as, at, in, over, across, beyond, with	Acc.	продолжать $f(z)$ за единичный круг to continue $f(z)$ beyond the unit circle; за период немногим более четырех лет in a period of a little over four years; за время t_0 at time t_0; Если за закон композиции принять сложение двух чисел из $I, \ldots$ If we take as[3] the law of composition the addition of two numbers of $I, \ldots$;

Preposition	*Case*	*Illustration*
за (cont.) for, as, at, in, over, across, beyond, with	Acc.	за один оборот in one revolution (per revolution); число частиц рассеянных за единицу времени the number of particles scattered per unit time;
	Instr.	за исключением величины A with the exception of the quantity A
из of, out of, by, from	Gen.	меньший из элементов A, B the smaller of the elements A, B; одно из множеств E_n one of the sets E_n; состоящий из конечного числа дуг consisting of a finite number of arcs; Из (1) следует, что . . . It follows from (1) that . . .; Многочлены определяются из равенств $A_i = B_i$ The polynomials are defined by the equalities $A_i = B_i$
из-за because of, from behind	Gen.	Последнюю из теорем не приводим из-за громоздкости предварительных условий We do not cite the last of the theorems because of the awkwardness of the preliminary conditions[4]
изнутри in, from within	Gen.	Жидкость вытекает через ds изнутри круга The liquid flows across ds from within the circle
исключая[5] except, except for	Acc.	Пусть u, v и U, V — две пары функций, обладающие всеми указанными в определении (6) свойствами, исключая отношение (1) Let u, v and U, V be two pairs of functions having all the properties mentioned in Definition (6) except for the relation (1)
к (ко) to, towards, at, on	Dat.	правая часть стремится к нулю the right-hand side tends to zero; P_n стремится к некоторому пределу P_n tends to some limit;

Preposition	*Case*	*Illustration*
к (ко) (cont.) to, towards, at, on	Dat.	произведение расходится к нулю the product diverges to zero; теорема применена к контуру охватывающему начало the theorem is applied to a contour which includes the origin; ко времени написания at the time of writing; замечания к предыдущей теореме remarks on the previous theorem
кончая until, ending with	Instr.	кончая октябрем until October
кроме except, besides	Gen.	кроме точек множества мера которого равна нулю except for a set of measure zero[6]; кроме случая, в котором ... except for the case in which ...
между between	Instr.	между этими точками between these points; отношение между уравнениями (1) и (2) the relation between equations (1) and (2)
на on, onto, at, about, by, for, into	Prep.	на границе $u(x, y) = 0$ on the boundary, $u(x, y) = 0$ умножая уравнение (8) на e^{-xt} и интегрируя, ... if we multiply (8) by e^{-xt} and integrate, ...;
	Acc.	ограничения на поведение $f(z)$ restrictions on the behavior of $f(z)$; отображая круг $\|w\| < 1$ на круг $\|z\| < 1, \ldots$ if we map the circle $\|w\| < 1$ onto the circle $\|z\| < 1, \ldots$ задача на обтекание a flow problem (a problem on flow); на расстояние r от начала at a distance r from the origin; вращение на некоторый угол a rotation about some angle; Области D_n разобьем на два класса We (shall) divide the domains D_n into two classes;

Preposition	*Case*	*Illustration*
на (cont.) on, onto, at, about, by, for, into	Acc.	сила на единицу объема force per unit volume с характеристиками, отличающимися от характеристик $f(z)$ на величину порядка ε with characteristics differing from the characteristics of $f(z)$ by a quantity of the order of ε
над over, above, at	Instr.	слой над x a fibre over x; высота над осью height above the axis; пики над точками $z = n$ the peaks over the points $z = n$
начиная с beginning with	Gen.	начиная с достаточно больших значений n beginning with sufficiently large values of n;
несмотря на in spite of, despite	Acc.	несмотря на то, что $f(x)$ непрерывна, . . . in spite of the fact that $f(x)$ is continuous, . . .
о (об, обо) on, about, concerning	Prep.	теорема о среднем значении mean-value theorem (theorem about the mean value); о высших инвариантах Хопфа on the higher Hopf invariants; об одном обобщении функций concerning a generalization of functions
около about, near, by, close to	Gen.	эмпирические значения j_p обычно составляют около $j_T/3$ empirical values of j_p are usually about one-third of j_T; Полное движение ускоряемых частиц можно описать колебаниями их около адиабатически изменяющейся равновесной орбиты The general motion of accelerated particles can be described by their oscillations about an adiabatically varying equilibrium orbit

Preposition	*Case*	*Illustration*
от from, of, on	Gen.	интеграл не зависит от выбора областей D_n the integral does not depend on the choice of the domains D_n; независимый от выбора базиса independent of the choice of basis; Мы переходим от одной системы к новой системе We go over from one system to a new system
относительно with respect to, over, about (concerning)	Gen.	гиперкомплексная система относительно коммутативного поля a hypercomplex system over a commutative field; Поле Σ расширения называется алгебраическим относительно Δ, если ... An extension field Σ is called algebraic over Δ if ... ; гармоническая мера E относительно области D the harmonic measure of E with respect to the domain D; относительно функции $T(t)$, см. § 2, п. 1 concerning the function $T(t)$, cf. § 2, par. 1
перед in front of, before, preceding, compared to	Instr.	Цифры в круглых скобках, стоящие перед различными группами обозначений Numbers in parentheses preceding various groups of symbols; Перед эпсилоновыми доказательствами вставляется интуитивный набросок Preceding the epsilon-proofs, there is an intuitive sketch
по by, on, in, according to, with respect to, up to	Dat.	по теореме 1 by Theorem 1; индукция по n induction on n; разложение по степеням z expansion in powers of z; первое слагаемое по модулю не превосходит ε the first term does not exceed ε in modulus;

Preposition	*Case*	*Illustration*
по (cont.) by, on, in, according to, with respect to, up to	Dat.	дифференцируя (19) по x и y, . . . if we differentiate (19) with respect to x and y, . . . лекция по теории идеалов a lecture on the theory of ideals; по отношению к дуге Γ with respect to the arc Γ; по отношению E modulo E; сходится по мере converges in measure; по всем некасательным путям along all non-tangential paths
под under, by, at	Instr.	под знаком интеграла under the integral sign; под углом ϑ at an angle ϑ; Под n-м корнем из единицы подразумеваем корень полинома $x^n - 1$ By an n-th root of unity we mean a root of the polynomial $x^n - 1$
после after, following	Gen.	после отображения B на B_1 following a mapping of B onto B_1; после подстановки after a substitution
при for, at, under, by, on	Prep.	при фиксированном r for fixed r; при всех $n > N_0$ for all $n > N_0$; при угле падания at the angle of incidence; при нормальном падении at normal incidence; при условиях теоремы 1 under the hypotheses of Theorem 1; При разложении по степеням x мы получаем ряд (1) By (on) expanding in powers of x, we obtain the series (1); при конформном отображении круга $\|w\| < 1$ на круг $\|z\| < 1$, . . . under a conformal mapping of the circle $\|w\| < 1$ onto the circle $\|z\| < 1$, . . .

Preposition	*Case*	*Illustration*
против against, opposite, facing	Gen.	против паза ротора opposite the slot of the rotor; против часовой стрелки counter-clockwise
путем by, by means of	Gen.	путем разложения по степеням x by means of an expansion in powers of x; путем сопоставления by way of contrast; Путем сравнения (1) с ранее установленным Гулдом выражением для $1 - 1$ выводится тождество $0 \equiv 0$. By comparison of (1) with an expression for $1 - 1$ established earlier by Gould, the identity $0 \equiv 0$ is deduced.
с (со) with, of, on	Instr.	со скоростью v with velocity v; с равенством только для $A = A$ with equality only for $A = A$; корень с порядком n a root of order n;
	Gen.	с другой стороны on the other hand; с 1952 г. since 1952; с бесконечно большой длиной волны of infinite wave length
согласно by, according to	Dat.	согласно предыдущему, $A = 0$ by the preceding, $A = 0$; согласно определению according to the definition
среди among	Gen.	среди экстримальных функций among the extremal functions
у[7] by, with, on, of	Gen.	у него решение he has a solution[8]; Изложение у нас более подробное, чем в [1] Our account is more detailed than [that given] in [1];

Preposition	*Case*	*Illustration*
у[7] (cont.) by, with, on, of	Gen.	Для молекул, у которых инверсионным удвоением пренебрегать нельзя, . . . For molecules whose inversion doubling cannot be neglected, . . .; Штрих у знаков суммы означает, что . . . The prime on the summation signs means that . . .
через across, by, in terms of	Acc.	поток через единичную площадку the flow across a unit area; выражаются через импульсы (they) are expressed in terms of the momenta; функция продолжается через дугу A the function is continued across the arc A; Обозначим через $[a]$, как обычно, целую часть числа a Let us denote by $[a]$, as is customary, the integral part of the number a; Элементы множества A могут быть обозначены через $a_1, a_2, \ldots$ The elements of the set A can be denoted by $a_1, a_2, \ldots$; прямы, не проходящие через начало straight lines not passing through the origin.

1. Forms in parentheses are used to facilitate the pronunciation of the resultant pair of words.
2. Adverbial participle of благодарить (to thank), meaning literally "thanking".
3. The word "as" is a bit smoother here than "for".
4. The reader of a reviewing journal will be familiar with such a statement!
5. This is the adverbial participle formed from исключать and means literally "excluding" or "excepting". The word has a second meaning in extensive use, for example

Исключая t из двух последних равенств, получаем $s = 1$.

If we eliminate t from the last two equalities, we obtain $s = 1$.

6. Literally, "except for points of a set, the measure of which is equal to zero"; the Russian is frequently phrased in this way.
7. An idiomatic way of expressing the sense of the English "to have" is by the use of this preposition.
8. Literally "By him is a solution".

§ 7. MISCELLANEOUS

7.1. Cardinal and Ordinal Numbers

The following table contains the usual cardinal and ordinal numbers:

1.	один (*m.*), одна (*f.*), одно (*n.*)	первый, первая, первое, first
2.	два (*m.*), две (*f.*), два (*n.*)	второй, вторая, второе, second, etc.

3.	три	третий, третья, третье
4.	четыре	четвертый
5.	пять	пятый
6.	шесть	шестой
7.	семь	седьмой
8.	восемь	восьмой
9.	девять	девятый
10.	десять	десятый
11.	одиннадцать	одиннадцатый
12.	двенадцать	двенадцатый
13.	тринадцать	тринадцатый
14.	четырнадцать	четырнадцатый
15.	пятнадцать	пятнадцатый
16.	шестнадцать	шестнадцатый
17.	семнадцать	семнадцатый
18.	восемнадцать	восемнадцатый
19.	девятнадцать	девятнадцатый
20.	двадцать	двадцатый
21.	двадцать один (*m*)	двадцать первый (*m.*)
	двадцать одна (*f.*)	двадцать первая (*f.*)
	двадцать одно (*n.*)	двадцать первое (*n.*) etc.
25.	двадцать пять	двадцать пятый
30.	тридцать	тридцатый
40.	сорок	сороковой
50.	пятьдесят	пятидесятый
60.	шестьдесят	шестидесятый
70.	семьдесят	семидесятый
80.	восемьдесят	восьмидесятый
90.	девяносто	девяностый
100.	сто	сотый
200.	двести	двухсотый
300.	триста	трехсотый
400.	четыреста	четырехсотый
500.	пятьсот	пятисотый
600.	шестьсот	шестисотый
700.	семьсот	семисотый
800.	восемьсот	восьмисотый
900.	девятьсот	девятисотый
1000.	тысяча	тысячный
10^6.	миллион	миллионный
10^9.	миллиард	миллиардный
10^{12}.	биллион	биллионный

The cardinal numbers are declined, and the details are given in 7.2. The ordinals are declined like adjectives and will not be treated further. The case of the noun qualified by a numeral is treated in 7.3.

It must be remarked that in mathematical Russian, as in mathematical English, it is customary to use digits rather than words to describe the number of objects under discussion, e.g., 12 групп (12 groups) rather than двенадцать групп (twelve groups).

7.2. The Declension of Numerals

The numeral один (one) agrees in gender, number and case with the noun; in this respect it is much like an adjective. The use of the plural will be shown by examples in 7.3.

	Masc.	*Fem.*	*Neut.*	*Plural*
Nom.	один	одна	одно	одни
Gen.	одного	одной	одного	одних
Dat.	одному	одной	одному	одним
Acc.	один	одну	одно	одни
Instr.	одним	одной	одним	одними
Prep.	одном	одной	одном	одних

The number два (two) has a feminine form (две), the neuter form coinciding with the masculine, and its declension is given in the table below.

	Masc.	*Fem.*	*Neut.*
Nom.	два	две	два
Gen.	двух	двух	двух
Dat.	двум	двум	двум
Acc.	два	две	два
Instr.	двумя	двумя	двумя
Prep.	двух	двух	двух

All other simple numerals do not distinguish gender, and the cases of the cardinal numbers ending in -ь (from пять to тридцать) are formed like those of the feminine nouns of 2.2 (4°), except for восемь which has a root change indicated in the following table:

Nom.	три	четыре	пять	восемь
Gen.	трех	четырех	пяти	восьми
Dat.	трем	четырем	пяти	восьми
Acc.	три	четыре	пять	восемь
Instr.	тремя	четырьмя	пятью	восемью
Prep.	трех	четырех	пяти	восьми

The numbers сорок (forty), девяносто (ninety) and сто (hundred) have the forms сорока, девяноста and ста, respectively, in all cases except the accusative which coincides with the nominative, while the numerals пятьдесят (fifty), шестьдесят (sixty), семьдесят (seventy) and восемьдесят (eighty) are declined as follows:

Nom.-Acc.	пятьдесят	шестьдесят	семьдесят	восемьдесят
Instr.	пятьюдесятью	шестьюдесятью	семьюдесятью	восемьюдесятью
All other	пятидесяти	шестидесяти	семидесяти	восьмидесяти

Among the cardinal numbers from двести (two hundred) to девятьсот (nine hundred), there are three distinct endings and the declensions are typified in the following table:

Nom.	двести (200)	триста (300)	пятьсот (500)
Gen.	двесот	трисот	пятьсот
Dat.	двестам	тристам	пятьстам
Acc.	двести	триста	пятьсот
Instr.	двестами	тристами	пятьстами
Prep.	двестах	тристах	пятьстах

The numbers тысяча, миллион, миллиард, etc., are treated as nouns and are declined accordingly.

The declension of a compound numeral such as двадцать пять (twenty-five) or тысяча три (a thousand and three) is achieved by the simultaneous declension of the component parts of the compound numeral. In forming the ordinal number of a compound numeral, only the last part is in the form of an adjective; thus, for the numbers just mentioned,

двадцать пятый twenty-fifth

тысяча третий thousand and third.

7.3. The Use of Numerals

It has been mentioned already that the number один agrees in case, number and gender with the noun which it qualifies. The plural form, одни, is used whenever the noun to which it refers has no singular, for example

Если одни часы колеблются с периодом T, . . .

If one clock vibrates with period T, . . .

A second use of the plural одни may occur with one of the alternative meanings of один (e.g. some, alone, etc.), for example

Одни математики согласились с Лобачевскому.

Some mathematicians agreed with Lobatchevsky.

A noun following one of the numbers два, три or четыре is usually in the genitive singular if the case of the numeral is nominative or accusative in the sentence. Thus for метр (meter)

Nom.	два метра[1]
Gen.	двух метров
Dat.	двум метрам
Acc.	два метра[1]
Instr.	двумя метрами
Prep.	двух метрах

1. Note that these forms are genitive singular while all other forms are the plural forms of the corresponding cases.

For all other numerals except compound numerals having два, три or четыре as the last number, the genitive plural of the noun is used in the nominative and accusative forms. The reader will find, however, that these rules are not followed as strictly as he might wish, but there is one compensating factor: There is seldom any doubt about the meaning of a Russian sentence involving the enumeration of mathematical objects. All the following illustrations are taken *verbatim* from current Soviet literature:

(1) Пусть i, j, k — три вектора единичной длины, . . .

Let i, j, k be three vectors of unit length, . . .

(2) Эти функции образуют шесть групп по четыре функции в каждой.

These functions form six groups with four functions in each group.

(3) Если угол между двумя зеркалами равен α, . . .

If the angle between the two mirrors is equal to α, . . .

(Here the phrase "two mirrors" does not appear in the capacity of a nominative or an accusative, but as the object of между, which governs the instrumental case, so that both numeral and noun appear in the instrumental case.)

(4) Вводя три единичных вектора i_1, i_2, i_3, . . .

If we introduce the three unit vectors, i_1, i_2, i_3, . . .

(Note that whenever an adjective is interposed between the numeral and the noun being qualified, the adjective is always *plural* even if the noun is in the genitive *singular*. The case of the interposed adjective seems to vary from writer to writer; some using the genitive plural and an equal number using the nominative or the accusative plural.)

(5) Пусть уравнение $L = 0$ имеет n различных корней.

Let the equation $L = 0$ have n distinct roots.

(Here the numerical n takes the genitive plural.)

(6) V является функцей 12 величин.

V is a function of 12 variables.

(7) Эти $4(N-1)$ уравнений дают $4(N-1)$ величины x_i, y_i, z_i, t_i.

These $4(N-1)$ equations yield the $4(N-1)$ quantities x_i, y_i, z_i, t_i.

7.4. Indefinite Numerals

In the illustrations (5) and (7) of 7.3, the numerals were unspecified and governed the genitive plural of the noun under consideration although the latter example contained an interesting deviation. The words много (many, much), мало (little, few), несколько (several, some, a few) are also considered to be indefinite numerals and are followed by the genitive plural whenever the noun under consideration can be counted and by the genitive singular whenever the noun denotes something which can be measured but not counted, e.g., энергия (energy) and свет (light).

(1) Приведем несколько примеров.

We cite a few examples.

(2) Имеется много различных вариантов.

Many different variants are possible.

(3) мало света.

a little light.

A

а, and, but, while; **не . . . , а . . . ,** not . . . , but . . . ; **а именно,** namely; **а не то,** or else; **а так же,** just as; **а так как,** and since, now as
а-, *prefix*, non-
абака, *f.*, abacus
абгомотопический, *adj.*, abhomotopy
абелевость, *f.*, commutativity
абелевский, *adj.*, abelian
абелевый, *adj.*, abelian
аберрационный, *adj.*, aberrational
аберрация, *f.*, aberration, deviation, error
абзац, *m.*, indentation, paragraph, item
абонент, *m.*, subscriber
абрис, *m.*, contour, outline, sketch
абсолютный, *adj.*, absolute
абсолютно, *adv.*, absolutely; **абсолютно наименьший вычет,** least positive residue
абсорбент, *m.*, absorbent
абсорбер, *m.*, absorber
абсорбировать, *v.*, absorb
абсорбирующий, *adj.*, absorbing, absorptive
абсорбция, *f.*, absorption
абстрагировать, *v.*, abstract
абстрагируясь, *adv. part.*, abstracting, generalizing, if we abstract
абстрактность, *f.*, abstractness, abstraction
абстрактный, *adj.*, abstract
абстракция, *f.*, abstraction
абсурд, *m.*, absurdity
абсурдность, *f.*, absurdity; **абсурдность допущенного очевидна,** the absurdity of the assumption is obvious
абсурдный, *adj.*, absurd, inept, preposterous
абсцисса, *f.*, abscissa, *x*-coordinate
авария, *f.*, accident, wreck, damage, mishap
авиа-, *prefix*, air-, aero-; e.g. **авиабаза,** airbase
авиационный, *adj.*, aviation
авиация, *f.*, aviation
автоблокировка, *f.*, automatic block system
автодистрибутивность, *f.*, autodistributivity
автодуальный, *adj.*, autodual; **автодуальное отображение,** autoduality
автоколебание, *n.*, auto-oscillation
автоколебательный, *adj.*, self-vibrating, self-oscillating
автокоррелированный, *adj.*, autocorrelated
автокорреляционный, *adj.*, autocorrelated, self-correlated
автокорреляция, *f.*, auto-correlation
автомат, *m.*, automatic machine; **автоматы,** *pl.*, automata
автоматизация, *f.*, automation
автоматизированный, *adj.*, automatized, automated
автоматизировать, *v.*, automatize
автоматизм, *m.*, automatism
автоматика, *f.*, automation
автоматически, *adv.*, automatically
автоматический, *adj.*, automatic
автомашина, *f.*, truck, motor vehicle, lorry
автомобиль, *m.*, motor car, autocar, automobile
автоморфизм, *m.*, automorphism
автоморфность, *f.*, automorphism, automorphy
автоморфный, *adj.*, automorphic
автономность, *f.*, autonomy, self-regulation
автономный, *adj.*, autonomous, self-governing, self-regulating
автопараллельный, *adj.*, self-parallel, autoparallel
автопилот, *m.*, automatic pilot, mechanical pilot, robot pilot
автополярность, *f.*, self-polarity

автополярный, *adj.*, self-polar, autopolar
автопроективитет, *m.*, autoprojectivity
автопроективный, *adj.*, self-projective, autoprojective
автор, *m.*, author
авторегрессивный, *adj.*, autoregressive
авторегрессионный, *adj.*, autoregressive
авторегрессия, *f.*, autoregression
автореферат, *f.*, review by the author
авторский, *adj.*, pertaining to author
автотопия, *f.*, autotopy
агглютинативный, *adj.*, agglutinative
агглютинирующий, *adj.*, agglutinating
аггрегат, cf. **агрегат**
аггрегатный, cf. **агрегатный**
агент, *m.*, agent, factor
агрегат, *m.*, aggregate, set, collection, assembly
агрегатный, *adj.*, aggregate, assembly
агрегация, *f.*, set, aggregate, collection
агрономический, *adj.*, agricultural
адаптация, *f.*, adaptation
адаптер, *m.*, adapter
адаптированный, *adj.*, adapted
адаптировать, *v.*, adapt
адвекция, *f.*, advection
аддитивность, *f.*, additivity
аддитивный, *adj.*, additive
аддиционный, *adj.*, additional, addition
адекватно, *adv.*, adequately, sufficiently, equally
адекватность, *f.*, adequacy, sufficiency
адекватный, *adj.*, adequate, sufficient, equal to
адиабата, *f.*, adiabatic curve
адиабатический, *adj.*, isentropic, adiabatic
адиабатичный, *adj.*, adiabatic
адиабатный, *adj.*, adiabatic
-адический, *suffix*, -adic
адресный, *adj.*, address
адсорбирование, *n.*, adsorption
адсорбированный, *adj.*, adsorbed
адсорбировать, *v.*, adsorb
адсорбция, *f.*, adsorption
адсорпция, *f.*, adsorption
адъюнкт, *m.*, adjoint, adjunct, cofactor
адэрентный, *adj.*, adherent
азарт, *m.*, gambling
азартный, *adj.*, gambling, risky; **азартная игра,** game of chance, gambling (game)
азимут, *m.*, azimuth
азимутальный, *adj.*, azimuth
азот, *m.*, nitrogen
академик, *m.*, academician
академия, *f.*, academy; **академия наук,** academy of sciences
аккомодация, *f.*, accommodation, adaptation
аккреция, *f.*, accretion
аккумулирование, *n.*, accumulation
аккумулированный, *adj.*, accumulated, stored
аккумулировать, *v.*, accumulate
аккумулятор, *m.*, accumulator, storage battery
аккумуляция, *f.*, accumulation
аккуратно, *adv.*, accurately, exactly, neatly
аккуратность, *f.*, accuracy, exactness, neatness, punctuality
аккуратный, *adj.*, accurate, exact, neat, regular
акселератор, cf. **акцелератор**
аксиальный, *adj.*, axial
аксиома, *f.*, axiom, postulate; **аксиома выбора**, axiom of choice
аксиоматизация, *f.*, axiomatization
аксиоматизировать, *v.*, axiomatize
аксиоматизируемость, *f.*, axiomatization, axiomatizability
аксиоматизируемый, *adj.*, axiomatizable
аксиоматизуемость, *f.*, axiomatizability
аксиоматика, *f.*, axiomatics
аксиоматический, *adj.*, axiomatic
аксонометрический, *adj.*, axonometric
аксонометрия, *f.*, axonometry, perspective geometry
акт, *m.*, act
актив, *n.*, assets
активатор, *m.*, activator, catalyst
активация, *f.*, activation, activization, sensitization

активизировать, *v.*, activate, promote
активностный, *adj.*, activity
активность, *f.*, activity; **нулевая активность,** excluded activity; **ненулевая активность,** included activity
активный, *adj.*, active, live
актиниевый, *adj.*, actinic, radioactive
актуальность, *f.*, urgency
актуальный, *adj.*, actual; urgent
акустика, *f.*, acoustics
акустический, *adj.*, acoustic
акцелератор, *m.*, accelerator
акцелерометр, *m.*, accelerometer, acceleration gauge
акцепт, *m.*, acceptance
акцептант, *m.*, acceptor
акцептировать, *v.*, accept
акцептование, *n.*, acceptance
акцептовать, *v.*, accept
акцептор, *m.*, acceptor
акцепторный, *adj.*, acceptor
акционер, *m.*, stockholder, shareholder
алгебра, *f.*, algebra
алгебраизация, *f.*, algebraization
алгебраический, *adj.*, algebraic
алгеброидный, *adj.*, algebroidal
алгоритм, (алгорифм), *m.*, algorithm; **алгоритм эвклида,** euclidean algorithm
алгоритмически, *adv.*, by an algorithm, algorithmically
алгоритмический, *adj.*, algorithmic, pertaining to an algorithm
алеф, *m.*, aleph
аликвотный, *adj.*, aliquot
аллотропический, *adj.*, allotropic
аллотропия, *f.*, allotropy
алмаз, *m.*, diamond; **решетка типа алмаза,** diamond-type lattice
алфавит, *m.*, alphabet; **по алфавиту,** alphabetically
алфавитно, *adv.*, alphabetically
алфавитный, *adj.*, alphabetical
алхимия, *f.*, alchemy
альтернатива, *f.*, alternative
альтернативный, *adj.*, alternative, alternate
альтернион, *m.*, alternion
альтернирование, *n.*, alternation, antisymmetrization
альтернированный, *adj.*, alternating, alternated
альтернирующий, *adj.*, alternating
алюминий, *adj.*, aluminum
амортизатор, *m.*, damper, shock absorber, buffer
амортизационный, *adj.*, amortization, buffer; **амортизационный запас,** buffer inventory
амортизация, *f.*, amortization
ампер, *m.*, ampere
ампервиток, *m.*, ampere turn
амперсекунда, *f.*, ampere-second
амплитуда, *f.*, amplitude
ампулка, *f.*, ampulla (small)
аналагматический, *adj.*, analagmatic
анализ, *m.*, analysis
анализатор, *m.*, analyzer
анализированный, *adj.*, analyzed
анализировать, *v.*, analyze
анализируемый, *adj.*, analyzable
аналитик, *m.*, analyser, analyst
аналитика, *f.*, analytics
аналитический, *adj.*, analytical, analytic
аналитичность, *f.*, analyticity
аналлагматический, *adj.*, analagmatic
аналог, *m.*, similarity, analogy; **статистический аналог,** statistical image
аналогический, *adj.*, analogical, analogous, similar
аналогично, *adv.*, analogously, similarly
аналогичный, *adj.*, analogous, similar; **быть аналогичным,** *v.*, be analogous (to), be similar (to)
аналогия, *f.*, analogy, similarity, comparison; **по аналогии,** by analogy (with); **проводить аналогию,** draw analogy (to, with)
анаморфоза, *f.*, anamorphism, anamorphosis
ангармонический, *adj.*, anharmonic; **ангармоническое отношение,** *n.*, cross-ratio
ангармоничность, *f.*, anharmonicity

ангстрем, *m.*, angstrom
анизометрический, *adj.*, anisometric
анизотропический, *adj.*, anisotropic
анизотропия, *f.*, anisotropy; **эффекты анизотропии,** anisotropic effects
анизотропность, *f.*, anisotropy
анизотропный, *adj.*, non-isotropic, anisotropic
анион, *m.*, anion
анкер, *m.*, anchor
анкета, *f.*, form, questionnaire
аннекс, *m.*, annex
аннигилятор, *m.*, annihilator
аннигиляторный, *adj.*, annihilator; **аннигиляторная алгебра,** annihilator algebra
аннигиляция, *f.*, annihilation
аннотация, *f.*, annotation
аннотированный, *adj.*, annotated
аннуитет, *m.*, annuity
аннулирование, *n.*, annulment, cancelation, nullification, annihilation, abrogation, abolition
аннулированный, *adj.*, annulled, canceled, annihilated
аннулировать, *v.*, annul, cancel, annihilate, nullify, abolish, abrogate, destroy
аннулироваться, *v.*, vanish
аннулируемость, *f.*, annihilation
аннулируемый, *adj.*, (being) annihilated
аннулирующая, *f.*, annihilator, nullifier
аннулятор, *m.*, annihilator
анnуляторный, *adj.*, annihilator
анод, *m.*, anode
анодный, *adj.*, anode
аномалия, *f.*, anomaly
аномальный, *adj.*, anomalous, irregular
анонимный, *adj.*, anonymous
анонс, *m.*, notice, announcement
анонсированный, *adj.*, advertised, announced, noted
анонсировать, *v.*, announce
ансамбль, *m.*, group, set, ensemble
антенна, *f.*, antenna
антецедент, *m.*, antecedent
антиавтоморфизм, *m.*, anti-automorphism
антианалитический, *adj.*, anti-analytic
антигомоморфизм, *m.*, anti-homomorphism
антижанр, *m.*, anti-genus
антиизоморфизм, *m.*, anti-isomorphism
антиизоморфный, *adj.*, anti-isomorphic
антиинволюция, *f.*, anti-involution
антиканонический, *adj.*, anti-canonical
антикоммутативность, *f.*, anti-commutativity
антикоммутатор, *m.*, anti-commutator
антикоммутативный, *adj.*, anti-commutative
антикоммутирование, *n.*, anti-commutation
антинейтрино, *n.*, antineutrino
антиномия, *f.*, antinomy
антипараллельный, *adj.*, antiparallel
антиплюриканонический, *adj.*, anti-pluricanonical
антипод, *m.*, antipode
антиподный, *adj.*, antipodal; **антиподное множество,** antipodal set
антипредставление, *n.*, anti-representation
антипроективный, *adj.*, antiprojective
антирефлексивность, *f.*, anti-reflexiveness, skew-reflexivity
антирод, *m.*, antigenus
антисимметрический, *adj.*, anti-symmetric, skew-symmetric, alternating
антисимметричность, *f.*, anti-symmetry, skew-symmetry
антисимметричный, *adj.*, skew-symmetric
антистоксовой, *adj.*, anti-Stokes, **анти·стокова линия,** anti-Stokes line
антитеза, *f.*, antithesis
антитетический, *adj.*, antithetic; **антитетическая переменная,** antithetic variate
антитонный, *adj.*, antitone
антиупорядоченный, *adj.*, anti-ordered, star-ordered, inversely ordered
антиферромагнетизм, *m.*, anti-ferromagnetism

антиформа, *f.*, anti-form
антицепь, *f.*, anti-chain, inverse chain
античастица, *f.*, antiparticle
античный, *adj.*, antique
антиэрмитовой, *adj.*, anti-Hermitian, skew-Hermitian
антье (от), greatest integer (in)
анционерный, *adj.*, joint-stock; **анционерный капитал,** capital stock, share, stock
апекс, *m.*, apex
апеллировать, *v.*, appeal
апериодический, *adj.*, aperiodic, non-periodic
апериодичность, *f.*, aperiodicity
апертура, *f.*, aperture, opening; **ограничение апертуры,** over-all aperture ratio
апертурный, *adj.*, aperture
апланатизм, *m.*, aplanatism
апогей, *m.*, apogee
аполярность, *f.*, apolarity, non-polarity
аполярный, *adj.*, apolar, non-polar
апосиндетический, *adj.*, aposyndetic
апосиндетично, *adv.*, aposyndetically
апостериори, *adv.*, a posteriori
апостериорный, *adj.*, a posteriori
апофема, *f.*, apothem
аппарат, *m.*, apparatus, means, instrument, device
аппаратурный, *adj.*, instrument, apparatus
аппликата, *f.*, *z*-coordinate
аппроксимативный, *adj.*, approximate
аппроксимационный, *adj.*, approximate, approximating, approximated
аппроксимация, *f.*, approximation
аппроксимировать, *v.*, approximate
аппроксимируемость, *f.*, approximability
аппроксимируемый, *adj.*, approximable, approximate, approximated
аппроксимирующий, *adj.*, approximating, approximate
аппроксимируя, *adv. part.*, approximating, if we approximate
априори, *adv.*, a priori
априорный, *adj.*, a priori
апробация, *f.*, approbation, approval
апробировать, *v.*, approve
апсида, *f.*, apsis, apse; **линия апсид,** line of apsides
ар, *m.*, are (100 square meters)
аргон, *m.*, argon
аргумент, *m.*, argument, amplitude, independent variable
аргументация, *f.*, argumentation
аргументировать, *v.*, argue
ареальный, *adj.*, areal
ареолярный, *adj.*, areolar
аристотелевский, *adj.*, Aristotelian
арифметика, *f.*, arithmetic
арифметико-геометрический, *adj.*, arithmetic-geometrical
арифметический, *adj.*, number-theoretic, arithmetical
арифмометр, *m.*, adding machine, comptometer, calculator
арка, *f.*, arch
арксинус, *m.*, arcsine
арктангенс, *m.*, arctangent
арочный, *adj.*, arch, arched
арретирование, *n.*, locking, holding, stopping
арретировочный, *adj.*, stopping, locking; **арретировочное приспособление,** stopping device, locking device, brake
арретирующий, *adj.*, stopping
архимедовость, *f.*, property of being Archimedian
архимедовский, *adj.*, Archimedian; **архимедовски расположенный,** *adj.*, Archimedian ordered
архимедовый, *adj.*, Archimedian
архитектура, *f.*, architecture
архитектурный, *adj.*, architectural
асимметрический, *adj.*, asymmetric
асимметричный, *adj.*, asymmetric
асимметрия, *f.*, asymmetry, skewness
асимптота, *f.*, asymptote
асимптотика, *f.*, asymptotics
асимптотический, *adj.*, asymptotic
асимптотичность, *f.*, asymptotic property
асинхроничный, *adj.*, non-synchronous

асинхронный, *adj.*, non-synchronous, asynchronous
аспект, *m.*, aspect, appearance
ассигнованный, *adj.*, assigned
ассоциативность, *f.*, associativity
ассоциативный, *adj.*, associative
ассоциатор, *m.*, associator
ассоциация, *f.*, association; **по ассоциации,** by association; **ассоциация качественных признаков,** contingency
ассоциированность, *f.*, association, associativity
ассоциированный, *adj.*, associated, associate
ассоциировать, *v.*, associate
ассоциирующий, *adj.*, associating
астатический, *adj.*, astatic, non-static
астигматизм, *m.*, astigmatism
астигматический, *adj.*, astigmatic
астроида, *f.*, astroid
астрологический, *adj.*, astrological
астрология, *f.*, astrology
астроном, *m.*, astronomer
астрономический, *adj.*, astronomical
астрономия, *f.*, astronomy
астроспектроскопия, *f.*, stellar spectroscopy
астрофизика, *f.*, astrophysics
астрофизический, *adj.*, astrophysical
асферический, *adj.*, non-spherical, aspherical
асферичность, *f.*, asphericity
атака, *f.*, attack; **угол атаки,** angle of attack
атмосфера, *f.*, atmosphere
атмосферический, *adj.*, atmospheric, atmosphere
атмосферный, *adj.*, atmospheric, atmosphere
атом, *m.*, atom
атомистический, *adj.*, atomistic
атомистичность, *f.*, property of being atomistic; **гипотеза атомистичности,** atomistic hypothesis
атомический, *adj.*, atomic
атомность, *f.*, atomicity
атомный, *adj.*, atomic
атрибут, *m.*, attribute, property, quality
атриодический, *adj.*, atriodic, non-triodic
аттеньюатор, *m.*, attenuator
аттенюатор, *m.*, attenuator, reducer
афелий, *m.*, aphelion
афортиори, *adv.*, a fortiori
аффикс, *m.*, affix
аффинитет, *m.*, affinity, affineness
аффинно, *adv.*, affinely, affine; **аффинно-евклидовой,** *adj.*, affine-Euclidean
аффинность, *f.*, affinity, affineness
аффинный, *adj.*, affine
аффинор, *m.*, affinor
ахромат, *m.*, achromat; **контактный ахромат,** contact achromat
ахроматизированный, *adj.*, achromatized; **ахроматизированный дублет,** achromatized doublet
ахроматизм, *m.*, achromation
ахроматический, *adj.*, achromatic
ациклический, *adj.*, acyclic
ацикличный, *adj.*, acyclic, non-cyclic
аэрация, *f.*, aeration
аэрогидродинамика, *f.*, aerohydrodynamics
аэродинамика, *f.*, aerodynamics
аэродинамический, *f.*, aerodynamic
аэронавтика, *f.*, aeronautics

Б

база, *f.*, basis, base, foundation
базировать, *v.*, base on, found, ground
базироваться, *v.*, be based on
базирующийся, *adj.*, based on
базис, *m.*, base, basis, foundation
базисный, *adj.*, base, basis; **базисное пространство,** base space
базовый, *adj.*, base; **базовый период,** base period; **базовый вес,** base weight
байесовский, *adj.*, Bayes, pertaining to Bayes; **байесовская стратегия,** Bayes strategy
бактерия, *f.*, bacteria
баланс, *m.*, balance
балансир, *m.*, beam, balance beam, balance wheel
балансированный, *adj.*, balanced
балка, *f.*, beam, girder
балл, *m.*, number, mark, point
баллистика, *f.*, ballistics
баллистический, *adj.*, ballistic
балловый, *adj.*, number-, mark-
банаховый, *adj.*, Banach; **банаховое пространство,** Banach space
барабан, *m.*, drum, roll, barrel
барицентрический, *adj.*, barycentric
барометр, *m.*, barometer
барометрический, *adj.*, barometric
бароскоп, *m.*, baroscope
баротропный, *adj.*, barotropic
барьер, *m.*, barrier, enclosure, rail, bar
барьерный, *adj.*, barrier
башня, *f.*, tower
беглый, *adj.*, sketchy, fluent, cursory
бегущий, *adj.*, running
бедный, *adj.*, poor
без, *prep.*, without; **безо,** minus, without
безаберрационный, *adj.*, without aberration, non-aberrational
безактиваторный, *adj.*, non-activated, unactivated, inactive
безвихревой, *adj.*, irrotational; **безвихревое течение,** irrotational flow
безвкусно, *adv.*, tastelessly, inelegantly
безводный, *adj.*, anhydrous, waterless, non-aqueous
безвозвратно, *adv.*, irrevocably, irreversibly
безвозвратный, *adj.*, irrevocable, irreversible, irretrievable
безвредный, *adj.*, harmless
безграничный, *adj.*, unlimited, boundless, unbounded
бездеятельность, *f.*, inertia, inactivity
бездивергенционный, *adj.*, with vanishing divergence, without divergence, solenoidal
бездоказательный, *adj.*, unproved
безизлучательный, *adj.*, non-radiating
безинерционный, *adj.*, inertia-free, without inertia
безинтегральный, *adj.*, integral-free
безламповый, *adj.*, tubeless
безлогарифмический, *adj.*, non-logarithmic
безмагнитный, *adj.*, non-magnetic
безмала, *adv.*, almost, nearly
безмерно, *adv.*, immeasurably
безмерность, *f.*, immeasurability, immensity
безмерный, *adj.*, immeasurable, immense, boundless, infinite
безнадежный, *adj.*, hopeless
безо, (cf. **без**) *prep.*, without, minus
безобидный, *adj.*, harmless
безоговорочно, *adv.*, unconditionally
безопасность, *f.*, safety, security
безопасный, *adj.*, safe, safety, foolproof
безосновательный, *adj.*, groundless, unfounded
безостановочный, *adj.*, unceasing, non-stop
безотносительно, *adv.*, irrespective
безотносительный, *adj.*, unconditional, absolute
безошибочно, *adv.*, correctly, without error

безошибочность, *f.*, faultlessness, infallibility
безошибочный, *adj.*, correct, exact, without error
безпредельный, *adj.*, unlimited, boundless
безразличие, *n.*, indifference; **поверхность безразличия,** indifference surface; **кривая общественного безразличия,** community indifference curve
безразличный, *adj.*, indifferent, neutral; **безразлично,** *pred.*, it makes no difference
безразмерный, *adj.*, dimensionless; **безразмерное число,** pure number
безрезультатный, *adj.*, without results
безупречный, *adj.*, faultless, irreproachable
безусловно, *adv.*, unconditionally, undoubtedly
безусловность, *f.*, absoluteness, certainty
безусловный, *adj.*, unconditional, absolute
безуспешный, *adj.*, unsuccessful, ineffective
безциркулярный, cf. **бесциркулярный**
безэлементный, *adj.*, element-free
бер-, cf. **брать**: **берем,** we take
берег, *m.*, shore, bank, coast
бернуллиевый, *adj.*, Bernoulli
беря, *adv. part.*, taking, if we take
бес-, *prefix*, -less, -free
беседа, *f.*, lecture, talk, conversation, debate, discussion
бесквадратный, *adj.*, square-free
бесквадратурный, *adj.*, quadrature-free
бескванторный, *adj.*, quantor-free, quantifier-free
бесконечно, *adv.*, infinitely, extremely, endlessly; **бесконечно малая (величина),** *f.*, infinitesimal; **бесконечно малый,** *adj.*, infinitesimal
бесконечномерный, *adj.*, infinite dimensional
бесконечно-длинный, *adj.*, infinitely long
бесконечнократный, *adj.*, infinite-to-one
бесконечнолистный, *adj.*, infinite sheeted
бесконечносвязный, *adj.*, of infinite connectivity
бесконечность, *f.*, infinity; **до бесконечности,** ad infinitum
бесконечно-удаленный, *adj.*, infinite, infinitely far; **бесконечно-удаленная точка,** point at infinity
бесконечный, *adj.*, infinite, endless, interminable, nonterminating
бесповоротный, *adj.*, irrevocable, irreversible, rotation-free
бесполезно, *adv.*, in vain, uselessly
бесполезность, *f.*, uselessness
бесполезный, *adj.*, useless
беспорядок, *m.*, disorder, confusion, chaos
беспорядочно, *adv.*, irregularly, in a random manner
беспорядочный, *adj.*, chaotic, disorderly, confused, irregular, random; **беспорядочная цепь,** disordered chain
беспредельный, *adj.*, boundless, infinite, unbounded
беспредметность, *f.*, pointlessness, aimlessness
беспредметный, *adj.*, pointless, aimless
беспрепятственно, *adv.*, without obstacles, easily
беспрерывно, *adv.*, continuously, without interruption
беспримесный, *adj.*, pure
беспристрастность, *f.*, impartiality
беспристрастный, *adj.*, unbiased, impartial; **беспристрастная выборка,** unbiased sample
бесселевый, *adj.*, Bessel
бесскобочный, *adj.*, without brackets, parenthesis-free
бессмертный, *adj.*, immortal, everlasting
бессмысленный, *adj.*, senseless, absurd
бессодержательный, *adj.*, empty
бесспиновой, *adj.*, spin-free, zero-spin
бесспорно, *adv.*, indisputably, without contradiction, unquestionably, undoubtedly

бесспорность, *f.*, indisputability, incontrovertibility
бесспорный, *adj.*, indisputable, incontrovertible, undeniable, self-evident
бессрочный, *adj.*, permanent
бесструктурный, *adj.*, formless, without structure
бессчетный, *adj.*, innumberable, uncountable
бесцельно, *adv.*, aimlessly, at random
бесцельность, *f.*, aimlessness, purposelessness, random character
бесцельный, *adj.*, aimless, purposeless, haphazard, random
бесценно, *adv.*, pricelessly, beyond price
бесценность, *f.*, pricelessness, inestimable value
бесценный, *adj.*, priceless, inestimable, invaluable
бесцентровый, *adj.*, without center
бесциркулярный, *adj.*, irrotational, circulation-free; **бесциркулярное обтекание,** irrotational flow
бесциркуляционный, *adj.*, irrotational, circulation-free; **бесциркуляционное обтекание,** irrotational flow
бесчисленный, *adj.*, uncountable, non-denumerable
бесчисленность, *f.*, non-denumerability, uncountability, innumerability
бета-распределение, *n.*, beta-distribution
бетатрон, *m.*, betatron
бета-функция, *f.*, beta-function
би-, *prefix*, bi-, di-
биаксиальный, *adj.*, biaxial
биаффинный, *adj.*, biaffine
библиографический, *adj.*, bibliographical
библиография, *f.*, bibliography
бивариантный, *adj.*, bivariant
бивектор, *m.*, bivector
бигармонический, *adj.*, biharmonic
бигармоничный, *adj.*, biharmonic
биградуированный, *adj.*, bigraded, twice-graded; **биградуированный модуль,** *m.*, bigraded module
бидифференцируемый, *adj.*, bidifferentiable, twice differentiable
бидуальный, *adj.*, bidual
биение, *n.*, beating, throbbing, pulsation; **частота биений,** beat frequency
биканонический, *adj.*, bicanonical
бикатегория, *f.*, bicategory
биквадрат, *m.*, fourth power, biquadratic
биквадратичный, *adj.*, biquadratic
биквадратный, *adj.*, biquadratic
бикомпакт, *m.*, compactum, bicompactum
бикомпактный, *adj.*, bicompact, compact; **бикомпактное пополнение,** *n.*, bicompactification, compactification
бикомплексный, *adj.*, bicomplex
билет, *m.*, ticket, card
билинейность, *f.*, bilinearity
билинейный, *adj.*, bilinear
бимодальный, *adj.*, bimodal
бимолекулярный, *adj.*, bimolecular
бинарный, *adj.*, binary
бинокулярный, *adj.*, binocular
бином, *m.*, binomial; **бином Ньютона,** binomial formula, binomial theorem
биномиальный, adj., binomial
бинормаль, *f.*, binormal
бинормальный, *adj.*, binormal
био-, *prefix*, bio-
биография, *f.*, biography
биодинамика, *f.*, biodynamics
биодинамический, *adj.*, biodynamic
биология, *f.*, biology
биологический, *adj.*, biological
биоматематика, *f.*, bio-mathematics
биометрия, *f.*, biometrics
биортогонализация, *f.*, biorthogonalization
биортогональность, *f.*, biorthogonality
биортогональный, *adj.*, biorthogonal
биортонормирование, *n.*, biorthonormalization
биотип, *m.*, biological type, species
биофизика, *f.*, biophysics
бипланарный, *adj.*, biplanar
биполярный, *adj.*, bipolar
бипризма, *f.*, biprism

бирациональный, *adj.*, birational
бирегулярный, *adj.*, biregular
бисектриса, *f.*, bisectrix, bisector
бисериальный, *adj.*, biserial
бисимметрия, *f.*, bisymmetry
биспинорный, *adj.*, bispinor
биссектриса, *f.*, bisectrix, bisector
биссекторный, *adj.*, bisector, bisecting
битернарный, *adj.*, biternary
бифакторный, *adj.*, bifactor, bifactorial
бифлекнодальный, *adj.*, biflecnode
биформа, *f.*, biform, double form
бифунктор, *m.*, bifunctor
бифуркационный, *adj.*, bifurcational, branching
бифуркация, *f.*, bifurcation, branching
бихэвиористический, *adj.*, behavioristic
бицикл, *m.*, bicircle; **единичный бицикл,** unit bicircle
бицилиндр, *m.*, bicylinder
бицилиндрический, *adj.*, bicylindrical
бициркулярный, *adj.*, bicircular
благодарный, *adj.*, grateful, appreciative
благодаря, *prep.*, thanks to, because of, due to
благоприятный, *adj.*, favorable; **благоприятный исход,** success
благоприятствовать, *v.*, favor, foster, be favorable (to)
благородный, *adj.*, rare, inert
блеск, *m.*, brightness, brilliance, brilliancy, glitter, lustre
блестящий, *adj.*, brilliant, shiny
блеф, *m.*, bluff, bluffing; **игра с блефом,** bluffing game
ближайший, *adj.*, nearest, next, immediate; **ближайший повод,** immediate cause; **при ближайшем рассмотрении,** on closer examination
ближе, *adv.*, nearer
ближний, *adj.*, near, neighboring
близ, *prep.*, near, close to
близиться, *v.*, approximate, approach, draw near
близкий, *adj.*, near, like, close, similar; **на близком растоянии,** at a short distance; **область, близкая к кругу,** nearly-circular domain; **бесконечно близкий от** A, infinitesimally close to A
близко, *adv.*, nearly
близкодействующий, *adj.*, short-range
близлежащий, *adj.*, neighboring, nearby, near
близнец, *m.*, twin; **близнецы,** *pl.*, twins, prime pair
близорукий, *adj.*, short-sighted, near-sighted, myopic
близорукость, *f.*, near-sightedness, myopia
близость, *f.*, proximity, nearness, closeness; **в непосредственной близости,** in immediate proximity (to); **пространство близости,** proximity space
блок, *m.*, block, unit, bloc; **блок ввода-вывода,** input-output unit
блоховский, *adj.*, Bloch, pertaining to Bloch
блочный, *adj.*, block; **блочный идеал,** block ideal
блуждание, *n.*, wandering; **случайное блуждание,** random walk
блуждать, *v.*, wander, walk
блуждающий, *adj.*, wandering, straying
бок, *m.*, side; **по бокам,** on each side, **бок о бок,** side by side; **вид с боку (вид сбоку),** side-view
боковой, *adj.*, lateral, side, profile
более, *adv.*, more; **более и более,** more and more; **более всего,** most of all; **тем более,** all the more; **более того,** and what is more; **более чем,** more than; **тем более, что,** especially as, as, the more so
болометрический, *adj.*, bolometric
болт, *m.*, bolt, pin
больше, *adv.*, greater (than), more, larger; **как можно больше,** as much as possible, as many as possible; **много больше,** much more; **больше не,** no more, not any more

больший, *adj.*, larger, greater; **по большей части,** mostly, for the most part; **самое большее,** at most, at the utmost

большинство, *n.*, majority; **в большинстве случаев,** in most cases

большой, *adj.*, big, large

бомбардировать, *v.*, bombard

борновский, *adj.*, Born, pertaining to Born

боровский, *adj.*, Bohr, pertaining to Bohr

бороздка, *f.*, groove, fissure

борьба, *f.*, struggle, fight

бочкообразный, *adj.*, barrel-type; **бочкообразная дисторсия,** barrel-type distortion

брак, *m.*, reject

браковать, *v.*, reject, discard

браковаться, *v.*, be rejected

браковка, *f.*, rejection, discarding

браковочный, *adj.*, rejected, discarded

бракующий, *adj.*, rejecting, discarding

брать, *v.*, take, obtain, originate, prevail, succeed; **брать производную,** *v.*, differentiate

брауэровский, *adj.*, Brouwerian, pertaining to Brouwer

брахистохрона, *f.*, brachistochrone

брахистохронный, *adj.*, brachistrochrone

брикет, *m.*, brick fuel, briquet

бродячий, *adj.*, stray, wandering

броневой, *adj.*, armored, protective

бросание, *n.*, throwing, tossing; **бросание монеты,** coin-tossing

бросать, (бросить), *v.*, throw

броуновский, *adj.*, Brownian

брошенный (from **бросать**) *adj.*, thrown, abandoned, deserted; **брошенное тело,** *n.*, projectile

брошюра, *f.*, brochure, pamphlet

брус, *m.*, beam, girder, bar, block, squared beam

брусковый, *adj.*, bar

брусок, *m.*, rod, rail, bar, stack; **бруски покрытия,** stacks of a covering

брусчатый, *adj.*, stacked, block; **брусчатое покрытие (с базой** *a*), stacked covering (over *a*)

брызгать (брызнуть), *v.*, sprinkle, squirt

будет (from **быть**), will, will be

будто, *conj.*, as if, as though; **будто бы,** supposedly, apparently

будут (cf. **быть**), *v.*, will, will be

будучи, *adv. part.* (from **быть**), being

будущее, *n.*, the future

будущий, *adj.*, future, next; **в будущий раз,** next time

будущность, *f.*, future

будящий, *adj.*, arousing, calling

буква, *f.*, letter (of alphabet); **буква в букву,** letter for letter

буквальный, *adj.*, literal

букет, *m.*, union (bouquet); **букет сфер,** union of spheres

буксование, *n.*, slipping, skidding

буксовать, *v.*, skid, slip, tow

булевский, *adj.*, Boolean

булевый, *adj.*, Boolean

бумага, *f.*, paper, document

бумажный, *adj.*, paper

бумеранг, *m.*, boomerang

Буняковский, *m.*, Buniakowski; **неравенство Буняковского,** Cauchy-Schwarz-Buniakowski inequality

бусина, *f.*, bead

бусинка, *f.*, bead

бутылка, *f.*, bottle; **бутылка Клейна,** Klein bottle

буфер, *m.*, shock absorber, cushion, buffer

буферный, *adj.*, buffer

бушевать, *v.*, make turbulent, storm, rage

бушель, *m.*, bushel

бушинг, *m.*, bushing

бушующий, *adj.*, turbulent, storming, raging

бы (*particle, indicating subjunctive or conditional*): **кто бы ни,** whoever; **что бы ни,** whatever; **когда бы ни,** whenever; **как бы,** no matter how, as if; **чем бы,** no matter by what

бывать, *v.*, be, happen, occur, take place

был (была, было, были), *v.* (*past of* **быть**), was, were

былое, *n.*, the past

былой, *adj.*, past, former
быстродействующий, *adj.*, high speed
быстрота, *f.*, speed, quickness, rapidity
быстрый, *adj.*, fast, quick, rapid
бэровский, *adj.*, Baire, pert. to Baire
бэта-функция, *f.*, beta function
бюджет, *m.*, budget; **линия бюджета,** budget line

В

в (во), *prep.*, in, into, at, to, toward; for, from, on, within; **в виде,** in the form of; **во многом,** in many instances; **в самом деле,** in fact; **в свете,** in view (of); **в случае,** in case (of)
в, *abbrev.*, **(вольт),** volt; **В,** *abbrev.* **(Восток),** East
вагон, *m.*, coach, carriage
вагонетка, *f.*, trolley, wagon
важность, *f.*, importance, significance
важный, *adj.*, important, significant
важнейший, *adj.*, most important
вакуум, *m.*, vacuum
вакуумный, *adj.*, vacuum
вал, *m.*, shaft, drum
валентность, *f.*, valency, valence
-валентный, *adj. suffix*, valent
валик, *m.*, cylinder, roller
вальдовский, *adj.*, Wald, pertaining to Wald; **вальдовское секвенциальное испытание,** sequential probability ratio test
валюация, *f.*, valuation
валютный, *adj.*, exchange; **валютный курс,** exchange rate (of currency)
вариант, *m.*, variant, alternate version
вариантность, *f.*, variance
вариационный, *adj.*, variational
вариация, *f.*, variation
варьирование, *n.*, variation
варьированный, *adj.*, varied, varying
варьировать, *v.*, vary, change, modify
варьироваться, *v.*, vary
варьирующий, *adj.*, varying, changing
варьируя, *adv. part.*, varying, if we vary
ватерлиния, *f.*, water line
ватт, *m.*, watt
ваттметр, *m.*, wattmeter
вблизи, *prep.*, near, close, not far from
вбок, *adv.*, sideways
вбрызгивать, *v.*, inject
введем (cf. **вводить**), we (shall) introduce, let us introduce
введение, *n.*, introduction; inlet, intake
введенный, *adj.*, introduced
введя, *adv. part.*, introducing, having introduced
вверх, *adv.*, up, upwards
ввести (cf. **вводить**) *v.*, introduce
ввиду, *prep.*, in view of; **ввиду того что,** as, in view of the fact that
ввинчивать (ввинтить), *v.*, screw, screw in
ввод, *m.*, inlet, lead-in, intake
вводить (ввести), *v.*, introduce
вводиться, *v.*, be introduced
вводный, *adj.*, introductory
вводя, *adv. part.*, introducing, if we introduce
вдаваться (вдаться), *v.*, devote one's self to; **вдаваться в детали,** go into details, refine, elaborate
вдавливание, *n.*, impression, stamping
вдали, *prep.*, far from, at a distance, beyond
вдвое, *adv.*, double, twice; **вдвое меньше,** half; **сложить вдвое,** *v.*, fold in two; **увеличить вдвое,** *v.*, double
вдобавок, *adv.*, in addition, besides
вдоль, *prep.*, along, down; *adv.*, lengthwise
вебер, *m.*, weber (unit), 10^8 maxwells
ведем (cf. **водить**), we lead, we conduct
ведется (cf. **водить**), is carried out, is conducted

ведомость, *f.*, list, sheet, record
ведущий (cf. **водить**), *adj.*, conductor, conducting, leading; **ведущий идеал,** conductor ideal, conductor; **ведущее начало,** fundamental principle; **ведущее колесо,** driving wheel
ведь, *conj.*, but, in fact, as a matter of fact; **но ведь это всем известно,** but this is well-known
веер, *m.*, fan
везде, *adv.*, everywhere
вездесущий, *adj.*, ubiquitous, omnipresent
вейлевский, *adj.*, Weyl, pertaining to Weyl; Weil, pertaining to Weil
век, *m.*, century, age
вековой, *adj.*, age-old, ancient, secular; **вековое уравнение,** secular equation
вексель, *m.*, note, bill; **норма учета векселей,** discount rate
вектор, *m.*, vector
векторно-матричный, *adj.*, vector-matrix
векторный, *adj.*, vectorial, vector; **векторное пространство,** vector space
вектор-столбец, *m.*, column vector
вектор-строка, *f.*, row vector
вел (вела, вело, вели), cf. **вести; вел себя, как . . .,** behaves like
великий, *adj.*, great; **ферма великая теорема,** Fermat's last theorem
величина, *f.*, magnitude, quantity, size, value, variable
вентиль, *m.*, valve, gate; **входной (выходной) вентиль,** in- (out-) gate
вентильный, *adj.*, valve
вентилятор, *m.*, ventilator
вентиляционный, *adj.*, ventilating
вера, *f.*, faith, belief, trust
веревка, *f.*, rope, string, cord
веревочный, *adj.*, cord, string, rope
веретено, *n.*, spindle
веретенообразный, *adj.*, spindle-shaped
верзор, *m.*, versor
верить, *v.*, believe
верификатор, *m.*, verifier
верификация, *f.*, verification
верифицируемый, *adj.*, verifiable
вернемся (cf. **вернуться**), we (shall) return
верно, *adv.*, correctly, probably
верность, *f.*, accuracy, correctness; **верность измерений,** accuracy of measurement
вернуться, *v.*, return
верный, *adj.*, valid, true, correct, reliable
вероятностник, *m.*, probabilist
вероятностный, *adj.*, probability; **вероятностная фуикция,** probability function, distribution function
вероятность, *f.*, probability
вероятный, *adj.*, probable, likely
вертикал, *m.*, vertical (instrument), vertical (astr.)
вертикаль, *f.*, vertical line, vertical (astr.)
вертикально, *adv.*, vertically
вертикальность, *f.*, verticality, vertical position
вертикальный, *adj.*, vertical, upright; **вертикальная проекция,** vertical projection, front view
верх, *m.*, top, upper part
верхний, *adj.*, upper, top; **верхняя гомология,** cohomology; **верхняя граница,** upper bound; **верхний предел,** upper bound, upper limit; **верхняя цена,** upper pure value (game theory); **верхний цикл,** cocycle
верхушка, *f.*, apex
вершина, *f.*, top, summit, apex, vertex; **расстояние от вершины до объекта,** object distance (optics)
вершинный, *adj.*, vertex
вес, *m.*, weight, influence, authority, position, system; **удельный вес,** specific weight, specific gravity; **на вес (=весом),** by weight
весовой, *adj.*, weight; **весовая функция,** weight function
вести (cf. **водить**), *v.*, lead, conduct
вести (повести), *v.*, conduct, direct
весь (вся, все), all, the whole of, everything

весьма, *adv.*, very, highly, greatly
ветвистость, *f.*, ramification
ветвистый, *adj.*, branching, ramified
ветвление, *n.*, branching, ramification, bifurcation
ветвь, *f.*, branch
ветвящийся, *adj.*, branching, ramified
ветер, *m.*, wind; **встречный ветер,** headwind
ветряк, *m.*, wind turbine
веха, *f.*, stake, landmark
вещественно, *adv.* (from **вещественный**): **вещественно замкнутый,** *adj.*, real-closed
вещественнозначный, *adj.*, real-valued
вещественность, *f.*, matter, substance
вещественный, *adj.*, real, material
вещество, *n.*, substance, matter
вещь, *f.*, thing, entity, piece; **вещь в себе,** thing in itself
веяние, *n.*, trend, tendency
взаимно, *adv.*, mutually, reciprocally, relatively; **взаимно исключающий друг друга,** *adj.*, mutually exclusive; **взаимно не пересекаться,** *v.*, be mutually disjoint, be mutually exclusive; **взаимно простой,** *adj.*, relatively prime, coprime, mutually disjoint
взаимнодополнительный, *adj.*, mutually disjoint, mutually complementary
взаимнообратный, *adj.*, inverse, reciprocal
взаимно-однозначно, *adv.*, in a one-to-one manner
взаимно-однозначный, *adj.*, one-to-one; **взаимно-однозначное соответствие,** one-to-one correspondence
взаимно-полярный, *adj.*, polar reciprocal
взаимно-простой, *adj.*, mutually disjoint, relatively prime, coprime
взаимносопряженный, *adj.*, self-conjugate
взаимность, *f.*, reciprocity, mutuality, duality
взаимный, *adj.*, mutual, reciprocal; **взаимная связь,** coupling
взаимодействие, *n.*, interaction, reciprocal action, reciprocity
взаимодействовать, *v.*, interact, act reciprocally
взаимодействующий, *adj.*, interacting
взаимозависимость, *f.*, interdependency
взаимозаменяемость, *f.*, interchangeability
взаимозаменяемый, *adj.*, interchangeable
взаимоисключающий, *adj.*, alternative, mutually exclusive
взаимоотношение, *m.*, mutual relation, correlation, inter-relation
взаимопревращение, *n.*, transmutation
взаимосвязь, *f.*, correlation, interconnection, interdependence, intercommunication
взаимосогласованность, *f.*, interconsistency, consistency
взамен, *prep.*, instead of, in return for
взвешенно-полиномиальный, *adj.*, weighted polynomial
взвешенный, *adj.*, weighted, weighed, suspended
взвешивание, *n.*, weighing, weighting
взвешивать (взвесить), *v.*, weigh
взгляд, *m.*, view, glance
взглядывать (взглянуть), *v.*, glance, look at
взлет, *m.*, flight, take-off, launching
взлетный, *adj.*, flight, take-off
взнос, *m.*, payment, fee, due
взойти, *v.* (*perf. of* **восходить** *and* **всходить**)
взрез, *m.*, cut, incision
взрыв, *m.*, explosion, detonation
взрывной (= **взрывчатый**), *adj.*, explosive; **взрывная волна,** blast wave
взяв, *adv. part.* (from **взять**), having taken
взятие, *n.*, taking; **взятие дополнения,** (operation of) taking the complement
взять (cf. **брать**) *v.*, take
взятыи, *adj.*, taken; **взят,** taken (short form)
вибратор, *m.*, vibrator, oscillator
вибрационный, *adj.*, vibrational

вибрация, *f.*, vibration, oscillation
вибрировать, *v.*, vibrate, oscillate
виброграф, *m.*, oscillograph
вибротехника, *f.*, vibrotechnics
вид, *m.*, aspect, form, view, kind, species, shape, mode; **в виде,** in the form of; **в виду,** in view of, on account of; **ни под каким видом,** on no account, by no means
видеть (увидеть), *v.*, see
видим (cf. **видеть),** we see
видимо, *adv.*, evidently, obviously, apparently
видимость, *f.*, visibility
видимый, *adj.*, apparent, visible, obvious
видно, *adv.*, obviously, evidently, apparently, it is seen, one can see, it is obvious; **как видно,** as is obvious; **как видно из сказанного,** as is obvious from what has been said
видоизменение, *n.*, modification transformation, change, alteration, version
видоизмененный, *adj.*, modified
видоизменять, *v.*, transform, modify, alter
Виеторисиан, *m.*, Vietoris complex
виеторисовский, *adj.*, Vietoris
визир, *m.*, sight, view-finder
визуальный, *adj.*, visual
вилка, *f.*, fork, plug, bracket
винеровский, *adj.*, Wiener, pertaining to Wiener
винт, *m.*, screw, propeller; **воздушный винт,** airscrew propeller; **шаг винта,** pitch of a screw
винтовой, *adj.*, screw, spiral, helical
вириал, *n.*, virial
вириальный, *adj.*, virial
виртуальный, *adj.*, virtual
висеть, *v.*, hang, overhang, be suspended
витой, *adj.*, twisted, spiral, turned
виток, *m.*, coil, loop, turn, convolution
вихревой, *adj.*, rotational, vortex, vortical, turbulent
вихрение, *n.*, vorticity
вихрь, *m.*, curl, rotation, vorticity, vortex, whirl
вклад, *m.*, contribution, investment; **сделать вклад в,** *v.*, contribute to
вкладывать, (вложить), *v.*, put in, invest, insert; imbed
вклеивание, *n.*, pasting in, pasting
включать, *v.*, enclose, insert, include, add; **включать себя,** *v.*, involve; **включать в себя,** *v.*, include
включая, *prep.*, including, inclusive of; *adv. part.*, including; **включая бесконечно удаленную точку**, including the point at infinity
включение, *n.*, inclusion, cut-in
включенный, *adj.*, included
включительно, *adv.*, inclusively, inclusive
вкравшийся, *adj.*, slipped in, slipping in
вкрадываться (вкрасться), *v.*, slip in (error)
вкратце, *adv.*, briefly, in short
вкус, *m.*, taste, manner, style; **дело вкуса,** a matter of taste
владеть, *v.*, possess, have, be master (of)
владеющий, *adj.*, possessing, having
власть, *f.*, rule, power, authority
влево, *adv.*, to the left
влечение, *n.*, tendency, inclination
влечет (cf. **влечь**), implies
влечь, *v.*, attract, draw, drag, bring, involve, necessitate, imply; **влечь за собой,** *v.*, imply, have as a consequence
вливающийся, *adj.*, flowing
влияние, *n.*, influence, impact; **функция влияния,** influence function, Green's function
влиять, *v.*, influence, affect
влияющий, *adj.*, influencing, affecting
вложение, *n.*, enclosure, insertion, imbedding, investment, inclusion; **вложение в целом,** global imbedding; **отображение вложения,** inclusion map
вложенный, *adj.*, imbedded, inserted enclosed; **вложенная цепь Маркова** imbedded Markov chain; **правильно (дико) вложенный,** *adj.*, tamely (wildly) imbedded

вложить, (*perf. of* **вкладывать**), put in, imbed, invest
вместе, *adv.*, together; **вместе с тем,** moreover, at the same time; **вместе с,** together with
вместимый, *adj.*, imbeddable
вместо, *prep.*, instead of, in place of
вмешательство, *n.*, interference, intervention
вмещение, *n.*, imbedding
вмещенный, *adj.*, imbedded
вначале, *adv.*, at the beginning; at first
вне, *prep.*, outside of, exterior to
вневписанный, *adj.*, circumscribed
внедрение, *n.*, introduction, intrusion, penetration
внезапно, *adv.*, suddenly, unexpectedly, abruptly
внезапный, *adj.*, sudden, abrupt
внеинтегральный, *adj.*, outside the integral, integrated; **внеинтегральный член,** the term outside the integral, the integrated term
внеконкурентный, *adj.*, uncompetitive; **внеконкурентное торможение,** uncompetitive inhibition (biophysics), (as disting. from **неконкурентное торможение,** non-competitive inhibition)
внеконтрольный, *adj.*, out of control
внеметаматематический, *adj.*, extrametamathematical
внеосевой, *adj.*, off the axis
внесение, *n.*, bringing in, insertion, entry, introduction
внести (cf. **вносить**), *v.*, bring in, insert
внетабличный, *adj.*, extratabular
внешне, *adv.*, outwardly, externally
внешний, *adj.*, exterior, external, superficial, outward, outer; **внешняя форма,** exterior form; **внешнее предельное множество,** superficial cluster set; **внешним образом,** *adv.*, externally
внешность, *f.*, exterior, appearance
вниз, *adv.*, down, downwards; **вниз по потоку,** downstream
внизу, *adv.*, below, at the bottom
внимание, *n.*, attention, notice; **принять во внимание,** *v.*, take into consideration
внимательный, *adj.*, attentive, intent, careful
вновь, *adv.*, anew, again, once again
внос, *m.*, introduction, importation
вносить, *v.*, bring in, insert, introduce
внося, *adv. part.*, introducing, if we introduce
вносящий, *adj.*, contributory, introducing
внутренне, *adv.*; **внутренне гомологичный,** *adj.*, intrinsically homologous, cobordant
внутренний, *adj.*, interior, inner, internal, intrinsic; **внутреннее расстояние,** intrinsic distance; **внутренняя гомология,** intrinsic homology, cobordism
внутренность, *f.*, interior, interiority; **внутренность угла,** angular domain, angular region
внутри, *prep.*, in, inside, interior to, on compact subsets of; **равномерно сходится внутри** *D*, is uniformly convergent on compact subsets of *D*
внутриблочный, *adj.*, interblock, intrablock
внутривидовой, *adj.*, intraspecific, intragroup
внутрикристаллический, *adj.*, crystalline, within the crystal, intracrystalline
внутримолекулярный, *adj.*, intramolecular
внутрисистемный, *adj.*, intrasystem, internal
внутрь, *prep.*, in, inside, inwards, toward the interior, into
внушать, *v.*, instil, suggest, inspire
внушенный, *adj.*, suggested
во (cf. **в**), *prep.*, in, into, at, to; **во время,** during; **во вторых,** secondly; **во всех отношениях,** in every respect; **во первых,** in the first place
вовлекать (вовлечь), *v.*, involve, implicate

вовсе, *adv.*, completely, entirely, at all, quite; **вовсе нет,** not at all
вогнутость, *f.*, concavity
вогнутый, *adj.*, concave; **вогнуто-выпуклый,** *adj.*, concave-convex
водить, *v.*, lead, conduct, steer
водопровод, *m.*, water pipe, water main
водопроницаемый, *adj.*, water permeable
водород, *m.*, hydrogen
водородоподобный, *adj.*, hydrogen-like
водородный, *adj.*, hydrogen
водохранилище, *n.*, reservoir
водяной, *adj.*, water
воедино, *adv.*, together
военный, *adj.*, military
возбудитель, *n.*, agent, stimulant, exciter, pulser
возбуждаемый, *adj.*, excitatory, excitable
возбуждать (возбудить), *v.*, excite, stimulate
возбуждающий, *adj.*, exciting, stimulating, excitatory
возбуждение, *n.*, motivation, stimulation, excitation; **цепь возбуждения,** energizing circuit (*comp.*)
возбужденный, *adj.*, excited; **возбужденное состояние,** upper state (of an atom)
возведение, *n.*, involution, raising (to a power), erection
возведенный, *adj.*, raised, elevated, derived, deduced
возвести (cf. **возводить**), *v.*, raise
возводить, *v.*, raise, erect; **возводить в третью степень,** *v.*, raise to the third power; **возводить в квадрат,** *v.*, square
возврат, *m.*, return, recover, restitution; **точка возврата,** cusp; **ребро возврата,** cuspidal edge, edge of regression
возвратить (cf. **возвращать**), return
возвратность, *f.*, reflexivity
возвратный, *adj.*, reflexive, recursion, recurring, reciprocal; **возвратная последовательность,** recursion relation; **возвратное уравнение,** reciprocal equation
возвращать, *v.*, return, give back, restore
возвращаясь, *adv. part.*, returning (to), reverting (to), if we return (to)
возвращение, *n.*, return, recurrence, replacement, regression; **выбор без возвращения,** sampling without replacement; **выбор с возвращением,** sampling with replacement
возвышать (возвысить), *v.*, raise, involve
возвышаться, *v.*, rise over, surpass
возвышение, *n.*, elevation, rise; **угол возвышения,** elevation angle
возвышенность, *f.*, height
возвышенный, *adj.*, high, elevated
воздействие, *n.*, action, effect
воздействовать, *v.*, act, influence, affect
воздействующий, *adj.*, acting, affecting
воздерживаться, *v.*, refrain (from), abstain (from)
воздух, *m.*, air
воздуховод, *m.*, air duct, air line
воздухопроницаемый, *adj.*, air-penetrating, air-penetrable
воздушный, *adj.*, air, aerial; **воздушный змей,** kite
возлагать, *v.*, lay, rest on
возле, *prep.*, next to, alongside, by
возможно, *adv.*, possibly, it is possible; **возможно лучшее,** best possible
возможность, *f.*, possibility, opportunity, chance
возможный, *adj.*, possible, feasible; **единственно возможный,** the only (one) possible
возмущать, *v.*, stir up, perturb, stir
возмущающий, *adj.*, disturbing, perturbation
возмущение, *n.*, perturbation, disturbance
возмущенный, *adj.*, perturbed
вознаграждение, *n.*, fee, reward, compensation
возникать, *v.*, arise, appear, spring up

возникающий, *adj.*, originating, arising from
возникновение, *n.*, origin, rise, beginning
возникнуть (cf. **возникать**), *v.*, arise
возобновляемый, *adj.*, renewed, renewable
возобновлять (возобновить), *v.*, renew, restore; resume
возражать, *v.*, object, take exception
возражение, *n.*, objection
возразить (cf. **возражать**), *v.*, object
возраст, *m.*, age
возрастание, *n.*, increase, rise, growth, increment
возрастать, *v.*, increase, grow, ascend
возрастающий, *adj.*, growing, increasing, accelerating, ascending
возрасти (cf. **возрастать**), *v.*, increase, grow
войдет (cf. **входить**), enters
войти (cf. **входить**), enter
война, *f.*, war, warfare
вокруг, *prep.*, around, round
волна, *f.*, wave
волнение, *n.*, disturbance
волнистость, *f.*, sinuosity
волнистый, *adj.*, sinuous, wavy; **волнистый круговой конус,** sinuous circular cone
волновод, *m.*, wave guide, wave conductor
волновой, *adj.*, pertaining to wave, wave
волнообразный, *adj.*, wavy, undulatory, undulating
волокнистый, *adj.*, pertaining to filament, fibrous, stringy
волокно, *n.*, filament, fibre, thread
вольтерровский, *adj.*, Volterra
волчок, *m.*, top, top molecule
вольт, *m.*, volt
вольтамперный, *adj.*, current-voltage, volt-ampere
воображаемый, *adj.*, imaginary, conceptual
воображать (вообразить), *v.*, imagine
воображаться, *v.*, seem
воображение, *n.*, imagination
воображенный, *adj.*, imaginary, imagined
вообразить (cf. **воображать**), *v.*, imagine
вообще, *adv.*, in general, generally; **вообще говоря,** generally speaking, in general
вооружение, *n.*, armament, equipment
вооруженный, *adj.*, armed, armed with, in possession of
вопреки, *prep.*, in spite of, against, despite, notwithstanding
вопрос, *m.*, question, problem, matter, issue; **вопрос состоит в том, что,** the question is
воронка, *f.*, whirlpool, funnel, crater
воронкообразный, *adj.*, funnel-shaped
ворота, *pl.*, gate, gates
восемь, *num.*, eight
восемьдесят, *num.*, eighty
воспламенение, *n.*, ignition
восположение, *n.*, fulfilment
восполнять (восполнить), *v.*, complete, fulfil, supply
воспользоваться, *v.*, take advantage of, use
воспрещать, *v.*, prohibit, forbid
восприимчивость, *f.*, susceptibility, receptivity, sensitivity
восприимчивый, *adj.*, susceptible, receptive, sensitive
воспринимаемый, *adj.*, perceptible
воспринимать, *v.*, perceive, interpret, absorb, receive
воспринимающий, *adj.*, receiving, stimulus-receiving
воспринятие, *n.*, perception
воспроизведение, *n.*, reproduction
воспроизведенный, *adj.*, reproduced
воспроизводимость, *f.*, reproducibility
воспроизводимый, *adj.*, reproducible
воспроизводительный, *adj.*, reproductive
воспроизводить (воспроизвести), *v.*, reproduce
воспроизводиться, *v.*, be reproduced
воспроизводство, *n.*, reproduction
воспроизводящий, *adj.*, reproducing; **воспроизводящее ядро,** reproducing kernel

восставить, *v.*, raise, erect; **восставить перпендикуляр (к),** *v.*, erect a perpendicular (to)
восстанавливать, *v.*, restore, reestablish, regenerate
восстановление, *n.*, restoration, renewal, reconstruction
восстановленный, *adj.*, reestablished, restored
восстановляющий, *adj.*, regenerating
восток, *m.*, east
восточный, *adj.*, eastern, easterly
восход, *m.*, rising, rise; **восход солнца,** sunrise
восходить (взойти), *v.*, go back (to)
восходящий, *adj.*, ascending
восхождение, *n.*, ascent, ascension; **прямое восхождение,** right ascension
восьмеричный, *adj.*, octuple, octal; **восьмеричный разряд,** octal digit
восьмерка, *f.*, eight, figure eight
восьми-, *prefix*, octo-, eight
восьмигранник, *m.*, octahedron
восьмигранный, *adj.*, octahedral
восьмиполюсник, *m.*, octopole, eight-terminal network
восьмиричный (=восьмеричный)
восьмиугольник, *m.*, octagon
восьмиугольный, *adj.*, octagonal
вот, there, here; here is, there is
вошедший, *adj.*, entered (into)
вошел (вошла, вошло, вошли), (cf. **входить**), entered
впервые, *adv.*, first, for the first time
вперед, *adv.*, forward; **вперед-назад (вперед и назад),** back and forth
впереди, *prep.*, in front of, before, ahead of
впечатление, *n.*, impression, influence, effect
впечатлительность, *f.*, impressionability, susceptibility
впечатлительный, *adj.*, impressionable, susceptible
вписанность, *f.*, refinement
вписанный, *adj.*, inscribed, refined; *A* **вписано в** *B*, *A* is a refinement of *B* (topology)
вписать (cf. **вписывать**), *v.*, inscribe, refine
вписывать, *v.*, inscribe, insert, enter, refine
впитывание, *n.*, absorption
впитывать, *v.*, absorb, take in
вплоть до, *prep.*, up to, till
вполне, *adv.*, entirely, fully, completely
вполне-непрерывный, *adj.*, completely continuous
вполне-приведенный, *adj.*, completely reducible
вполнеприменимость, *f.*, complete applicability
впоследствии, *adv.*, afterwards, later on, subsequently
вправе, *adv.*, justified; **быть вправе,** *v.*, have the right to
вправо, *adv.*, to the right
впредь, *adv.*, henceforth, from now on
впрочем, *conj.*, besides, however, though
впрыскивание, *n.*, injection
впрыскивать, *v.*, inject
впрыснутый, *adj.*, injected
вращательно, *adv.*, rotationally; **вращательно эллиптический,** *adj.*, spheroidal
вращательно-колебательный, *adj.*, rotationally oscillatory
вращательный, *adj.*, rotary, rotational
вращать, *v.*, revolve, rotate, turn
вращающийся, *adj.*, rotating, revolutionary
вращение, *n.*, rotation, revolution, gyration
вред, *m.*, harm, injury, damage
временами, *adv.*, at times, from time to time
временно, *adv.*, temporarily, provisionally
временной, *adj.*, time, pertaining to time, temporal
временный, *adj.*, temporary, provisional
время, *n.*, time, tense; **в то время,** at that time; **по временам,** from time to time; **со времени,** since

времяобразный, *adj.*, time-like, time
вроде, *prep.*, like; **нечто вроде,** a kind of
Вронскиан, *m.*, Wronskian (determinant)
вряд ли, *adv.*, hardly, scarcely
все (cf. **весь**), all
все, *adv.*, always, all the time, still; **все время,** all the time; **все еще,** still; **все же,** nevertheless; **все равно,** all the same; **все таки,** nevertheless
всевозможный, *adj.*, various, different, all kinds of, all sorts, all possible
всегда, *adv.*, always; **как всегда,** as ever
всегда-истинность, *f.*, identity
всегда-истинный, *adj.*, identity, identically true, always true, identically valid
всегдашний, *adj.*, usual, customary
всего (*gen.* of **весь**); *adv.*, in all, all together
всего-навсего, *adv.*, in all, only
вселение, *n.*, establishment, installation
вселенная, *f.*, universe
всемирный, *adj.*, universal, world-wide
всеобщий, *adj.*, universal, general
всеобщность, *f.*, generality, universality
всеобъемлющий, *adj.*, universal, comprehensive
Всесоюзный, *adj.*, All-Union
всесторонний, *adj.*, manifold, multifold, comprehensive, detailed
всецело, *adv.*, wholly, completely, entirely, exclusively
вскрывать (вскрыть), *v.*, open, reveal, disclose
вслед, *adv.*, *prep.*, after
вследствие, *prep.*, so that, in consequence of, on account of
вспоминать, *v.*, remember, recollect, recall
вспомогательный, *adj.*, auxiliary, subsidiary
вспыхивать (вспыхнуть), *v.*, flash, flare up, burst into flames
вспышка, *f.*, flash, outbreak
вставка, *f.*, insertion, imbedding
вставлять (вставит), *v.*, put (in), introduce
встреча, *f.*, meeting, contact; **точка встречи,** point of contact
встречать (встретить), *v.*, meet, encounter, occur; **может встретиться,** it may occur, we may come across
встречающийся, *adj.*, encountered, met, meeting
встречный, *adj.*, coming from the opposite direction, counter-; **встречный ветер,** headwind
встряхивание, *n.*, shaking, shaking up
вступать, *v.*, enter, enter into
вступающий, *adj.*, entering
вступление, *n.*, introduction, entry
всходить (взойти), *v.*, rise, ascend, mount
всюду, *adv.*, everywhere; **почти всюду** almost everywhere; **всюду определенный,** *adj.*, completely defined, everywhere defined
вся (cf. **весь**), all
всякий, *adj.*, any, each, every; **во всяком случае,** in any case; **на всякий случай,** to make sure, to be on the safe side
вт., *abbrev.* **(ватт),** watt
вторгающийся, *adj.*, incoming, intruding
вторично, *adv.*, for the second time
вторичный, *adj.*, second, secondary, derived
второй, *adj.*, second
второстепенный, *adj.*, secondary, unimportant, minor
втрое, *adv.*, thrice, in three
вход, *m.*, entry, entrance, input
входить, *v.*, enter, come in, go in; be contained in; **входить в состав,** *v.*, form, be a part of
входной, *adj.*, entering, entrance, input; **входные данные,** input data; **входной зрачок,** entrance pupil; **входной сигнал,** input signal
входящий, *adj.*, entering, incoming, reëntrant
вхождение, *n.*, entrance, appearance, occurrence
вы, *pron.*, you
выбираемый, *adj.*, selective
выбирать (выбрать), *v.*, choose, select

выбирая, *adv. part.*, choosing, selecting, if we choose

выбор, *m.*, choice, selection, option, sampling; **выбор решения,** decision making; **выбор без возвращения,** sampling without replacement; **случайный выбор,** random sampling, **простой случайный выбор,** simple sampling; **пристрастный выбор,** biased sampling; **аксиома выбора,** axiom of choice

выборка, *f.*, sampling, sample, excerpt, selection, access (*comp.*); **время выборки,** access time (*comp.*)

выборный, *adj.*, sample

выборочный, *adj.*, sampling, sample, selective; **выборочная проверка,** spot check; **выборочная функция,** sample distribution function; **выборочный контроль,** sampling, testing; **выборочный контроль по количественному признаку,** sampling by variables; **выборочная функция,** choice function, selector

выбраковываться, *v.*, be thrown out, be discarded, be rejected

выбранный, *adj.*, chosen, selected

выбрасывание, *n.*, rejection

выбрасывать (выбросить), *v.*, reject, throw out

выбрать (cf. **выбирать**), *v.*, choose, select

выброс, *m.*, ejection, rejection

выбросить (cf. **выбрасывать**), *v.*, reject, throw out

выброшенный, *adj.*, thrown out, rejected

выбывший, *adj.*, leaving, quitting

выведение, *n.*, deduction, derivation

выведенный, *adj.*, brought out, revealed, derived, developed

выведывать, *v.*, find out, reveal

вывели (cf. **вывести**), deduced

выверка, *f.*, alignment

вывести (cf. **выводить**), *v.*, deduce, derive

вывод, *m.*, conclusion, deduction, inference, derivation; **делать вывод,** *v.*, conclude

выводимость, *f.*, deducibility

выводимый, *adj.*, deductive, derived, deducible, derivable

выводить (вывести), *v.*, deduce, derive, conclude, lead out

выглядеть, *v.*, discover, seem, appear

выгода, *f.*, advantage, benefit, gain, profit, interest; **функция выгоды,** utility function

выгодность, *f.*, utility

выгодный, *adj.*, advantageous, profitable

выгоднейший, *adj.*, most advantageous

выдающийся, *adj.*, outstanding, prominent, salient

выдвигать (выдвинуть), *v.*, advance, put forth, adduce, introduce

выдвинутый, *adj.*, introduced, advanced, promoted, risen

выделение, *n.*, isolation, separation, selection, secretion, discharge

выделенный, *adj.*, chosen, isolated, singled out, preferred

выделяемый, *adj.*, separating

выделять (выделить), *v.*, select, extract, distinguish, isolate

выдерживать, *v.*, withstand, sustain, endure

выдержка, *f.*, self-control, restraint, excerpt, exposure; **на выдержку,** at random

выждать (cf. **выжидать**), wait for

выживание, *n.*, survival, endurance; **функция выживания,** fatigue function

выжидать (выждать), *v.*, wait for

вызванный, *adj.*, due (to), caused by, summoned

вызвать (cf. **вызывать**), call, summon

выздоровевший, *adj.*, recovered

вызов, *m.*, call, summons, challenge

вызываемый, *adj.*, evoked

вызывать (вызвать), *v.*, call, summon, induce, cause, involve

выигрывать (выиграть), *v.*, benefit, win, gain

выигрыш, *m.*, prize, winnings, gain, advantage, score, payoff; **функция выигрыша,** payoff function

выйти (cf. **выходить**), *v.*, leave, go out; **выйти за пределы,** fall outside the limits
выкидывание, *n.*, rejection
выкидывать (выкинуть), *v.*, throw out, discard
выкинутый, *adj.*, eliminated, discarded, thrown out; **с выкинутой,** except for, with the exception of
выкладка, *f.*, calculation, computation, laying out
выключатель, *m.*, switch: **управляющий выключатель,** control switch
выключать, *v.*, switch, switch off
выключение, *n.*, cut-off
выколотый, *adj.*, punctured, deleted, pricked
вылет, *m.*, flight, take-off
вылетающий, *adj.*, flying out, outgoing; **вылетающая частица,** outgoing particle
выметаемый, *adj.*, swept out
выметание, *n.*, sweeping, sweeping out; **выметание мер,** balayage
вынимание, *n.*, removal, withdrawal
вынимать (вынуть), *v.*, take out, remove
вынос, *m.*, export, exportation
выносить (вынести), *v.*, take out, carry out, endure
вынуждать (вынудить), *v.*, force, constrain
вынуждающий, *adj.*, forcing, constraining
вынужденный, *adj.*, forced, constrained, compelled; **вынужденное движение,** forced vibration, forced motion
вынудить (cf. **вынуждать**), force, compel
вынутый, *adj.*, drawn, taken
выпадать (выпасть), *v.*, fall out, come out, fall, occur
выпадение, *n.*, shedding, falling out, appearance
выписывать (выписать), *v.*, write out, extract
выплата, *f.*, payment
выполнение, *n.*, realization, fulfilment
выполненный, *adj.*, fulfilled, realized
выполнимость, *f.*, realizability, practicability, feasibility
выполнимый, *adj.*, feasible, practicable, realizable, satisfiable
выполнять (выполнить), *v.*, fulfil, implement, carry out, accomplish
выполняться (выполниться), *v.*, be fulfilled, be realized
выполняющий, *adj.*, fulfilling, satisfying
выпрямимый, *adj.*, rectifiable
выпрямитель, *m.*, rectifier
выпрямление, *n.*, rectification, straightening
выпрямленный, *adj.*, rectified, straightened
выпрямлять (выпрямить), *v.*, rectify, straighten
выпрямляющий, *adj.*, rectifying, straightening; **выпрямляющий контакт,** rectifying contact
выпрямляющийся, *adj.*, straightening, being straightened, being rectified
выпукло-компактный, *adj.*, convex-compact
выпуклость, *f.*, convexity, convexification
выпуклый, *adj.*, convex, bulging, prominent, distinct
выпуск, *m.*, outlet, output, product, discharge, emission; **граница возможного выпуска продукции,** production-possibility frontier; **программирование выпуска продукции,** production programming; **матрица выпуска,** output matrix
выпускаемый, *adj.*, output; **выпускаемые продукты,** output goods
выпускать, *v.*, emit, let out, turn out, issue
выпучивание, *n.*, swelling, buckling
выпучивать (выпучить), *v.*, swell, protrude
выпущенный, *adj.*, emitted
вырабатывать (выработать), *v.*, make, manufacture, generate, produce
вырабатываться (выработаться), *v.*, be developed, be elaborated on

выработка, *f.*, development, elaboration
выравненный, *adj.*, adjusted, aligned, evened; **выравненные измерения,** adjusted measurements
выравнивание, *n.*, smoothing, levelling, alignment, equalization, fit
выравнивать (выровнять), *v.*, align, straighten, fit, smooth, level
выражать (выразить), *v.*, express, convey; **выражать в числах,** *v.*, evaluate
выражаться (выразиться), *v.*, be expressed, manifest itself
выражающий, *adj.*, expressing
выражение, *n.*, expression
выраженный, *adj.*, expressed, delineated; **выраженный через,** expressed in terms of
выразимость, *f.*, expressibility
выразительный, *adj.*, indicative, expressive, significant
выразить, cf. **выражать**
вырастать, *v.*, grow, increase, develop
вырез, *m.*, cut, excision
вырезаемый, *adj.*, cut
вырезание, *n.*, excision, cut, cutting out; **отображение вырезания,** excision map
вырезанный, *adj.*, cut out
вырезать, *v.*, cut out, excise
вырождаться (выродиться), *v.*, degenerate, degenerate into
вырождающийся, *adj.*, degenerating, degenerate
вырождение, *n.*, degeneration, confluence, degeneracy
вырожденность, *f.*, degeneracy, degeneration
вырожденный, *adj.*, degenerate, confluent, singular
выросший, *adj.*, evolved, developed
вырывание, *n.*, ejection, forcing out, extraction; **вырывание электрона,** ejection of an electron
высасывание, *n.*, exhaustion, wearing out, sucking out
высасывать, *v.*, exhaust, suck out
высвобождать, *v.*, free, let out, disengage, disentangle, release
высвобождение, *n.*, release
высекаемый, *adj.*, cut, being cut
высекать (высечь), *v.*, cut, cut out, carve, excise
высечение, *n.*, cut, excision
высечка, *f.*, carving, cutting, excision
выскабливание, *n.*, scraping, scraping out
высказанный, *adj.*, expressed, stated
высказывание, *n.*, expression, statement, proposition; **исчисление высказываний,** propositional calculus
высказывать, *v.*, state, express
выскакивать (выскочить), *v.*, jump out
высокий, *adj.*, high, tall, elevated
высоко, *adv.*, highly, high
высоковакуумный, *adj.*, high-vacuum
высоко-вероятный, *adj.*, high-probability, highly probable
высоковольтный, *adj.*, high-voltage
высококачественный, *adj.*, high-quality
высокомолекулярный, *adj.*, of high molecular weight
высокопробный, *adj.*, high-standard
высокоскоростной, *adj.*, high-speed
высокосортный, *adj.*, high-grade
высокочастотный, *adj.*, high-frequency
высокочувствительный, *adj.*, highly sensitive
высота, *f.*, height, altitude, pitch, elevation
выставлять (выставить), *v.*, advance, display, expose
выступ, *m.*, protuberance, salient, jut
выступающий, *adj.*, expressed, set forth, outstanding
высший, *adj.*, higher, advanced, superior, highest, supreme; **высшая точка,** peak
высыпание, *n.*, emptying, pouring out
выталкивать (вытолкать), *v.*, push out, force out, eject
вытекать (вытечь), *v.*, imply, flow out, run out, follow, ensue, arise from

вытеснение, *n.*, displacement, dislodgment, exclusion
вытесненный, *adj.*, displaced
вытесняемый, *adj.*, being displaced
вытравленный, *adj.*, etched, corroded
вытравливать, *v.*, corrode, etch
вытягивание, *n.*, extraction, elongation, stretching
вытягивать (вытянуть), *v.*, draw out, extract, pull out, stretch, extend,
вытянутый, *adj.*, prolate, stretched, elongated, prolonged, extracted
выхлопной, *adj.*, exhaust, escape; **выхлопной газ,** exhaust gas
выход, *m.*, exit, outcome, output, discharge, yield, result
выходить, *v.*, go out, leave, get out, appear; **вышло что,** it appeared that, it turned out that; **выходить за пределы,** fall outside the limits
выходной, *adj.*, output, outside; **выходные данные,** output data
выходящий, *adj.*, outgoing, leaving, emanating
вычеркивание, *n.*, crossing out, deletion, cancellation
вычеркивать, *v.*, to cross out, cancel, delete, eliminate
вычерченный, *adj.*, traced, drawn
вычерчивание, *n.*, drawing, tracing
вычерчивать (вычертить), *v.*, draw, trace
вычесть (cf. **вычитать**), *v.*, subtract
вычет, *m.*, residue, deduction, remainder
вычетный, *adj.*, residue, residual
вычисление, *n.*, calculation, computation, evaluation
вычисленный, *adj.*, calculated, computed, estimated
вычислимость, *f.*, computability
вычислимый, *adj.*, computable
вычислитель, *m.*, computer, calculator, calculating machine
вычислительный, *adj.*, computing, calculating, digital
вычислять (вычислить), *v.*, compute, calculate
вычитаемое, *n.*, subtrahend
вычитание, *n.*, subtraction, deduction
вычитать (вычесть), *v.*, subtract, deduct
вычитающий, *adj.*, subtracting
выше, *prep.*, above, higher, beyond; **выше доказанный,** *adj.*, proved above
вышедший, *adj.*, published
вышеизложенный, *adj.*, stated above, set forth above
вышел (вышла, вышло, вышли), *past tense* of **выходить**
вышеописанный, *adj.*, described above
вышеприведенный, *adj.*, above mentioned, foregoing, aforesaid
вышесделанный, *adj.*, made above
вышеуказанный, *adj.*, previously mentioned, above, above mentioned
вышеупомянутый, *adj.*, above cited, above mentioned
выявитель, *m.*, detector
выявить, *v.*, show, make, manifest
выявление, *n.*, exposure, detection
выяснение, *n.*, clearing up, determination, elucidation
выясненный, *adj.*, cleared up, determined
выяснять (выяснить), *v.*, explain, elucidate, clarify
вьеторисовский, *adj.*, Vietoris, pertaining to Vietoris; **вьеторисовский цикл,** Vietoris cycle
вязкий, *adj.*, viscous
вязко-пластический, *adj.*, visco-plastic
вязкость, *f.*, viscosity
вялый, *adj.*, inert, slack, dull

Г

г. (*abbrev.*, **год, года**), year
гадание, *n.*, guessing, guess-work
гадать (погадать), *v.*, guess, conjecture
газ, *m.*, gas
газета, *f.*, gazette, newspaper
газовый, *adj.*, gas, gaseous
газодинамика, *f.*, gas dynamics
газокалильный, *adj.*, incandescent
газообразный, *adj.*, vapor, gaseous, gas; **газообразная фаза,** *f.*, vapor phase
газопровод, *m.*, gas conduit, gas pipeline
галактика, *f.*, galaxy
галактический, *adj.*, galactic
галоид, *m.*, haloid
гальванический, *adj.*, galvanic
гальваномагнитный, *adj.*, galvano-magnetic
гальванометр, *m.*, galvanometer
гамильтониан, *m.*, hamiltonian
гамма-функция, *f.*, gamma-function
гантель, *m.*, dumb-bell shaped figure; **гантели,** *pl.*, dumb-bells
гарантировать, *v.*, guarantee
гарантируемый, *adj.*, guaranteed
гарантирующий, *adj.*, guaranteeing
гарантия, *f.*, guarantee, security, assurance
гармонизировать, *v.*, harmonize (with), be in keeping (with), go (with)
гармоника, *f.*, harmonics, harmonic curve, harmonic; **зональная гармоника,** zonal harmonic; **объемная гармоника,** solid harmonic
гармонический, *adj.*, harmonic; **линейная гармоническая функция,** *f.*, line harmonic; **точечная гармоническая функция,** *f.*, point harmonic
гармоничность, *f.*, harmonicity
гармоничный, *adj.*, harmonic
гасить, *v.*, extinguish, quench
гасящий, *adj.*, quenching
Гаусдорф, *prop. name*, Hausdorff (usually **Хаусдорф**)
гаусс, *m.*, gauss (unit)
гауссовый, *adj.*, gaussian; **гауссовы суммы,** gaussian sums; quadratic partitions
гашение, *m.*, extinguishing
гашеный, *adj.*, extinguished, quenched, slaked
гвоздь, *m.*, nail, stud
где, *adv.*, where; **где бы ни,** wherever; **где бы то ни было,** no matter where; **где-либо,** somewhere; **где-нибудь,** somewhere; **где-то,** somewhere
геделизировать, *v.*, Gödelize
геделевский, *adj.*, Gödel, pertaining to Gödel
гейзенберговский, *adj.*, Heisenberg
гексагональный, *adj.*, hexagonal
гексаэдр, *m.*, hexahedron
гексаэдроид, *m.*, hexahedroid, hexahedron
гектар, *m.*, hectare (10,000 sq. m.)
гекто-, *prefix*, hecto-
гелий, *m.*, helium
геликоид, *m.*, helicoid
геликоидальный, *adj.*, helical, helicoidal
гелио-, *prefix*, helio-
гелиоцентр, *m.*, heliocenter
гелиоцентрический, *adj.*, heliocentric
геми-, *prefix*, hemi-; semi-
ген, *m.*, gene
генеральный, *adj.*, general; **генеральная совокупность,** parent population, general population, universe
генератор, *m.*, generator
генератрис, *m.*, generatrix, generator
генерация, *f.*, generation
генерировать, *v.*, generate, produce
генерируемый, *adj.*, generated, produced
генетика, *f.*, genetics
генетический, *adj.*, genetic
гений, *m.*, genius

генотип, *m.*, genotype; **распределение генотипов,** genotype distribution; **частота генотипов,** genotype frequency
генри, *m.*, henry
географический, *adj.*, geographical
геодезическая, *f.*, geodesic
геодезический, *adj.*, geodesic, geodetic; **геодезическая окружность,** geodesic circle, geodesic
геодезия, *f.*, geodesy
геология, *f.*, geology
геомагнитный, *adj.*, geomagnetic
геометральный, *adj.*, geometric
геометрический, *adj.*, geometric; **геометрическое место (точек),** geometric locus; locus
геометрия, *f.*, geometry
геострофический, *adj.*, geostrophic
геофизический, *adj.*, geophysical
геоцентр, *m.*, geocenter
геоцентрический, *adj.*, geocentric
герб, *m.*, arms, heads; **герб или надпись,** heads or tails
германий, *m.*, germanium
герметизированный, *adj.*, hermetically sealed
герметизировать, *v.*, seal hermetically
герметический, *adj.*, hermetic; **герметически закрытый,** *adj.*, hermetically sealed; **герметическая кабина,** pressurized cabin
герц, *m.*, hertz, cycle per second
гессиан, *m.*, Hessian
гетерогенность, *f.*, heterogeneity
гетерогенный, *adj.*, heterogeneous
гибель, *f.*, loss, ruin, catastrophe, destruction, death; **коэффициент гибели,** death-rate
гибкий, *adj.*, flexible
гибкость, *f.*, flexibility, pliability
гигантский, *adj.*, large, giant; **гигантские простые числа Мерсена,** large Mersenne primes
гидравлика, *f.*, hydraulics
гидравлический, *adj.*, hydraulic
гидратированный, *adj.*, hydrated
гидро-, *prefix*, hydro-
гидродинамика, *f.*, hydrodynamics
гидродинамический, *adj.*, hydrodynamic
гидрология, *f.*, hydrology
гидромеханика, *f.*, hydromechanics, fluid mechanics
гидромеханический, *adj.*, hydromechanical
гидростатика, *f.*, hydrostatics
гидростатический, *adj.*, hydrostatic
гильбертовый, *adj.*, Hilbert; pertaining to Hilbert; **гильбертово пространство,** Hilbert space; **гильбертовый кирпич,** Hilbert cube
гимназия, *f.*, gymnasium (school)
гипер-, *prefix*, hyper-
гипереареальный, *adj.*, hyperareal
гипербола, *f.*, hyperbola
гиперболический, *adj.*, hyperbolic
гиперболичный, *adj.*, hyperbolic
гилерболоид, *m.*, hyperboloid
гипервещественный, *adj.*, hyper-real
гипергеометрический, *adj.*, hypergeometric
гиперквадрика, *f.*, hyperquadric
гиперкомплексный, *adj.*, hypercomplex
гиперкоммутаториальный, *adj.*, hypercommutatorial
гиперконечный, *adj.*, hyperfinite
гиперконус, *m.*, hypercone
гиперкуб, *m.*, hypercube
гиперлиния, *f.*, hyperline, hypercurve
гипермаксимальный, *adj.*, hypermaximal
гиперметрический, *adj.*, hypermetric
гипернильпотентный, *adj.*, hypernilpotent
гипернорма, *f.*, hypernorm
гипернормальный, *adj.*, hypernormal
гипероктаэдральный, *adj.*, hyperoctahedral
гиперон, *m.*, hyperon
гиперпараллелепипед, *m.*, hyperparallelepiped
гиперпеременный, *adj.*, hypervariable
гиперплоскость, *f.*, hyperplane

гиперповерхностный, *adj.*, hypersurface
гиперповерхность, *f.*, hypersurface, form
гиперпримарный, *adj.*, hyperprimary
гиперпростой, *adj.*, hypersimple
гиперсоприкасающийся, *adj.*, hyperosculating
гиперсфера, *f.*, hypersphere
гиперсферический, *adj.*, hyperspherical, hypersphere
гиперфокальный, *adj.*, hyperfocal
гиперфрагмент, *m.*, hyper-fragment
гиперцентр, *m.*, hypercenter
гиперцикл, *m.*, hypercycle
гиперциркуль, *m.*, hypercompasses
гиперцоколь, *m.*, hyper-base, hypersocle
гипершар, *m.*, hypersphere
гиперэллипсоид, *m.*, hyperellipsoid
гиперэллиптический, *adj.*, hyperelliptic
гипокомпактный, *adj.*, hypocompact
гипотеза, *f.*, hypothesis, conjecture
гипотенуза, *f.*, hypotenuse
гипотетический, *adj.*, hypothetical
гипоциклоида, *f.*, hypocycloid
гипоэллиптический, *adj.*, hypoelliptic
гировертикаль, *m.*, gyrovertical
гиромагнитный, *adj.*, gyromagnetic; **гиромагнитное отношение,** gyromagnetic ratio
гироскоп, *m.*, gyroscope, gyro
гироскопический, *adj.*, gyroscopic
гиря, *f.*, weight
гистерезис, *m.*, hysteresis
гисто-, *prefix*, histo-
гистограмма, *f.*, histogram, bar chart
гл., *abbrev.* **(глава),** chapter; *abbrev.* **(гектолитр),** hectoliter
гл. о. (гл. обр.), *abbrev.* **(главным образом),** chiefly, mainly
глава, *f.*, chapter
главный, *adj.*, principal, essential, main; **главный диаметр,** principal axis; **главная нормаль,** principal normal; **главное отображение,** principal map; **главное произведение,** principal bundle; **главное значение (Коши),** (Cauchy) principal value; **главным образом,** chiefly, mainly; **главная часть,** principal part, dominant part; **главная точка (простого конца),** principal point (of prime end)
гладкий, *adj.*, smooth
гладкость, *f.*, smoothness
глаз, *m.*, eye
гласить, *v.*, state, say
гласный, *adj.*, public, open
гласящий, *adj.*, stating
глиссирование, *n.*, gliding, slipping
глобальный, *adj.*, global
глобус, *m.*, globe
глубина, *f.*, depth, intensity, profundity
глубокий, *adj.*, deep, profound
глушитель, *m.*, muffler, silencer
гнездный, *adj.*, nesting, nested
гнездо, *n.*, nest, nesting
гнездовой, *adj.*, nested, nesting
гномон, *m.*, gnomon
гномонический, *adj.*, gnomonic, gnomonical
говорить, *v.*, speak, say, indicate
говоря, *adv. part.*, saying, speaking, if we say; **вообще говоря,** generally speaking, in general; **иначе говоря,** in other words
год, *m.*, year
годиться, *v.*, suit, be fit for, be suitable for
годичный, *adj.*, a year's, of a year
годный, *adj.*, fit, valid, non-defective
годовой, *adj.*, yearly, annual
годограф, *m.*, hodograph
голландский, *adj.*, Dutch
головка, *f.*, head, knob
голоморф, *m.*, holomorph
голоморфно-полный, *adj.*, holomorphically complete
голоморфность, *f.*, property of being holomorphic, holomorphy
голоморфный, *adj.*, holomorphic
голономия, *f.*, holonomy
голономный, *adj.*, holonomic
гомалоидный, *adj.*, homaloidal

гомеоморф, *m.*, homeomorph, homeomorphic image
гомеоморфизм, *m.*, homeomorphism
гомеоморфность, *f.*, homeomorphism
гомеоморфный, *adj.*, homeomorphic
гомогенный, *adj.*, homogeneous
гомографический, *adj.*, homographic
гомографичный, *adj.*, homographic
гомография, *f.*, homography
гомогруппа, *f.*, homogroup
гомологический, *adj.*, homologous, homology, homological
гомологичность, *f.*, homology
гомологичный, *adj.*, homologous, homology
гомология, *f.*, homology; **верхняя гомология,** cohomology; **группа гомологий,** homology group; **внутренняя гомология,** cobordism
гомоморф, *m.*, homomorph
гомоморфизм, *m.*, homomorphism; **гомоморфизм в,** into homomorphism, homomorphism into; **гомоморфизм на,** onto homomorphism, homomorphism onto
гомоморфный, *adj.*, homomorphic; **гомоморфный по объединениям,** *adj.*, join-homomorphic
гомотетичный, *adj.*, homothetic
гомотетия, *f.*, homothety, homothetic transformation, dilation
гомотопический, *adj.*, homotopic, homotopy
гомотопия, *f.*, homotopy
гомотопность, *f.*, being homotopic, homotopy
гомотопный, *adj.*, homotopic, homotop
гомотропия, *f.*, homotropy
гомоцентрический, *adj.*, homocentric, concentric
гониометр, *m.*, goniometer
гониометрия, *f.*, goniometry
гораздо, *adv.*, much, far, considerably
горение, *n.*, combustion, burning
гореть, *v.*, burn
горизонт, *m.*, horizon
горизонталь, *f.*, horizontal, contour line, level
горизонтальный, *adj.*, horizontal
горицикл, *m.*, oricycle
горло, *n.*, throat; **течение в горле сопла,** throat flow; **радиус горла,** throat radius
горловой, *adj.*, throat, striction; **горловая точка (линейчатой поверхности),** throat, central point (of a ruled surface); **горловая линия,** striction line
господствовать, *v.*, dominate, predominate, majorize
господствующий, *adj.*, dominating, majorizing
готический, *adj.*, Gothic
готовый, *adj.*, ready, ready for, prepared for; **готовый продукт,** assembly
гофрированный, *adj.*, corrugated
гравиметрический, *adj.*, gravimetric
гравитационный, *adj.*, gravitational
гравитация, *f.*, gravitation, gravity
гравитирующий, *adj.*, gravitating
градиент, *m.*, gradient
градиентный, *adj.*, gradient
градуирование, *n.*, graduation, calibration
градуированный, *adj.*, graduated, calibrated, graded
градуировать, *v.*, graduate, calibrate, scale, grade
градуировка, *f.*, calibration, calibrating, graduation
градуировочный, *adj.*, graduated, calibrated
градуируемый, *adj.*, gradable, capable of being graduated
градус, *m.*, degree
градусный, *adj.*, degree
грамм, *m.*, gram; (*gen. pl.* = **грамм**)
грамматом, *m.*, gram atom
граммолекула, *f.* (also **грамм-молекула,** *f.*), gram molecule
грандиозный, *adj.*, mighty, grand, immense

гранецентрированный, *adj.*, face-centered; **гранецентрированная кубическая решетка,** face-centered cubic (lattice)
граничащий, *adj.*, adjacent, adjoining, next to
граничение, *n.*, demarcation
граничить, *v.*, bound, adjoin, border (on), abut
граничный, *adj.*, boundary, bounding; **граничное множество,** cluster set; ∇**-граничный,** *adj.*, coboundary; **нижнее граничное множество,** greatest lower cluster set; **угловое граничное множество,** angular cluster set; **граничный оператор,** face operator, boundary operator
граница, *f.*, boundary, limit, frontier
-гранный, *suffix*, -hedral, -faced; *n*-**гранная игральная кость,** *n*-faced die
грань, *f.*, face, side, bound; **нижняя грань,** (greatest) lower bound; *q*-**мерная грань,** *q*-face
грассмановский, *adj.*, Grassman; **грассмановское многообразие,** Grassman manifold
грассмановый, *adj.*, Grassman
граф, *m.*, graph
графа, *f.*, column, linear complex, complex
график, *m.*, graph, diagram, chart, schedule
графить, *v.*, rule, draw
графический, *adj.*, graphic, schematic, diagrammatic
графленый, *adj.*, ruled
графо-аналитический, *adj.*, graphico-analytic, graph-analytic
гребенка, *f.*, comb, rack
гребень, *m.*, crest, ridge, comb
греко-латинский, *adj.*, Greco-Latin; **греко-латинский квадрат,** Greco-Latin square; Eulerian square
греть, *v.*, heat, warm
греческий, *adj.*, Greek; **греческая буква,** Greek letter
Гринвич, Greenwich; **долгота от Гринвича,** longitude from Greenwich
гриновый, *adj.*, Green, Green's
громадный, *adj.*, large, vast, immense
громоздить, *v.*, pile up, heap up
громоздкий, *adj.*, cumbersome, bulky, unwieldy, awkward, tedious
громоздко, *adv.*, clumsily, inconveniently
громоздкость, *f.*, awkwardness, inconvenience
громоздок, *m.*, bulk
грубо, *adv.*, roughly; **грубо говоря,** roughly speaking
грубооднородный, *adj.*, roughly uniform
грубый, *adj.*, rough, coarse, crude, raw, gross; **грубая ошибка,** gross error; **грубый критерий,** quick test
груз, *m.*, load, goods, freight
грунт, *m.*, ground, bottom, soil
грунтовой, *adj.*, ground, prime
группа, *f.*, group, cluster, batch
группирование, *n.*, grouping, classification
группированный, *adj.*, divided in groups, grouped, classified, tabulated
группировать, *v.*, group, classify
группироваться, *v.*, cluster, group
группировка, *f.*, grouping, classification, organization, alignment
группировочный, *adj.*, grouped, grouping, group
групповой, *adj.*, group, grouped, raw; **групповой момент,** raw moment, grouped moment
группоид, *m.*, groupoid
грушевидный, *adj.*, pear-shaped
гуморалный, *adj.*, humoral
густо, *adv.*, densely, thickly
густой, *adj.*, dense, thick
густота, *f.*, density, thickness
гц., *abbrev.* **(герц),** Hertz; cycle per second

Д

да, *part.*, yes; *part. of subj.*, let; *conj.*, and, but

даваемый, *adj.*, given

давать, *v.*, give; **дадим,** let us give, we shall give; **дадут,** (they) will give; **дается,** is given

давление, *n.*, pressure, stress

давний, *adj.*, old, ancient

давно, *adv.*, for long, long ago; **давно известный,** familiar, well known

давность, *f.*, antiquity, remoteness

дадим, cf. **давать**

даже, *part.*, even, even though; **если даже,** even if

даламбериан, *m.*, d'Alembertian, wave operator

далее, *adj.*, further, later; then; **и так далее,** etc., and so on

далекий, *adj.*, remote, distant

далеко, *adv.*, far, far off, by far; **далеко не,** by far not, far from being

дальнейший, *adj.*, further, furthest, subsequent; **в дальнейшем,** later on, in what follows, in the sequel

дальнодействие, *n.*, long-range action

дальнодействующий, *adj.*, long-range, far-ranging

дальнозоркий, *adj.*, far-sighted

дальнозоркость, *f.*, long sight, far-sightedness

дальномер, *m.*, range finder

дальность, *f.*, distance, range, ranging

дальше, *adv.*, farther, farther on, later

дан (дана, дано, даны), [short form of **данный,** given]; **пусть дан,** given, let there be given

данные, *pl.*, data; **выходные данные,** output data; **приводить данные,** *v.*, cite data

данный, *adj.*, given

даром, *adv.*, in vain, for nothing, to no purpose, free, gratis

дата, *f.*, date

датчик, *m.*, transmitter, data unit, generator

дать (cf. **давать**), *v.*, give

два, *num.*, two

двадцатигранник, *m.*, icosahedron

двадцать, *num.*, twenty

дважды, *adv.*, twice

две, *num.*, two

двенадцатигранник, *m.*, dodecahedron

двенадцатиричный, *adj.*, duodecimal

двенадцать, *num.*, twelve

двести, *num.*, two hundred

двигатель, *m.*, motor, engine

двигательный, *adj.*, motive

двигать, *v.*, move, set in motion, advance, promote

двигающий, *adj.*, motive, moving, driving

движение, *n.*, movement, motion; **вращательное движение,** rotation, rotary motion; **количество движения,** momentum; **момент количества движения,** angular momentum, moment of momentum; **полное движение,** general motion; **политропическое движение,** polytropic expansion

движимость, *f.*, mobility, movable property

движимый, *adj.*, movable, mobile

движок, *m.*, slide, movable indicator

движущий, *adj.*, moving, motive, driving, propelling

движущийся, *adj.*, moving; **движущийся объект,** moving object, moving target

двинуть (cf. **двигать**), move

двое, *n.*, two, pair

двоеточие, *n.*, colon

двоить, *v.*, double

двоично-десятичный, *adj.*, binary-decimal, coded decimal; **двоично-десятичный счетник,** binary-decimal counter

двоично-кодированный, *adj.*, binary-coded
двоично-рациональный, *adj.*, dyadic, binary; dyadic rational, binary rational
двоичный, *adj.*, binary
двойка, *f.*, two, pair
двойник, *m.*, double
двойной, *adj.*, double, dual, compound, two-base, binary; **двойное отношение,** *n.*, cross-ratio, anharmonic ratio; **двойная стрелка,** double arrow, implication
двойственность, *f.*, duality; **теорема двойственности,** duality theorem; **двойственность себе,** *f.*, self-duality
двойственный, *adj.*, dual, reciprocal; **двойственный себе,** *adj.*, self-reciprocal, self-dual
двоякий, *adj.*, two-fold, double
двояко, *adv.*, in two ways, doubly
двояковогнутый, *adj.*, concavo-concave, doubly concave, biconcave
двояковыпуклый, *adj.*, convexo-convex, doubly convex, biconvex
двоякокруговой, *adj.*, bicircular
двоякопериодический, *adj.*, doubly periodic
двоякопреломляющий, *adj.*, doubly refracting
дву- (двух-), *prefix*, bi-, di-, two-
двуадический, *adj.*, dyadic
двугранный, *adj.*, dihedral, two-sided
двудольный, *adj.*, bi-partite
двузначность, *f.*, two-valued property; **точка двузначности**, ambiguous point
двузначный, *adj.*, two-valued, two-digit, two-to-one
двукратный, *adj.*, repeated, double, reiterated
двулистный, *adj.*, two-sheeted; **двулистное накрытие,** double covering, two-sheeted covering
двум (cf. **два**), (to) two
двумерный, *adj.*, two-dimensional, bivariate
двуместный, *adj.*, two-place; **двуместная функция,** function of two variables
двумостный, *adj.*, double bridge
двумя (cf. **два, две**), two
двунормовой, *adj.*, double-norm
двупараметрический, *adj.*, two-parameter
двуполостный, *adj.*, two-sheeted
двупредельный, *adj.*, two-limit, either-or, go-and-not-go
двупятиричный (=двупятеричный), *adj.*, biquinary
двусвязный, *adj.*, doubly-connected
двуслойный, *adj.*, two-sheeted, two-layer, double-layer
двусмысленность, *f.*, ambiguity
двусмысленный, *adj.*, ambiguous, equivocal
двустепенный, *adj.*, two-phase, bigrade
двусторонний, *adj.*, two-sided, double-sided, bilateral
двусторонно-инвариантный, *adj.*, bilaterally invariant
двуточечно, *adv.*, pair-wise
двуточечный, *adj.*, two-point, double point, pair-wise
двуугольник, *m.*, lune, figure having two angles
двух (cf. **два, две**), two, of two
двух- (=дву-), *prefix*, bi-, di-, two-
двухатомный, *adj.*, diatomic
двухвариантный, *adj.*, bivariant
двухвидовой, *adj.*, two-way; **двухвидовая классификация,** two-way classification
двухвыборочный, *adj.*, two-sample
двухгранный, *adj.*, dihedral
двухкомпонентный, *adj.*, two-component
двухмерный, *adj.*, two-dimensional
двухместный, *adj.*, two-place, binary
двухнуклонный, *adj.*, two-nucleon
двухосный, *adj.*, biaxial
двухпараметрический, *adj.*, two-parameter
двухполюсник, *m.*, dipole, bipole

двухполюсный, *adj.*, bipolar, two-pole
двухпутный, *adj.*, two-lane
двухрядный, *adj.*, two-row
двухсерийный, *adj.*, biserial, diserial
двухсотый, *adj.*, two hundredth
двухсторонний, *adj.*, bilateral, two-sided, two-way
двухступенчатый, *adj.*, two-stage, two-step, two-phase, two-level
двухтактный, *adj.*, two-stroke, two-cycle
двухточечный, *adj.*, two-point, double-point
двухфазный, *adj.*, two-phase
двухфотонный, *adj.*, two-photon
двухчастичный, *adj.*, two-particle; **двухчастичное взаимодействие,** two-particle system
двухшпунтовый, *adj.*, double-channel
двухэлементный, *adj.*, two-element
двучлен, *m.*, binomial
двучленный, *adj.*, binomial
дебаевский, *adj.*, Debye; **дебаевская температура,** Debye temperature; **дебаевское приближение,** Debye approximation
дебит, *m.*, yield, output, debit
деблокирование, *n.*, unblocking
деблокировать, *v.*, unblock
девиата, *f.*, variance
девиационный, *adj.*, deviation
девиация, *f.*, deviation
девяносто, *num.*, ninety
девятиричный, *adj.*, nonary
девятиточечный, *adj.*, nine-point, consisting of nine points; **девятиточечная окружность,** nine-point circle
девятнадцать, *num.*, nineteen
девятый, *adj.*, ninth
девять, *num.*, nine
дедекиндовость, *f.*, Dedekind property
дедекиндовый, Dedekind
дедуктивно, *adv.*, deductively; **дедуктивно равные формулы,** interdeducible formulas
дедуктивный, *adj.*, deductive
дедукция, *f.*, deduction
дезориентация, *f.*, disorientation, disorder
действенность, *f.*, effectiveness, efficiency, activity; **траектория действенности выпуска продукции,** production efficiency locus
действенный, *adj.*, efficient, effective, active
действие, *n.*, operation, effect, action, rule; **действием,** by means (of); **область действия,** scope, area of action
действительно, *adv.*, really, in fact, real; **действительно замкнутый,** *adj.*, real-closed
действительнозначный, *adj.*, real-valued
действительность, *f.*, reality, validity
действительный, *adj.*, real, true, actual, present
действовать, *v.*, act, operate, function
действующий, *adj.*, operating, acting, effective
дейтерий, *m.*, deuterium
дейтрон, *m.*, deuteron
декада, *f.*, decade
декартовый, *adj.*, Cartesian
декаэдр, *m.*, decahedron
деквантификация, *f.*, dequantification
декодирование, *n.*, decoding
декодировать, *v.*, decode
декремент, *m.*, decrement
делать, *v.*, make, do; **делать вывод,** *v.*, conclude
делаться, *v.*, become, get, grow, happen
деление, *n.*, division, partition; **деление круга,** *n.*, cyclotomy; **деление пополам,** *n.*, bisection; **полином деления круга,** *m.*, cyclotomic polynomial; **поле деления окружности,** *n.*, cyclotomic field
деленный, *adj.*, divided; **деленный на,** divided by, divided into
делимое, *n.*, dividend
делимостный, *adj.*, divisibility
делимость, *f.*, divisibility
делимый, *adj.*, divisible

делитель, *m.*, divisor; **делитель нуля,** zero divisor; **общий наибольший делитель,** greatest common divisor; **сдвинутый делитель,** shifted divisor, shifted divider
делительный, *adj.*, dividing; **делительное устройство,** divider
делить, *v.*, divide, divide into; **делить пополам,** *v.*, bisect
дело, *n.*, business, matter, affair, case; **в самом деле,** indeed, in fact
деловой, *adj.*, business, practical
дельта, *f.*, delta; **дельта-функция,** delta-function
дельтоид, *m.*, deltoid, delta-shaped region
деля, *adv.*, *part.*, dividing, on dividing, if we divide; **деля на** 2π, dividing by 2π, if we divide by 2π
делянка, *f.*, allotment, plot, lot
демографический, *adj.*, demographic
демография, *f.*, demography
демодуляция, *f.*, demodulation
демонстрационный, *adj.*, demonstration
демонстрировать, *v.*, demonstrate, show
демпфирование, *n.*, damping, shock absorption, buffer action
демфированный, *adj.*, damped, damped out
демпфировать, *v.*, damp, damp out
дендрит, *m.*, dendrite
денежный, *adj.*, monetary, financial
денситометр, *m.*, densitometer
деполяризация, *f.*, depolarization; **коэффициент деполяризации,** depolarizing factor
дерево, *n.*, tree, graph
держать, *v.*, hold, keep; **держать пари,** bet
держаться, *v.*, hold, adhere to; **держаться темы,** keep to the subject
дерзкий, *adj.*, daring, bold
дерзость, *f.*, boldness
дериват, *m.*, derivative
деривация, *f.*, derivation
дескриптивный, *adj.*, descriptive
дескрипция, *f.*, description
десяти-, *prefix*, ten-, deca-
десятикратный, *adj.*, tenfold
десятилетие, *n.*, decade
десятиугольник, *m.*, decagon
десятично-двоичный, *adj.*, decimal-binary
десятичный, *adj.*, decimal; **десятичная дробь,** decimal fraction; **десятичный знак,** decimal point; **десятичный логарифм,** common logarithm
десятка, *f.*, ten, the ten (cards)
десяток, *m.*, decade, ten
десятый, *adj.*, tenth
десять, *num.*, ten
детализация, *f.*, detailing
детализированный, *adj.*, detailed
деталь, *f.*, detail
детальный, *adj.*, detailed
детектирование, *n.*, detection
детектор, *m.*, detector, spark indicator
детекторный, *adj.*, detection; **детекторный приемник,** crystal receiver, detector
детерминант, *m.*, determinant
детерминация, *f.*, determination
детерминированный, *adj.*, determinate, determined
детерминистический, *adj.*, deterministic
детерминисткий, *adj.*, deterministic
дефект, *m.*, defect, deficiency, imperfection; **индекс дефекта,** index of error; deficiency index; **дефект массы,** mass excess
дефективный, *adj.*, defective
дефектный, *adj.*, imperfect, faulty, defect, defective; **дефектная группа,** defect group
дефектоскопия, *f.*, flaw detection
дефинитивный, *adj.*, definitive
дефинитный, *adj.*, definite
дефиниция, *f.*, definition
дефицит, *m.*, deficit, deficiency
дефицитный, *adj.*, scarce, deficient, deficit
дефлятор, *m.*, deflator
дефляция, *f.*, deflation
дефокусировка, *f.*, defocusing; **электрическая дефокусировка,** electric defocusing

деформационный, *adj.*, deformation, distortion; **деформационная ∇-цепь,** deformation cochain
деформация, *f.*, deformation, distortion, strain; **тензор деформации,** strain tensor
деформирование, *n.*, deformation, distortion
деформированный, *adj.*, deformed, distorted
деформировать, *v.*, deform, distort
деформироваться, *v.*, be deformed
деформируемый, *adj.*, deformable
деформирующий, *adj.*, deforming, distorting
децибел, *m.*, decibel
дециль, *m.*, decile
децимальный, *adj.*, decimal
децимация, *f.*, decimation
дешевый, *adj.*, cheap, inexpensive
дешифратор, *m.*, decoder
дешифрировать, *v.*, decipher
деятельность, *f.*, activities, work, activity
джоуль, *m.*, joule
дзета-функция, *f.*, zeta function
ди-, *prefix*, di-, bi-, two-
диагонализация, *f.*, diagonalization
диагонализуемость, *f.*, diagonability, diagonalizability
диагонализуемый, *adj.*, diagonable, diagonalizable, diagonalized
диагональ, *f.*, diagonal
диагональный, *adj.*, diagonal
диаграмма, *f.*, diagram, graph
диаграммный, *adj.*, diagrammatic
диада, *f.*, dyad
диадический, *adj.*, dyadic
диалектика, *f.*, dialectics
диалектически, *adv.*, dialectically
диалектический, *adj.*, dialectical
диамагнетизм, *m.*, diamagnetism
диамагнитный, *adj.*, diamagnetic; **диамагнитная восприимчивость атома,** diamagnetic susceptibility of an atom
диаметр, *m.*, diameter
диаметрально, *adv.*, diametrically; **диаметрально противоположный,** diametrically opposite
диаметральный, *adj.*, diametrical
диаметрический, *adj.*, diametrical
диапазон, *m.*, range, compass, spectral band, span; **диапазон шкалы,** scale range
диастатический, *adj.*, diastatical
диафрагма, *f.*, diaphragm, aperture, stop
дивектор, *m.*, divector, screw
дивергенция, *f.*, divergence
дивиатор, *m.*, deviator; **дивиатор напряжения,** stress deviator, voltage deviator
дивизор, *m.*, divisor, ideal
дигомология, *f.*, dihomology
диграф, *m.*, directed graph, digraph
дидактика, *f.*, didactics
дидактический, *adj.*, didactic
дизъюнктивный, *adj.*, disjunctive
дизъюнктность, *f.*, disjointness, disjunction
дизъюнктный, *adj.*, disjoint, disjunct
дизъюнкция, *f.*, disjunction; **разделительная дизъюнкция,** exclusive disjunction; **неразделительная дизъюнкция,** inclusive disjunction
дико, *adv.*, wildly; **дико вложенный,** *adj.*, wildly imbedded
диктовать, *v.*, dictate
дилатация, *f.*, dilatation, expansion, broadening, extension
дилемма, *f.*, dilemma
дилюция, *f.*, dilution
дина, *f.*, dyne
динамика, *f.*, dynamics
динамический, *adj.*, dynamic, power, forced
динод, *m.*, dynode
диод, *m.*, diode
диодный, *adj.*, diode
диофантовый, *adj.*, Diophantine
диполь, *m.*, dipole, doublet
дипольный, *adj.*, dipole
дирамация, *f.*, diramation; **точка дирамации,** diramation point

директор, *m.*, director, head
директорский, *adj.*, managerial, director
директриса, *f.*, directrix
диск, *m.*, disk, dial; **диск единиц,** units dial; **диск десятков,** tens dial; **диск сотен,** hundreds dial
дисквалифицирующий, *adj.*, rejection, disqualifying
дисковый, *adj.*, disk, circular
дисконтинуум, *m.*, discontinuum
дискообразный, *adj.*, disk-shaped, circular
дискредитирующий, *adj.*, discrediting, discounting
дискретно, *adv.*, discretely
дискретность, *f.*, discreteness
дискретный, *adj.*, discrete
дискриминант, *m.*, discriminant
дискриминантный, *adj.*, discriminant
дискриминатор, *m.*, discriminator
дискриминация, *f.*, discrimination
дискуссия, *f.*, discussion, debate
дискутировать, *v.*, discuss
дискутироваться, *v.*, be discussed
дислокационный, *adj.*, dislocation; **дислокационная линия,** dislocation line
дислокация, *f.*, dislocation; **теория дислокаций,** dislocation theory
дисольвента, *f.*, dissolvent
дисольвентный, *adj.*, dissolvent
дисперсивный, *adj.*, dispersive, dispersible
дисперсионный, *adj.*, dispersing, dispersion, variance; **дисперсионный анализ,** analysis of variance; **дисперсионное отношение,** variance ratio
дисперсия, *f.*, dispersion, scattering, deviation, variance
дисперсность, *f.*, dispersibility
дисперсный, *adj.*, dispersible
диспозиционный, *adj.*, disposition
диссертация, *f.*, thesis, dissertation
диссипативный, *adj.*, dissipative, damping
диссипация, *f.*, dissipation, damping
диссонировать, *v.*, be in discord, be out of tune
диссонирующий, *adj.*, discordant, dissonant; **диссонирующие перестановки,** discordant permutations
диссоциация, *f.*, dissociation; **энергия диссоциации,** dissociation energy
диссоциировать, *v.*, dissociate
дистальный, *adj.*, distal, distant, remote
дистанционный, *adj.*, distant, remote
дистанция, *f.*, distance, interval, range
дисторсия, *f.*, distortion
дистрибутивность, *f.*, distributivity
дистрибутивный, *adj.*, distributive
дисциплина, *f.*, discipline, branch of science
дифрагированный, *adj.*, diffracted
дифракция, *f.*, diffraction
диффеоморфизм, *m.*, diffeomorphism, differentiable homeomorphism
дифферент, *m.*, trim; **угол дифферента,** angle of trim
дифференциал *m.*, differential; **дифференциал образов,** transformed differential; **дифференциал прообразов,** original differential
дифференциально-разностный, *adj.*, difference-differential
дифференциальный, *adj.*, differential
дифференциатор, *m.*, differentiator
дифференциация, *f.*, differentiation
дифференцирование, *n.*, differentiation
дифференцированный, *adj.*, differentiated
дифференцировать, *v.*, differentiate, distinguish
дифференцируемость, *f.*, differentiability
дифференцируемый, *adj.*, differentiable
дифференцируя, *adv. part.*, differentiating, if we differentiate
диффрагированный, *adj.*, diffracted
диффрагировать, *v.*, diffract
диффракционный, *adj.*, diffraction, diffracting; **диффракционная решетка,** diffracting screen, diffraction grating
диффракция, *f.*, diffraction
диффузионный, *adj.*, diffusion, diffusive

диффузия, *f.*, diffusion
диффузный, *adj.*, diffuse; **диффузное отражение света,** diffuse reflection of light
диффундировать, *v.*, diffuse, spread
диффундирующий, *adj.*, diffusing
дихотомизированный, *adj.*, dichotomized
дихотомический, *adj.*, dichotomous
дихотомия, *f.*, dichotomy
дихромат, *m.*, dichromat, dichromatic
диэдр, *m.*, dihedron; **группа диэдра,** dihedral group
диэдральный, *adj.*, dihedral
диэлектрик, *m.*, dielectric, non-conductor
диэлектрический, *adj.*, dielectric, non-conducting
длина, *f.*, length, path; **длина свободного пробега,** free path; **средняя длина свободного пробега,** mean free path; **в длину,** lengthwise; **во всю длину,** all along, the full length of
длинно, *adv.*, long, at length
длинноволновый, *adj.*, long wavelength
длинный, *adj.*, long, lengthy
длительность, *f.*, duration
длительный, *adj.*, long, protracted, prolonged
длиться, *v.*, last, continue
для, *prep.*, for; **для того чтобы,** in order that
длящийся, *adj.*, lasting, permanent
дневной, *adj.*, daily, day
днище, *n.*, bottom
дно, *n.*, bottom, ground; **вверх дном,** upside-down
до, *prep.*, until, up to, to; **до сих пор,** up to now; **до тех пор пока,** until; **до этих пор,** until now; **дополнение** *A* **до полного пространства,** the complement of *A* with respect to the whole space
добавка, *f.*, component, addition
добавление, *n.*, addition, supplement
добавлять (добавить), *v.*, supplement, add, annex, append
добавочный, *adj.*, additional, supplementary
добиваться (добиться), *v.*, attain, obtain, achieve
доброкачественный, *adj.*, high quality
добыча, *f.*, extraction, output, gain
доведение, *n.*, bringing to, finishing up
доверенность, *f.*, warrant, trust, confidence
доверенный, *adj.*, trusted, confidential
доверие, *n.*, trust, confidence, credit
доверительный, *adj.*, fiducial, confidential, confidence; **доверительное распределение,** fiducial distribution; **доверительный контур,** confidence contour; **доверительная вероятность,** fiducial probability; **доверительная область,** confidence region; **доверительный уровень,** confidence level; **доверительный предел,** confidence limit
доверять, *v.*, trust, commit to
довод, *m.*, reason, argument
доводить, *v.*, bring to, reduce to
доводка, *f.*, finishing, sizing
довольно, *adv.*, enough, sufficiently
довольствоваться, *v.*, be satisfied
догадаться (cf. **догадываться**), conjecture, surmise
догадка, *f.*, conjecture, guess
догадываться, *v.*, conjecture, surmise, guess
догма, *f.*, dogma
догматичный, *adj.*, dogmatic
договариваться, *v.*, reach, come to, arrange
догружение, *n.*, loading
догруженный, *adj.*, loaded
додекаэдр, *m.*, dodecahedron
Додж, *m.*, Dodge; **план Доджа,** Dodge's plan, continuous inspection plan
доживать, *v.*, live until, attain the age of
дожигание, *n.*, afterburning
дожигать, *v.*, burn up
дожидаться, *v.*, wait, await
доза, *f.*, batch, dose

дозволенный, *adj.*, permitted, authorized, legal
дозволительный, *adj.*, permissible
дозволять (дозволить), *v.*, permit, allow
дозвуковой, *adj.*, subsonic
дойти (cf. **доходить**), *v.*, go as far as, reach, come to
дойдя, *adv. part.*, having come that far, having reached
док, *m.*, dock
докажем (cf. **доказать**), we shall prove, let us prove
доказанный, *adj.*, proved, that which has been proved; **выше доказанный,** proved above; **считать доказанным,** *v.*, take for granted
доказательный, *adj.*, demonstrative, convincing, conclusive
доказательство, *n.*, proof, demonstration, argument
доказать (cf. **доказывать**), *v.*, prove, demonstrate; **что и требовалось доказать,** Q.E.D.
доказуемый, *adj.*, demonstrable, provable
доказываемый, *adj.*, (that which is) being proved
доказывать (доказать), *v.*, prove, demonstrate, argue
доклад, *m.*, report, lecture
докладчик, *m.*, speaker, lecturer
докритический, *adj.*, subcritical
докторский, *adj.*, doctoral
документ, *m.*, document
документация, *f.*, documentation
долг, *m.*, debt; **погашение долга,** amortization
долгий, *adj.*, long
долго, *adv.*, long, (for) a long time
долговечность, *f.*, longevity, durability
долгопериодный, *adj.*, long-period; **долгопериодное возмущение,** long-period perturbation
долгосрочный, *adj.*, long-term, long-range
долгота, *f.*, longitude, length
должать, *v.*, borrow, owe
должен, *predic.*, must, owe; **должно быть,** must be, should be
долженствовать, *v.*, be obliged, be forced
должный, *adj.*, due, proper
дологический, *adj.*, prelogical
дольше, a longer time
доля, *f.*, part, segment, fraction
доминанта, *f.*, majorant, dominant
доминирование, *n.*, prevalence, domination
доминировать, *v.*, dominate, prevail, predominate
доминирующий, *adj.*, dominating, dominant
донный, *adj.*, ground, base
донор, *m.*, donor
донорный, *adj.*, donor
доопределение, *n.*, extension of a definition, supplementing of a definition, extension, determination
доопределенный, *adj.*, predetermined, extended
доопределять (доопределить), *v.*, define, determine, complete a definition
дополнение, *n.*, addition, supplement, complement, complementation; **алгебраическое дополнение,** cofactor; **дополнение множества,** complement of a set; **структура с дополнением,** complemented lattice; **дополнение до полного квадрата,** completing the square; **дополнение** *A* **до полного пространства,** the complement of *A* with respect to the whole space
дополненный, *adj.*, complemented
дополнительно, *adv.*, in addition
дополнительный, *adj.*, further, additional, supplementary, complementary, complement, adjugate
дополняемый, *adj.*, complemented
дополнять (дополнить), *v.*, supplement, complement, add to, amplify
допредельный, *adj.*, limit, limiting; **допредельное распределение,** limiting distribution

допуск, *m.*, tolerance, admittance
допускаемость, *f.*, admissibility
допускать (допустить), *v.*, tolerate, admit, allow; **допускается,** it is assumed
допускающий, *adj.*, admitting, allowing, permitting, giving
допуская, *adv. part.*, assuming, allowing, supposing, if we assume; **допуская от противного, что,** if, to the contrary, we assume that . . .; **допуская противное,** assuming the contrary, if we assume the contrary
допустим (from **допускать**), let us take, let us assume
допустимость, *f.*, admissibility, permissibility, tolerance
допустимый, *adj.*, admissible, permissible, tolerance
допустить (cf. **допускать**), suppose, assume
допущение, *n.*, assumption, hypothesis
допущенный, *adj.*, permitted, admitted, assumed
дорога, *f.*, road, way, path; **управление дорогой,** traffic control
дорожка, *f.*, path, track, trail
досадный, *adj.*, disappointing, unfortunate
доска, *f.*, board, plank
дословно, *adv.*, literally, word for word, verbatim
дословный, *adj.*, literal, verbatim
доставленный, *adj.*, supplied, furnished
доставляемый, *adj.*, supplied, furnished
доставлять, *v.*, supply, furnish, deliver
достаточно, *adv.*, sufficiently; it is sufficient
достаточность, *f.*, sufficiency
достаточный, *adj.*, sufficient, ample
достигаемость, *f.*, accessibility, attainability
достигать, *v.*, reach, achieve, attain
достигнутый, *adj.*, achieved, reached
достижение, *n.*, achievement, attainment
достижимый, *adj.*, accessible, attainable; **достижимая подгруппа,** composition subgroup
достичь (cf. **достигать**), reach, attain
достоверность, *f.*, truth, reliability, certainty
достоверный, *adj.*, authentic, reliable, certain; **достоверное событие,** certain event
достоинство, *n.*, merit, dignity
достопримечательность, *f.*, remarkable sight, curiosity
достопримечательный, *adj.*, noteworthy, remarkable
доступный, *adj.*, accessible, available, understandable
досягаемость, *f.*, range, attainability, accessibility
досягаемый, *adj.*, accessible, attainable
доупорядочение, *n.*, ordering
доход, *m.*, income, profit; **общий доход,** aggregate profit; **чистый годовой доход,** net revenue, net yearly profit
доходить, *v.*, go as far as, reach
дочерний, *adj.*, daughter, derived; **дочернее ядро,** product, daughter nucleus
дошел (дошла, дошло, дошли), (past of **доходить**), reached, went as far as
древесина, *f.*, wood
древний, *adj.*, ancient, old
древность, *f.*, antiquity
древо, *n.*, tree
древовидный, *adj.*, tree-like, tree, dendrite; **древовидная полезность,** utility tree
дрейф, *m.*, drift, leeway
дробление, *n.*, subdivision, pulverization
дробно-квадратичный, *adj.*, quadratic fractional
дробно-линейный, *adj.*, linear-fractional, bilinear
дробно-рациональный, *adj.*, rational, bilinear
дробный, *adj.*, fractional
дробовой, *adj.*, shot, shooting; **дробовой эффект,** shot noise, shot effect

дробь, *f.*, fraction, quotient; **непрерывная дробь,** continued fraction; **простейшая дробь,** partial fraction; **производная дроби,** derivative of a quotient
дроссельный, *adj.*, throttle, choke
дросселирование, *n.*, throttling, choking
друг, *m.*, friend, other; **друг друга,** each other, one another, mutually; **друг за другом,** one after another; **друг от друга,** from each other; **друг с другом,** with each other
другой, *adj.*, other, another, different; **другими словами,** in other words; **с другой стороны,** on the other hand; **в другом месте,** elsewhere
дружественный, *adj.*, amicable, **дружественные числа,** amicable numbers
дуализация, *f.*, dualization
дуализировать, *v.*, dualize
дуализируемый, *adj.*, dualizable, dualized
дуализм, *m.*, dualism
дуалистический, *adj.*, dualistic
дуальность, *f.*, duality
дуальный, *adj.*, dual
дублер, *m.*, dual, double, understudy
дублет, *m.*, doublet, duplicate
дублетный, *adj.*, doublet; **расстояние между дублетными линиями,** doublet separation
дубликат, *m.*, duplicate, replica, copy
дублирование, *n.*, doubling, duplication
дублированный, *adj.*, doubled, duplicated
дублировать, *v.*, double, duplicate
дублирующий *adj.*, duplicating, duplication, doubling, redundant
дуга, *f.*, arc, arch
дуговой, *adj.*, arc
дугообразно, *adv.*, arc-wise
дугообразный, *adj.*, arched, bow-shaped, arc, arc-wise
дужка, *f.*, small arc, parenthesis
думать (подумать), *v.*, think, believe, mean, intend
душа, *f.*, soul; **на душу,** per capita, per head
дым, *m.*, smoke
дыра, *f.*, hole
дырка, *f.*, hole
дырочный, *adj.*, hole; **дырочная ловушка,** hole trap
дюйм, *m.*, inch

Е

евклидовой, *adj.*, Euclidean; **евклидовое пространство,** Euclidean space
евклидовский, *adj.*, Euclidean
его (cf. **он, оно**), *pron.*, his, its; him, it
едва, *adv.*, hardly, just
единение, *n.*, union, unity
единица, *f.*, unit, identity, identity element; **единица счета,** count; **единица длины,** unit of length; **единица измерения,** unit, unit of measurement
единично-треугольный, *adj.*, unit triangular
единичный, *adj.*, unit, single, individual, identity, monic, unitary; **единичный круг,** unit circle; **единичная окружность,** unit circle; **игра с единичным наблюдением числовой величины,** game with a numerical-valued single observation
единовременно, *adv.*, once only, once
единообразие, *n.*, uniformity
единообразный, *adj.*, uniform
единственно, *adv.*, uniquely, only, solely; **единственно возможный,** the only (one) possible

единственность, *f.*, uniqueness; **теорема единственности,** uniqueness theorem
единственный, *adj.*, unique, only
единый, *adj.*, single, unique, indivisible; **единое целое,** *n.*, unit
ее (cf. **она**), *pron.*, her, hers, it, its
ежегодник, *m.*, annual, year-book
ежегодно, *adv.*, annually, yearly
ежегодный, *adj.*, yearly, annual
ежели, *conj.*, if, in case
ежемесячный, *adj.*, monthly
ежеминутно, *adv.*, at every instant, continually
ежеминутный, *adj.*, continual, incessant
ей (cf. **она**), *pron.*, (to) her, (to) it
еле, *adv.*, hardly, scarcely
емкостный, *adj.*, capacity, capacitance, induction, capacitative
емкость, *f.*, capacity, content, capacitance; **емкость регистра,** register length
ему (cf. **он, оно**), *pron.*, (to) him, (to) it
если, *conj.*, if; **если и,** even if; **в случае, если,** in case; **если не,** unless
естественно, *adv.*, naturally
естественный, *adj.*, natural, intrinsic
естество, *n.*, nature, substance
естествознание, *n.*, natural science
есть (cf. **быть**), is, there is, are
еще *adv.*, still, yet, as yet, more; **все еще,** still; **еще во время,** as far back as; **еще один,** another, one more

Ж

жанр, *m.*, genus, genre
жданный, *adj.*, expected
ждать, *v.*, expect, await
же, *conj.*, and, but, as for, even, still; **точно так же,** in just the same way; **один и тот же,** the same, one and the same; **тот же (то же),** the same; **он (оно) же,** the very same; **так же,** also
желаемый, *adj.*, desired
желание, *n.*, desire
желанный, *adj.*, desired
желательность, *f.*, desirability
желательный, *adj.*, desirable; **желательно,** it is desirable
желать, *v.*, desire, wish
железный, *adj.*, ferrous, iron; **железная дорога,** *f.*, railway, railroad
железо, *n.*, iron
желоб, *m.*, groove, trough, gutter, chute
желтый, *adj.*, yellow
жертвовать, *v.*, sacrifice, donate
жесткий, *adj.*, rigid, hard, tough, inflexible, stringent
жестко, *adv.*, rigidly, inflexibly, stringently
жесткость, *f.*, rigidity, inflexibility, stiffness
живой, *adj.*, living, alive, vivid
животный, *adj.*, animal
живучесть, *f.*, survival, vitality
жидкий, *adj.*, liquid, fluid
жидкость, *f.*, liquid, fluid
жизнь, *f.*, life
жир, *m.*, fat, grease
жирновычерченный, *adj.*, heavily drawn
жирный, *adj.*, fat, greasy, bold-face, heavy
жордановый, *adj.*, Jordan; **жорданова область,** Jordan domain
жребий, *m.*, toss, lot, fate; **бросается жребий,** a coin is tossed
жужжащий, *adj.*, humming, buzzing
журнал, *m.*, periodical, journal

З

за, *prep.*, for, as, at, in, over, across beyond, with
заблуждение, *n.*, fallacy, error
забой, *m.*, drift, cut, face
заболевание, *n.*, disease
забота, *f.*, responsibility, care
заботиться, *v.*, take care, be concerned about
забракованный, *adj.*, rejected
забраковать (cf. **браковать**), *v.*, reject, condemn
забываемый, *adj.*, forgotten, neglected
забывать (забыть), *v.*, forget, neglect
забывчивость, *f.*, forgetfulness
заведение, *n.*, institution, establishment
заведомо, *adv.*, automatically, trivially, a fortiori, knowingly; *pred.*, it is automatic (that), it is trivial (that), it is (well) known (that)
завершать, *v.*, complete, conclude
завершающий, *adj.*, concluding, final
завершение, *n.*, completion, end
завершенность, *f.*, completeness
завершенный, *adj.*, completed, final
зависание, *n.*, hovering (aerodyn.)
зависеть, *v.*, depend, depend on
зависимость, *f.*, dependence, relation, function; **в зависимости от,** depending on, subject to
зависимый, *adj.*, dependent, dependent on, related
зависящий, *adj.*, depending; **зависящий от,** depending on
завихрение, *n.*, turbulence, vorticity
завихренность, *f.*, vorticity
завихряющий, *adj.*, turbulent, swirling
завышенный, *adj.*, overstated, excessive
заглавие, *n.*, title, heading
заглавный, *adj.*, title, capital; **заглавный лист,** title page; **заглавная буква,** capital letter
заголовок, *m.*, title, heading
загружать (загрузить), *v.*, load, charge
загруженность, *f.*, load, charge
загруженный, *adj.*, loaded, charged
загрузка, *f.*, loading, charge, load
загрязнение, *n.*, contamination, impurity
задаваемый, *adj.*, prescribed, defined (by)
задавать (задать), *v.*, set, assign, give, pose, define, plot
задаваясь, *adv. part.*, being given, given, if we are given
задавшись, *adv. part.*, given, having been given; **задавшись** $\varepsilon > 0$, given $\varepsilon > 0$
задание, *n.*, task, job, assignment, representation; **задание кривых в параметрической форме,** parametric representation of curves
заданный, *adj.*, given, prescribed, defined; **наперед заданный,** *adj.*, preassigned
задать, (cf. **задавать**), *v.*, set, assign, give; **задаться целью,** set a goal
задача, *f.*, problem, task; **задача коши,** Cauchy problem; **краевая задача,** boundary value problem
задачник, *m.*, set of problems, problem book
задающий, *adj.*, setting, assigning, giving; **задающий контур,** drive circuit (*comp.*)
заделанный, *adj.*, embedded, clamped closed, fixed
заделать, cf. **заделывать**
заделка, *f.*, sealing, closing, stopping up
заделывать (заделать), *v.*, fix, seal, close, stop up
задерживать (задержать), *v.*, detain, delay
задерживающий, *adj.*, delaying, delay, inhibitory
задержка, *f.*, delay, lag; **звуковая линия задержки на проволоке,** wire-type acoustic delay; **корпус линии задержки,** tank; **ртутная линия задержки,** mercury tank;

задержка импульса на один главный импульс, one-pulse time delay; **задержка импульса на один разряд,** one-pulse time delay; **схема задержки,** delay circuit; **цепь задержки,** inhibit circuit

задний, *adj.*, back, rear; **задняя кромка,** trailing edge

зажим, *m.*, clip, clamp

заземление, *n.*, grounding, ground

заземленный, *adj.*, grounded, ground

зазор, *m.*, clearance, margin, tolerance

заимствованный, *adj.*, borrowed, taken from

заимствовать, *v.*, borrow, adopt, copy

заинтересованный, *adj.*, interested

заинтересовать, *v.*, interest

зайчик, *m.*, reflection of a lightbeam

заказ, *m.*, order

заказчик, *m.*, client, customer

заканчивать (закончить), *v.*, finish, complete

заканчивающийся, *adj.*, ending

заклад, *m.*, mortgage, investment

закладная, *f.*, mortgage, investment

закладывать, *v.*, lay, put, establish, mortgage

заклеенный, *adj.*, glued, pasted

заклеивание, *n.*, pasting

заклеивать, *v.*, paste, glue

заклейка, *f.*, stopping up, pasting up

заклиненный, *adj.*, wedged

заключать, *v.*, enclose, include, contain, conclude; **заключать в себе,** *v.*, imply

заключаться, *v.*, be contained, consist, be confined

заключающий, *adj.*, including, inclusive of

заключающийся, *adj.*, contained, included

заключение, *n.*, conclusion, inference, inclusion, confinement

заключенный, *adj.*, contained, confined, concluded, included; **заключено строго внутри,** strictly contained in

заключительный, *adj.*, final, concluding, conclusive

закодированный, *adj.*, coded

закодировать, *v.*, code, encode

закон, *m.*, law, rule, principle

законность, *f.*, validity, legitimacy

законный, *adj.*, valid, legitimate

закономерность, *f.*, regularity, conformity

законченность, *f.*, completeness

законченный, *adj.*, completed, complete

закончить (cf. **заканчивать**), *v.*, finish, complete

закорачивающий, *adj.*, short-circuiting

закрепить (cf. **закреплять**), *v.*, fasten, fix, consolidate

закрепление, *n.*, fixing, fastening

закрепленный, *adj.*, fixed, fastened, secured

закреплять (закрепить), *v.*, fasten, fix, consolidate

закругление, *n.*, curving, curve, curvature, rounding

закругленный, *adj.*, rounded, rounded off, curved

закруглять (закруглить), *v.*, round, round off

закрученный, *adj.*, twisted

закручивание, *n.*, twisting, winding

закручивать (закрутить), *v.*, twist, curl

закручивающий, *adj.*, twisting, turning; **закручивающая пара,** torque

закрывать (закрыть), *v.*, close, shut, shut off, close down

закупка, *f.*, purchase

закупоренный, *adj.*, corked, sealed, stopped up

залив, *m.*, gulf

замедление, *n.*, deceleration, retarding, slowing down, delay

замедленный, *adj.*, delayed, retarded, decelerated

замедлять, *v.*, slow down, retard, decelerate

замедляющий, *adj.*, decelerating

замена, *f.*, substitution, replacement, exchange, change; **замена переменных,** change of variables; **структура с заменой,** exchange lattice

заменимость, *f.*, interchangeability, replaceability
заменимый, *adj.*, interchangeable, replaceable
заменитель, *m.*, substitute
заменяемость, *f.*, interchangeability, replaceability
заменяемый, *adj.*, interchangeable, replaceable
заменять (заменить), *v.*, substitute, replace, interchange
заменяющий, *adj.*, substituting, replacing
замеренный, *adj.*, measured
замерзание, *n.*, freezing
заметив, *adv. part.*, having noted, having observed
заметить (cf. **замечать**), *v.*, note, observe, remark
заметка, *f.*, note, notice, paragraph
заметно, *adv.*, noticeably, appreciably
заметный, *adj.*, noticeable, appreciable
замечание, *n.*, remark, observation
замечательный, *adj.*, remarkable, unusual
замечать (заметить), *v.*, notice, remark, note, observe
замечая, *adv. part.*, remarking, observing; **замечая что,** if we observe that
замещаемый, *adj.*, replaced, replaceable
замещать (заместить), *v.*, replace, substitute
замещение, *n.*, replacement, substitution, insertion
замещенный, *adj.*, replaced, substituted
замкнутость, *f.*, closure, completeness
замкнутый, *adj.*, closed, isolated, closure; **замкнутый относительно эквивалентности,** closed under equivalence; **замкнутая петля, замкнутый цикл,** closed loop
замкнуть (cf. **замыкать**), *v.*, close
замороженный, *adj.*, frozen
замощение, *n.*, covering, filling, filling out, paving
замыкаемый, *adj.*, subtended
замыкание, *n.*, closing, closure, completion; **короткое замыкание,** short circuit; **алгебра замыкания,** *f.*, closure algebra
замыкать (замкнуть), *v.*, close
замысел, *m.*, intention, plan, project
занимательный, *adj.*, amusing, entertaining
занимать (занять), *v.*, occupy, take up
заниматься, *v.*, be occupied with, be engaged in, busy oneself with
занимающийся, *adj.*, dealing with
заново, *adv.*, anew, again
занумерованный, *adj.*, numbered, indexed
занумеровывать (занумеровать), *v.*, number, numerate, index
занятие, *n.*, occupation, pursuit
занятость, *f.*, employment
занятый, *adj.*, occupied
занять (cf. **занимать**), occupy, borrow
заняться, *v.*, occupy oneself, busy oneself with
заострение, *n.*, cusp, point; **точка заострения,** spinode, cusp
заостренный, *adj.*, pointed, peaked, cusped
запад, *m.*, west
западный, *adj.*, west, western
запаздывание, *n.*, delay, lag, lateness
запаздывать, *v.*, be late, lag, lag behind, retard
запаздывающий, *adj.*, lagging, retarded, retarding
запас, *m.*, store, supply, stock, reserve, inventory
запасать (запасти), *v.*, accumulate, store, reserve
запасающий, *adj.*, storing, storage
запасенный, *adj.*, accumulated
запасной, *adj.*, spare, reserve; **запасной капитал,** *m.*, capital stock
запертый, *adj.*, closed, locked; **запертый мультивибратор,** monostable multivibrator
запираться, *v.*, close, shut, stop
записываемый, *adj.*, describable

записывать (записать), *v.*, write, write down, note
записываться (записаться), *v.*, register, be inscribed
записывая, *adv. part.*, writing, if we write
запись, *f.*, notation, entry, listing, writing; **сигнал записи,** write signal; **формирователь записи,** write driver; **носитель записи,** recording medium; **запись рядом,** juxtaposition
запишется (cf. **записаться**), will be written
заплата, *f.*, patch
заплетать (заплести), *v.*, braid
заплетенный, *adj.*, braided, linked
запоздать (cf. **запаздывать**), be late, lag, retard
заполнение, *n.*, filling, completing; **команда заполнения счетчика повторений,** load repeat counter instruction
заполненность, *f.*, population; **заполненность вращательных уровней,** population of rotational levels
заполненный, *adj.*, completed, solid, filled; **заполненный носитель,** solid carrier
заполнять, *v.*, fill, fill out
заполняющий, *adj.*, filling
запоминание, *n.*, mention, reminder, memory, storage
запоминать, *v.*, remember, memorize, store
запоминающий, *adj.*, remembering, memory, storage; **запоминающая схема,** memory circuit, storage circuit
запотевание, *n.*, condensation (of moisture)
запрет, *m.*, exclusion, prohibition; **принцип запрета Паули,** Pauli exclusion principle; **схема запрета,** inhibit circuit
запрещать, *v.*, forbid, prohibit, inhibit
запрещение, *n.*, prohibition, inhibition
запрещенный, *adj.*, prohibited, inhibited
запрос, *m.*, inquiry
запуск, *m.*, start, launching
запускать, *v.*, start, launch, throw
запутанность, *f.*, complexity, intricacy
запутанный, *adj.*, tangled, intricate, involved
запыленность, *f.*, dust content
запятая, *f.*, comma, decimal point; **к пятому знаку после запятой,** to (in) the fifth decimal place
заражение, *n.*, infection, contamination, contagion; **распределение (типа) заражения,** contagious distribution
заранее, *adv.*, in advance, hitherto, beforehand; **как это заранее ясно,** as is already clear
зарегистрированный, *adj.*, registered, recorded, observed
зарегистрировать, *v.*, register
зародыш, *m.*, germ, embyro, conception
зарождаться, (зародиться), *v.*, be conceived, originate, arise
зарождение, *n.*, origin, beginning, conception
заряд, *m.*, charge, load, supply; **нулевой заряд,** zero charge
зарядка, *f.*, charging, loading
зарядный, *adj.*, charge, load, suppiy
зарядовый, *adj.*, charge; **зарядовая сингулярность,** charge singularity
заряжать, *v.*, charge, load
заряжающий, *adj.*, charging
заряженный, *adj.*, charged, loaded, live
засасывать, *v.*, suck in, draw in
заседание, *n.*, meeting, conference, session
засечка, *f.*, cut, notch, mark, intersection; **засечка времени,** timing
заслонение, *n.*, shielding, screening
заслонять, *v.*, cover, hide, screen, shield
заслуга, *f.*, merit; **заслуги,** *pl.*, services
заслуживать, *v.*, deserve, earn
заставлять (заставить), *v.*, force, compel, make
застой, *m.*, stagnation, depression
застрахованный, *adj.*, insured, immune
застревать (застрять), *v.*, stick, get stuck, get trapped

затвердевание, *n.*, solidification, hardening, congealing
затвор, *m.*, lock, bar, shutter
затем, *adv.*, then, next, thereupon; **затем что,** since, as
затенять, *v.*, shade, darken
затмевать, *v.*, darken, cover, eclipse
затмение, *n.*, eclipse; **полное затмение,** total eclipse
зато, *conj.*, in return, on the other hand
заторможенный, *adj.*, braked, deferred, delayed, constrained; **заторможенное вращение,** hindered rotation
затормозить, *v.*, brake, hinder, slow down
затрагивать, *v.*, affect, touch upon
затрата, *f.*, expenditure, outlay, input; **вектор затрат,** input vector; **анализ затрат,** input analysis
затрачиваемый *adj.*, required, spent, expended, input
затрачивать (затратить), *v.*, spend, expend
затронутый, *adj.*, touched upon, affected
затронуть (cf. **затрагивать**), *v.*, touch upon, affect
затруднение, *n.*, difficulty
затрудненный, *adj.*, difficult
затруднительно, *adv.*, with difficulty
затруднительный, *adj.*, difficult
затруднять, *v.*, hamper, impede, make difficult
затухание, *n.*, damping, decay, dying out, fading, attenuation; **экспоненциальное затухание,** exponential decay; **коэффициент затухания,** damping factor
затухать (затухнуть), *v.*, damp, fade; be damped, die down
затухающий, *adj.*, damping, fading; **затухающее колебание,** damped oscillation; **затухающие колебания,** underdamping; **затухающее отображение,** fading mapping
затушевание, *n.*, shading, tinting
затушевывать, *v.*, shade, tint
заузленный, *adj.*, knotted
заучивать (заучить), *v.*, learn
зафиксировать, *v.*, fix, settle
захват, *m.*, range, scope, span, capture, claw, fastener; **сечение захвата (частиц),** capture cross-section (of particles)
захватывать, *v.*, seize, take, engage
заход, *m.*, setting; **заход солнца,** sunset
зацепление, *n.*, linkage, engagement, gearing; **коэффициент зацепления,** linking coefficient, looping coefficient
зацепленный, *adj.*, linked, engaged
зацеплять (зацепить), *v.*, link, lock, engage
зацепляться, *v.*, catch, catch on
зацепляющий, *adj.*, linking, engaging
зачастую, *adv.*, often, frequently
зачем, *adv.*, why, what for, wherefore
зачем-то, *adv.*, for some purpose or other
зачеркивание, *n.*, striking out, deletion
зачеркивать, *v.*, cross out, delete
зашифрование, *n.*, coding, encoding
заштрихованный, *adj.*, shaded, hatched
заштриховывать, *v.*, shade, hatch
зашунтированный, *adj.*, shunted, shunt
защемленный, *adj.*, fixed, fastened
защита, *f.*, defence, cover, protection; **схема защиты,** protection circuit
защитный, protective, protection; **защитная схема,** protection circuit
защищать (защитить), *v.*, defend, protect
защищенный *adj.*, guarded, protected, screened
заявление, *n.*, announcement
заявленный, *adj.*, claimed, stated, declared
заявлять (заявить), *v.*, announce
звезда, *f.*, star
звездно (from **звездный**); *adv.*, **звездно ограниченный,** *adj.*, star-bounded; **звездно конечный,** *adj.*, star-finite
звездный, *adj.*, star, pertaining to star, star-shaped, sidereal; **звездная сходимость,** star convergence
звездовидный, *adj.*, star-like
звездообразный, *adj.*, star-shaped

звездочка, *f.*, asterisk
звездчатый, *adj.*, star-shaped
звено, *n.*, link, unit, group, component (part); **интегрирующее звено,** integrating factor
звеньевой, *adj.*, link, member
звук, *m.*, sound
звуковой, *adj.*, sound, pertaining to sound, sonic, audio
звукозапись, *f.*, sound recording
звукоизоляционный, *adj.*, sound-proof
звукометрия, *f.*, sound ranging
звуконепроницаемый, *adj.*, sound-proof
звукопроводность, *f.*, sound conductivity
звукоулавливание, *n.*, sound detection, sound ranging
звукоулавливатель, *m.*, sound detector, sound ranger
звучать, *v.*, sound, resound, ring
звучащий, *adj.*, sounding, vibrating
звучность, *f.*, sonority; **звучность в комнате,** room sonority
здесь, *adv.*, here; **здесь и там,** here and there
здоровый, *adj.*, healthy, strong, sound
здравый, *adj.*, sensible
зеленый, *adj.*, green
землемер, *m.*, surveyor
землемерный, *adj.*, geodetic
землетрясение, *n.*, earthquake; **очаг землетрясения,** seismic center, seismic focus
земля, *f.*, earth
земной, *adj.*, earth, terrestrial
зенит, *m.*, zenith
зенитный, *adj.*, zenith, anti-aircraft
зеркало, *n.*, mirror
зеркальноподобный, *adj.*, mirror-like
зеркальный, *adj.*, mirror, mirror-like, specular; **зеркальное отображение,** mirror image; **зеркальное отражение (преломление),** specular reflection (refraction)
зигбановский, *adj.*, Siegbahn, pertaining to Siegbahn
зигзаг, *m.*, zigzag
зигзагообразный, *adj.*, zigzag
зиждиться, *v.*, be based on, be founded on
зиккурат, *m.*, pyramidal tower, series of terraces
зима, *f.*, winter
зимний, *adj.*, winter; **зимнее солнцестояние,** winter solstice
змеевидный, *adj.*, coiled, wound, snake-like; **змеевидный континуум,** snake-like continuum
знаем (cf. **знать**), we know
знак, *m.*, sign, symbol, mark; **двоичный знак,** bit, binary digit; **критерий знаков,** sign test
знакомить, *v.*, acquaint with, introduce to
знакомство, *n.*, familiarity (with), acquaintance
знакомый, *adj.*, familiar, known
знакоопределенность, *f.*, property of having fixed sign
знакоопределенный, *adj.*, of fixed sign
знакопеременный, *adj.*, with alternating signs, skew symmetric, alternating; **знакопеременная группа,** alternating group
знакоположительный, *adj.*, of positive terms; **знакоположительный ряд,** series of positive terms
знакопостоянный, *adj.*, of constant signs, of constant terms
знакочередующийся, *adj.*, alternating in sign, alternating; **знакочередующийся ряд,** alternating series
знаменатель, *m.*, denominator, ratio; **общий знаменатель,** common denominator; **знаменатель подобия,** similarity ratio
знамение, *n.*, sign
знаменательный, *adj.*, significant, important
знаменитый, *adj.*, famous
знание, *m.*, knowledge, learning
знатность, *f.*, eminence
знатный, *adj.*, distinguished, eminent
знаток, *m.*, expert
знать, *v.*, know

значащий, *adj.*, significant; **значащий разряд,** *m.*, significant digit; **значащая цифра,** *f.*, significant digit
значение, *n.*, value, meaning, sense, significance, valuation; **иметь значение,** *v.*, mean; **собственное значение,** *n.*, eigenvalue
значимость, *f.*, significance; **предел значимости,** significance limit; **уровень значимости,** significance level
значимый, *adj.*, significant; **значимое отклонение,** significant deviation
значит, *part.*, so, then, hence
значительно, *adv.*, considerably, significantly
значительный, *adj.*, considerable, significant
значить, *v.*, mean, signify, imply
значиться, be, be mentioned, appear
-значный, *suffix*, -valued
значок, *m.*, index, subscript, mark
золото, *n.*, gold
золотой, *adj.*, golden, gold; **золотая середина,** golden mean
зона, *f.*, zone; **зона действия,** effective area
зональность, *f.*, zonality
зональный, *adj.*, pertaining to zone, zonal; **поверхностная зональная функция,** surface zonal harmonic; **телесная зональная функция,** solid zonal harmonic
зонд, *m.*, probe, sound
зрачок, *m.*, pupil (optics); **входной зрачок,** entrance pupil; **выходной зрачок,** exit pupil
зрелость, *f.*, maturity, readiness, ripeness
зрелый, *adj.*, mature, ripe
зрение, *n.*, sight, view; **с принципиальной точки зрения,** fundamentally; **обман зрения,** optical illusion; **точка зрения,** point of view
зреть, *v.*, mature, perceive
зритель, *m.*, spectator; *pl.*, audience
зрительный, *adj.*, visual, optical
зуб, *m.*, tooth
зубчатка, *f.*, cog-wheel, rack-wheel
зубчатый, *adj.*, toothed, serrate, cogged; **зубчатое колесо,** cog-wheel

И

и, *conj.*, and, and then; **и . . . и,** both . . . and; (*often used as an untranslated indication of emphasis*)
ибо, *conj.*, because, for, since
игла, *f.*, needle, spine
иглообразный, *adj.*, needle-shaped
игнорировать, *v.*, ignore, disregard
игра, *f.*, play, game; **теория игр,** theory of games; **верхняя цена игры,** upper pure value; **игра с возможностью кооперирования,** cooperative game; **игра с нулевой суммой,** zero-sum game; **игра с ограничениями,** constrained game; **игра с (усеченной) последовательной выборкой,** (truncated) sequential game; **игра с фиксированным объемом выборки,** fixed sample-size game; **игра с единичным испытанием,** game with a single experiment; **игра с полной информацией,** perfect information game; **игра с выпуклой функцией выигрыша,** game with convex payoff
игральный, *adj.*, playing, game; **игральная кость,** die
играть, *v.*, play; **играть роль,** play a part in, play the (a) rôle
игрок, *m.*, player, gambler
идеал, *m.*, ideal
идеализатор, *m.*, idealizer
идеализированный, *adj.*, idealized

идеализм, *m.*, idealism
идеальный, *adj.*, ideal, perfect; **идеальный газ,** ideal gas
идемпотент, *m.*, idempotent
идемпотентность, *f.*, idempotency
идемпотентный, *adj.*, idempotent
идентификация, *f.*, identification
идентифицировать, *v.*, identify
идентифицируемость, *f.*, identifiability
идентифицируемый, *adj.*, identifiable
идентифицирующий, *adj.*, identifying, identification; **идентифицирующее отображение,** identification map
идентичный, *adj.*, identical
идеографический, *adj.*, ideographic
идет (cf. **идти**), he (she, it) goes
идея, *f.*, idea, notion, concept
идиома, *f.*, idiom
идиоматический, *adj.*, idiomatic
идти (cf. **ходить**), *v.*, go
идут (cf. **идти**), they go
идущий, *adj.*, going, operating, running
иерархия, *f.*, hierarchy
иератический, *adj.*, according to rank, hierarchical
из, *prep.*, from, out of
избавлять (избавить), *v.*, save, save from
избавляться (избавиться), *v.*, be rid of, get rid of
избегать (избежать, избегнуть), *v.*, avoid, evade
избежание, *n.*, avoidance, evasion; **во избежание,** in order to avoid
избежать, cf. **избегать**
избиравшийся, *adj.*, chosen, selected
избирательность, *f.*, selectivity
избирательный, *adj.*, selective
избыток, *m.*, surplus, excess
избыточность, *f.*, excessiveness, redundancy; **по избыточности,** excessively
избыточный, *adj.*, surplus, redundant, excessive, excess; **избыточный заряд,** excess charge, surcharge; **примитивные** *k*-**избыточные числа,** primitive *k*-nondeficients; **избыточное число,** abundant number

известие, *n.*, information, news
известно (cf. **известный**), it is known, it is well known
известный, *adj.*, known, well-known
извивающиися, *adj.*, winding, twisting, crinkly
извилистый, *adj.*, twisting, winding
извлекать (извлечь), *v.*, extract; **извлекать корень,** extract the root
извлечение, *n.*, extraction; **извлечение корня,** taking the root
извлеченный, *adj.*, extracted, derived
извне, *adv.*, from without, from the outside
извращение, *n.*, distortion, misinterpretation
изгиб, *m.*, bend, curve, winding, flexion
изгибание, *n.*, bending, curving, deformation
изгибать (изогнуть), *v.*, bend
изгибающий, *adj.*, bending; **изгибающий момент,** bending moment
изготавливать (изготовить), *v.*, make, manufacture
изготовление, *n.*, manufacture, preparation
издание, *n.*, edition, publication
издательство, *n.*, publisher, publishing house
изделие, *n.*, product, make, article
издержка, *f.*, cost, expense
из-за, *prep.*, because of, from behind
излагаемый, *adj.*, stated, set forth
излагать (изложить), *v.*, state, present, set forth
излишек, *m.*, excess, surplus
излишне (cf. **излишний**), it is unnecessary
излишний, *adj.*, unnecessary, superfluous, redundant
изложение, *n.*, account, presentation
изложенный, *adj.*, stated, set forth
изложить (cf. **излагать**), *v.*, explain, set forth
излом, *m.*, break, fracture
излучаемость, *f.*, radiativity
излучаемый, *adj.*, emitted, radiated

излучатель, *m.*, emitter, radiator
излучательный, *adj.*, radiant; **излучательная способность,** radiant emittance
излучать, *v.*, radiate
излучение, *n.*, radiation, emanation
измельчение, *n.*, refinement; **измельчение сетки,** mesh refinement
изменение, *n.*, change, variation, alteration; **область изменения,** range (of a function); **функция с ограниченным изменением,** function of bounded variation
измененный, *adj.*, changed, altered, transformed
изменчивость, *f.*, variability, changeability, unsteadiness, variation; **коэффициент изменчивости размаха,** coefficient of variation of range
изменяемость, *f.*, variability
изменяемый, *adj.*, variable, changeable
изменять (изменить), *v.*, change, alter
изменяться, (измениться), *v.*, vary, change, be changed
измерение, *n.*, measurement, dimension; **число измерения,** dimension
измеренный, *adj.*, measured, dimensioned
измеримость, *f.*, measurability
измеримый, *adj.*, measurable; *B*-**измеримый,** *adj.*, Borel measurable, measurable (*B*)
измеритель, *m.*, measuring instrument, gauge, index
измерительный, *adj.*, measuring, metering
измерять (измерить), *v.*, measure
измеряющий, *adj.*, measuring
изначальный, *adj.*, initial
изношенность, *f.*, deterioration, exhaustion
изнутри, *adv.*, outwards; *prep.*, in, from within
изо (cf. **из**), *prep.*, from
изобара, *f.*, isobar
изобарический, *adj.*, isobaric
изобарный, *adj.*, isobaric
изобилие, *n.*, abundance, profusion
изобиловать, *v.*, abound
изобильный, *adj.*, profuse, abundant
изображаемый, *adj.*, being represented, being depicted
изображать (изобразить), *v.*, represent, depict, map
изображение, *n.*, representation, image, transform; **изображение по Лапласу,** Laplace transform
изображенный, *adj.*, represented, depicted
изображено (cf. **изображенный**), depicted, represented
изобразимость, *f.*, representability
изобразимый, *adj.*, representable
изобразить (cf. **изображать**), *v.*, represent
изобретатель, *m.*, inventor
изобретательность, *f.*, ingenuity, inventiveness
изобретать, *v.*, invent, devise
изобретение, *n.*, invention
изобретенный, *adj.*, invented, developed
изогения, *f.*, isogeny
изогенный, *adj.*, isogenous, of the same origin
изогнутость, *f.*, state of being curved, curvature
изогнутый, *adj.*, bent, curved
изогнуть (cf. **изгибать**), *v.*, bend
изогональный, *adj.*, isogonal
изогонический, *adj.*, isogonal
изоклина, *f.*, isocline
изоклинальный, *adj.*, isocline
изолированный, *adj.*, isolated
изолировать, *v.*, isolate, insulate
изолируемый, *adj.*, capable of being isolated, isolable
изолятор, *m.*, insulator, isolator
изоляция, *f.*, isolation, insulation
изомер, *m.*, isomer
изомерный, *adj.*, isomeric
изометрически, *adv.*, isometrically
изометрический, *adj.*, isometric
изометричный, *adj.*, isometric
изометрия, *f.*, isometry
изоморфизм, *m.*, isomorphism

изоморфно, *adv.*, isomorphically
изоморфный, *adj.*, isomorphic
изопериметрический, *adj.*, isoperimetric
изопериметрия, *f.*, isoperimetry
изотерма, *f.*, isotherm
изотермически-асимптотический, *adj.*, isothermally asymptotic
изотермический, *adj.*, isothermal
изотермично-реализуемый, *adj.*, isothermally realizable
изотермичный, *adj.*, isothermal
изотонный, *adj.*, isotone, isotonic
изотоп, *m.*, isotope
изотопический, *adj.*, isotopic, isotopy
изотопия, *f.*, isotopy
изотропический, *adj.*, isotropic
изотропия, *f.*, isotropy
изотропность, *f.*, isotropy
изотропный, *adj.*, isotropic; **изотропный вектор,** null vector
изохорический, *adj.*, of constant volume
изоэндоморфизм, *m.*, isoendomorphism
изоэнергетический, *adj.*, of equal energy, isoenergetic
израсходованный, *adj.*, spent, used
израсходовать, *v.*, spend, use up, deliver
изредка, *adv.*, occasionally
изучать, *v.*, study
изучающий, *n.*, investigator; *adj.*, studying, investigating
изучение, *n.*, study
изученный, *adj.*, studied, investigated
изъятие, *n.*, exception, removal, exclusion, elimination; **без изъятия,** without exception; **изъятие капитала (из вкладов),** disinvestment of capital
изъятый, *adj.*, excepted, omitted
изъять, *v.*, withdraw, remove, exclude, except
изымать (изъять), *v.*, remove, exclude, except
изэнтропический, *adj.*, of equal entropy, isentropic, iso-entropic
изэнтропия, *f.*, isentropy, iso-entropy
изящество, *n.*, refinement, elegance
изящный, *adj.*, refined, elegant
икосаэдр, *m.*, icosahedron; **группа икосаэдра,** icosahedral group
икс-лучи, *pl.*, X-rays
или, *conj.*, or; **или . . . или,** either . . . or; **схема «или»,** “or”-circuit
иллюзия, *f.*, illusion
иллюминатор, *m.*, illuminator, side-light
иллюминация, *f.*, illumination
иллюминированный, *adj.*, illuminated
иллюминировать, *v.*, illuminate
иллюстративный, *adj.*, illustrative
иллюстрация, *f.*, illustration
иллюстрированный, *adj.*, illustrated
иллюстрировать, *v.*, illustrate
иллюстрирующий, *adj.*, illustrating
им (cf. **он, они**), *pron.*, (by) him, (by) it, (to) them
имевшийся, *adj.*, possessed, (which was) had
имеем (cf. **иметь**), we have
имени (cf. **имя**), in the name of
именно, *adv.*, namely
именование, *n.*, name, nomenclature
именованный, *adj.*, concrete, definite; **именованное число,** concrete number
именовать, *v.*, name, denote
именуемый, *adj.*, called, named
иметь, *v.*, have; **иметь дело,** deal (with), have to do (with); **иметь значение,** mean, have meaning; **иметь место,** occur, take place, hold, be valid; **иметь силу,** be valid; **иметь в виду,** keep in mind, bear in mind
иметься, *v.*, be, exist, have
имеющий, *adj.*, having; **имеющий силу,** *adj.*, valid
имеющийся, *adj.*, available, existing
имея (from **иметь**), *adv. part.*, having, if we have; **имея в виду,** keeping in mind, bearing in mind; **имея дело (с),** dealing (with), in connection (with)
ими (cf. **они**), (by) them
имитировать, *v.*, imitate
имитирующий, *adj.*, imitating
иммерсионный, *adj.*, immersion

иммунитет, *m.*, immunity
иммунный, *adj.*, immune
импеданс, *m.*, impedance
импедансный, *adj.*, impedance
импликативный, *adj.*, implicative
импликация, *f.*, implication
импортация, *f.*, importation
импредикабельность, *f.*, impredicativity, impredicability
импредикабельный, *adj.*, impredicable, impredicative
импримитивность, *f.*, imprimitivity
импримитивный, *adj.*, imprimitive
импульс, *m.*, impulse, pulse, linear momentum, momentum; **задержка импульса на один главный импульс,** one-pulse time delay; **острый (узкий) импульс,** spike pulse; **частота следования импульсов,** pulse repetition; **группа импульсов,** word; **импульс сложения,** add pulse (*comp.*); **импульс переноса,** carry pulse (*comp.*); **импульс суммы,** sum pulse (*comp.*)
импульсный, *adj.*, impulse, impact, pulse, momentum
имущество, *n.*, property
имя, *n.*, name
иначе, *adv.*, otherwise, or else, differently; **иначе говоря,** in other words
инвариант, *m.*, invariant
инвариантность, *f.*, invariance
инвариантный, *adj.*, invariant
инвентарный, *adj.*, inventory
инверсионный, *adj.*, inversion; **инверсионное удвоение,** inversion doubling; **инверсионный спектр,** inversion spectrum
инверсия, *f.*, inversion, inverting, reversal
инверсно, *adv.*, inversely
инверсный, *adj.*, inverse
инвертировать, *v.*, invert
инвертирующий, *adj.*, inverting; **инвертирующая схема,** inverter circuit
инверторный, *adj.*, inverter, inverting; **инверторная схема,** inverter circuit
инвестирование, *n.*, investment
инвестировать, *v.*, invest
инволюта, *f.*, involute
инволютивный, *adj.*, pertaining to involute, involutory, involution
инволюторный, *adj.*, involutory, involution
инволюционный, *adj.*, involutory, involution
инволюция, *f.*, involution
ингибитор, *m.*, inhibitor
индекс, *m.*, index, subscript; **индекс вверху,** superscript; **индекс внизу,** subscript; **индекс неожиданности,** surprise index
индекс-нуль, *m.*, index zero
индексировать, *v.*, index
индексирующий, *adj.*, indexing; **индексирующее множество,** indexing set
индефинитный, *adj.*, indefinite
индивид, *m.*, individual
индивидуальный, *adj.*, individual, specific
индивидуум, *m.*, individual
индикатор, *m.*, indicator, marker, indicator function
индикаторный, *adj.*, indicator, pertaining to indicator, indicated; **индикаторное показание,** indicator reading
индикатриса, *f.*, indicatrix, index; **индикатриса рассеяния,** dispersion index
индуктивно, *adv.*, inductively
индуктивность, *f.*, inductance
индуктивный, *adj.*, inductive
индуктированный, *adj.*, induced
индуктировать, *v.*, induce, proceed by induction
индукционный, *adj.*, inductive, induction
индукцированный, *adj.*, induced
индукция, *f.*, induction, displacement; **вектор электрической индукции,** electric displacement vector; **вектор магнитной индукции,** magnetic displacement vector
индуцированный, *adj.*, induced, produced; **индуцированное произведение,** induced bundle

индуцировать, *v.*, induce
индуцируемый, *adj.*, inducible, induced
инертность, *f.*, inertness, sluggishness, inertia
инертный, *adj.*, inert, inactive
инерционный, *adj.*, inertial; **инерционное движение,** inertial motion
инерция, *f.*, inertia, momentum
инжектированный, *adj.*, injected
инжектировать, *v.*, inject
инжектор, *m.*, injector
инжекторный, *adj.*, injector
инжекция, *f.*, injection; **инжекция частиц,** particle injection
инженер, *m.*, engineer
инженерный, *adj.*, engineering
инициатор, *m.*, initiator, pioneer
инкубационный, *adj.*, incubation
иновидный, *adj.*, different, different-looking
иногда, *adv.*, sometimes
иной, *adj.*, different, other
инородность, *f.*, heterogeneity
иностранный, *adj.*, foreign
инспектор, *m.*, inspector
инспекция, *f.*, inspection; **план непрерывной инспекции,** continuous inspection plan
институт, *m.*, institute
инструкция, *f.*, instruction, control
инструмент, *m.*, instrument, tool
ин-та, *abbrev.* **(института),** of the institute
интеграл, *m.*, integral; **интеграл свертки,** convolution, convolution integral, Faltung; **интеграл пуассона,** Poisson integral
интегральный, *adj.*, integral
интеграция, *f.*, integration
интегрирование, *m.*, integration; **интегрирование по частям,** integration by parts
интегрированный, *adj.*, integrated
интегрировать, *v.*, integrate
интегрируемость, *f.*, integrability
интегрируемый, *adj.*, integrable; **интегрируемый с квадратом,** square integrable
интегрирующий, *adj.*, integrating; **интегрирующее звено,** *n.*, integrating factor; **интегрирующий множитель,** *m.*, integrating factor; **интегрирующее устройство,** integrator
интегрируя, *adv. part.*, integrating, if we integrate
интегро-дифференциальный, *adj.*, integro-differential
интеллект, *m.*, intellect
интеллектуальность, *f.*, intellectuality
интеллектуальный, *adj.*, intellectual
интенсивность, *f.*, intensity
интенсиональный, *adj.*, intensional (log.)
интенция, *f.*, intension (log.)
интервал, *m.*, interval, space; **с интервалами,** at intervals
интерес, *m.*, interest, profit
интересный, *adj.*, interesting
интересовать, *v.*, interest, attract
интерквартильный, *adj.*, interquartile; **интерквартильная широта,** interquartile range
интеркомбинационный, *adj.*, intercombinative, intercombinatory
интеркомбинация, *f.*, intercombination
интерполирование, *m.*, interpolation
интерполированный, *adj.*, interpolated
интерполировать, *v.*, interpolate
интерполяционный, *adj.*, interpolational, interpolated
интерполяция, *f.*, interpolation
интерпретация, *f.*, interpretation
интерпретировать, *v.*, interpret
интерпретируемость, *f.*, interpretability
интерференционный, *adj.*, interference; **интерференционная полоса,** fringe
интерференцированный, *adj.*, interference
интерференция, *f.*, interference
интерферировать, *v.*, interfere
интерферометр, *m.*, interferometer
интранзитивный, *adj.*, intransitive

интуитивно, *adv.*, intuitively
интуитивный, *adj.*, intuitive
интуиционизм, *m.*, intuitionism
интуиционистический, *adj.*, intuitionistic
интуиционистский, *adj.*, intuitionistic
интуиция, *f.*, intuition
инфекционный, *adj.*, contagious, infectious
инфинитезимально, *adv.*, infinitesimally
инфинитезимально - изотопический, *adj.*, infinitesimally isotopic
инфинитезимальный, *adj.*, infinitesimal
инфлекционный, *adj.*, inflectional
информация, *f.*, information; **теория информации,** information theory; **канал информации,** trunk; **блок информации,** message
инфракрасный, *adj.*, infra-red
инфрамногочлен, *m.*, infrapolynomial
инцидент, *m.*, incident
инцидентность, *f.*, incidence; **матрица инцидентности,** incidence matrix
инцидентный, *adj.*, incident, incidental, incidence
инъективный, *adj.*, injective; **инъективный себе,** self-injective
инъекция, *f.*, injection
иным (from **иной**), by other; **иным путем,** by other means; **иными словами,** in other words
ион, *m.*, ion
ионизационный, *adj.*, ionization, ionized
ионизация, *f.*, ionization
ионизированный, *adj.*, ionized
ионизировать, *v.*, ionize
ионный, *adj.*, ionic; **ионная решетка,** ionic lattice
ионосфера, *f.*, ionosphere
ионизованный, *adj.*, ionized
ирис, *m.*, iris
ирисовый, *adj.*, iris
иррациональность, *f.*, irrationality
иррациональный, *adj.*, irrational
иррегулярность, *f.*, irregularity
иррегулярный, *adj.*, irregular
иррефлексивность, *f.*, irreflexiveness, irreflexivity
иррефлексивный, *adj.*, irreflexive
искажаемость, *f.*, distortability, distortion
искажать (исказить), *v.*, distort, alter
искажение, *n.*, distortion
искаженный, *adj.*, distorted
искатель, *m.*, researcher
искать, *v.*, seek, look
исключать (исключить), *v.*, exclude, except, eliminate
исключающий, *adj.*, excluding, eliminating, exclusive; **исключающий друг друга,** *adj.*, mutually exclusive
исключая, *prep.*, except, excepting; **не исключая,** not excepting; **исключая случай, когда . . .,** except when . . .; *adv. part.*, excluding, eliminating, excepting, if we eliminate, if we exclude
исключение, *n.*, exclusion, exception, elimination
исключенный, *adj.*, excluded, exceptional; **правило исключенного третьего,** law of the excluded middle
исключительно, *adv.*, exceptionally, exclusively, solely, only
исключительный, *adj.*, exceptional, unusual, exclusive
исключить (cf. **исключать**), exclude, eliminate
искомое, *n.*, unknown, unknown quantity, desired quantity
искомый, *adj.*, desired, sought for
искра, *f.*, spark
искривление, *n.*, twist, bend, deformation, distortion
искровой, *adj.*, spark; **искровой спектр,** spark spectrum
искривленный, *adj.*, curved, twisted, distorted, warped
искривлять, *v.*, bend, twist, distort, warp
искусник, *m.*, expert
искусный, *adj.*, expert, skilful, clever
искусственно, *adv.*, artificially, synthetically

искусственность, *f.*, artificiality
искусственный, *adj.*, artificial
испарение, *n.*, evaporation, vaporization; *pl.*, fumes
испарять (испарить), *v.*, evaporate, vaporize
исполнительный, *adj.*, control, executive; **исполнительный механизм на самолете,** automatic pilot
исполнять, *v.*, execute, fulfil
использовав, *adv. part.*, having used, having applied
использование, *n.*, use, utilization, employment; **повторное использование,** reuse
использованный, *adj.*, used, utilized
использовать, *v.*, make use of, exploit, utilize
используемый, *adj.*, used, being used, utilized
используя, *adv. part.*, using, if we use
исправление, *n.*, correction, improvement, revision
исправленный, *adj.*, revised, corrected
исправлять (исправить), *v.*, correct, revise, repair
испускаемый, *adj.*, emitted
испускание, *n.*, emission, radiation, ejection
испускать (испустить), *v.*, emit
испущенный, *adj.*, emitted
испытание, *n.*, trial, test, experiment; **испытание на нагрев,** heat test, heat run; **испытание в рабочих условиях,** performance test; **испытание долговечности,** life test, longevity test
испытатель, *m.*, tester
испытательный, *adj.*, test, trial, experimental, testing; **испытательный прибор,** testing device
испытующий, *adj.*, testing, test; **испытующая функция,** test function
испытываемый, *adj.*, experimental
испытывать (испытать), *v.*, undergo, experience, test
исследование, *n.*, investigation, research, analysis, discussion, tracing; **исследование операций,** operations research
исследованный, *adj.*, investigated, explored, examined, traced
исследователь, *m.*, investigator, researcher
исследовательский, *adj.*, research
исследовать, *v.*, investigate, analyze, trace
исследуемый, *adj.*, being investigated
истекать (истечь), *v.*, flow out, run out, elapse, expire
истечение, *n.*, outflow, discharge, expiration
истечь (cf. **истекать**)
истина, *f.*, truth
истинность, *f.*, truth; **таблица истинности,** truth table; **значение истинности,** truth value
истинный, *adj.*, true, correct, proper, faithful; **истинное подмножество,** proper subset; **работа в истинном масштабе времени,** real-time operation; **истинный масштаб времени,** real-time
исток, *m.*, source
истокообразно, *adv.*, according to source, sourcewise; **истокообразно представленная функция,** sourcewise representable function
истолкование, *n.*, interpretation
истолкователь, *m.*, interpreter, commentator
истолковательный, *adj.*, explanatory
истолковывать, *v.*, interpret, construe
истопник, *m.*, stoker
история, *f.*, history
источник, *m.*, source, origin; **функция источника,** source function; **источник питания,** supply
истощать, *v.*, exhaust, drain
истощение, *n.*, exhaustion
истощимый, *adj.*, exhaustible
исход, *m.*, outcome, result
исходим (from **исходить**), we start from

исходить, *v.*, come from, start from, emanate

исходный, *adj.*, initial, original, primitive, input, parent, assumed; **возвращать в исходное положение,** reset; **исходный документ,** source document; **исходное уравнение,** input equation; **исходные данные,** input data; **исходная формула,** assumption formula

исходя, *adv. part.*, starting from, beginning with

исчезать (исчезнуть), *v.*, vanish, disappear

исчезающий, *adj.*, vanishing, disappearing

исчезновение, *n.*, vanishing, disappearance

исчерпаемый, *adj.*, exhaustible

исчерпание, *n.*, exhaustion

исчерпанный, *adj.*, exhausted, settled

исчерпывание, *n.*, exhaustion; **процесс исчерпывания,** exhaustion process

исчерпывать (исчерпать), *v.*, exhaust, drain, settle

исчерпываться, *v.*, become exhausted

исчерпывающий, *adj.*, exhausting, exhaustive

исчисление, *n.*, calculus, computation; **исчисление высказываний,** propositional calculus; **исчисление предикатов,** predicate calculus; **исчисление одноместных предикатов,** one-place predicate calculus; **исчисление задач,** problem calculus; **чистое исчисление предикатов,** pure predicate calculus; **узкое исчисление предикатов,** restricted predicate calculus

исчислимый, *adj.*, calculable, countable

итак, *conj.*, thus, so

итеративный, *adj.*, iterated, repeated, iterative

итерационный, *adj.*, iterated, repeated, iterative; **итерационный цикл,** iterative loop

итерация, *f.*, iteration, iterate; **цикл итерации,** iterative loop

итерированный, *adj.*, iterated

итерировать, *v.*, iterate, repeat

и т. д., *abbrev.* **(и так далее),** and so on, etc.

итог, *m.*, sum, total, result; **в конечном итоге,** as the final result; **отрицательный итог,** negative balance; **подведение итога,** tally

итого, *adv.*, in all, altogether

итоговый, *adj.*, concluding, summarizing, total

ищем, ищет, (cf. **искать**), we seek, he seeks

ищется (cf. **искать**), is sought

их, *pron.*, (from **они**), their, them

ищущий, *adj.*, seeking

Й

йордановый (cf. **Жордановый**), *adj.*, Jordan, pertaining to Jordan

К

к, *prep.*, to, towards, at, on
кабель, *m.*, cable
кабина, *f.*, cabin, booth
каверна, *f.*, cavity
кавитационный, *adj.*, cavity, cavitational
кавитация, *f.*, cavitation
кавычки, *pl.*, quotation marks
каждый, *adj.*, every, each
кажется (from **казаться**), it seems
кажущийся, *adj.*, seeming, apparent
казаться, *v.*, seem, appear
кайзер, *m.*, kayser (unit of wave number, cm^{-1})
кайма, *f.*, border, edge
как, *adv.*, how, as, what; **как раз,** just, exactly; **как . . ., так и,** both . . . and; **как только,** as soon as; **как бы то ни было,** however that may be, be that as it may
как-либо, *adv.*, somehow
как-нибудь, *adv.*, somehow, anyhow
как-никак, *adv.*, after all
каков, *adj.*, what kind, what; **каково бы ни,** whatever
какой, *pron.*, what, what kind, which
какой-либо (cf. **какой-нибудь**) *part.*, some, some kind of
какой-нибудь, *pron.*, some, some kind of, any
кактоид, *m.*, cactoid
каление, *n.*, incandescence
калибр, *m.*, gauge, calibre
калибрование, *n.*, calibration
калибровать, *v.*, calibrate
калибровка, *f.*, calibration, graduation, graduating
калибровочно-инвариантный, *adj.*, gauge-invariant
калибровочный, *adj.*, caliber, gauge; **калибровочное преобразование,** gauge transformation
калильный, *adj.*, heat, incandescent
калориметрический, *adj.*, calorimetric
калорический, *adj.*, caloric, thermal
калория, *f.*, calorie
каменный, *adj.*, immovable, hard, stony, lifeless
камера, *f.*, chamber, camera
камертон, *m.*, tuning fork
канавка, *f.*, groove, slot
канал, *m.*, canal, channel, conduit, duct; **канал информации,** trunk, information channel; **поверхность канала,** canal surface
каналовый, *adj.*, canal, channel; **каналовая поверхность,** canal surface
канат, *m.*, rope, cable
кандидат, *m.*, kandidat (academic degree), candidate
кандидатский, *adj.*, pertaining to kandidat
канонизировать, *v.*, reduce to canonical form
канонический, *adj.*, canonical, classical, accepted; **канонический базис,** canonical basis; **канонический вид,** canonical form
канторовый, *adj.*, Cantor, pertaining to Cantor
канцелярский, *adj.*, office, clerical
капилляр, *m.*, capillary
капиллярный, *adj.*, capillary
капитал, *m.*, capital
капиталовложение, *n.*, investment, capital investment
капитальный, *adj.*, general, capital, fundamental, substantial
капля, *f.*, drop; **вес капли,** drop weight; **висячая капля,** hanging drop; **жидкая капля,** drop of liquid
карбид, *m.*, carbide
кардановский, *adj.*, Cardano, pertaining to Cardano
кардинальный, *adj.*, cardinal, principal; **кардинальное число,** cardinal number
кардиограмма, *f.*, cardiogram
кардиоида, *f.*, cardioid

каретка, *f.*, carriage, frame
карлик, *m.*, dwarf (star)
карманный, *adj.*, pocket
карта, *f.*, map, chart, card; **колода карт,** pack of playing cards
картина, *f.*, picture, situation
картограф, *m.*, cartographer
картографический, *adj.*, cartographical
картон, *m.*, cardboard, carton
картотека, *f.*, card-file, file
карточный, *adj.*, card; **карточная игра,** card game
касание, *n.*, contact, tangency; **точка касания,** point of contact, point of tangency
касательная, *f.*, tangent
касательно, *prep.*, touching, concerning; *adv.*, tangentially
касательный, *adj.*, tangent, tangential
касаться (коснуться), *v.*, touch, be tangent, concern; **что касается,** concerning, as to, relating to
касающийся, *adj.*, tangent, touching (upon), concerning
каскад, *m.*, cascade, waterfall
каскадный, *adj.*, cascade, step-by-step; **каскадный перенос,** step-by-step carry; **каскадная теория ливней,** shower theory
катализатор, *m.*, catalyst
катание, *n.*, rolling
катаракта, *f.*, cataract
катастрофа, *f.*, catastrophe, disaster
катать (катить), *v.*, roll, drive, wheel
категорический, *adj.*, categorical
категоричность, *f.*, categoricity, category
категоричный, *adj.*, categorical
категория, *f.*, category, class
катеноид, *m.*, catenoid, catenary surface
катет, *m.*, perpendicular, leg of a right triangle
катион, *m.*, cation
катить (cf. **катать**), *v.*, roll
катиться, *v.*, roll
катод, *m.*, cathode
катодный, *adj.*, cathode; **катодный осциллограф,** oscilloscope
катушка, *f.*, spool, coil, reel; **индукционная катушка,** induction coil
катящийся, *adj.*, rolling, roll
каустический, *adj.*, caustic; **каустическая линия,** caustic, focal curve
кафедра, *f.*, chair (professorial)
качание, *n.*, oscillation, vibration, swinging, rolling
качательный, *adj.*, vibrating, oscillatory
качать (качнуть), *v.*, roll, swing, wheel
качаться, *v.*, oscillate, swing, rock
качественный, *adj.*, qualitative, quality
качество, *n.*, quality, property; **контроль качества,** quality control; **в качестве,** in the capacity of, as
качка, *f.*, rolling, swinging
квадрант, *m.*, quadrant
квадрантный, *adj.*, quadrant
квадрат, *m.*, square; **в квадрате,** squared
квадратик, *m.*, small square
квадратически, *adv.*, quadratically, to the second power
квадратический, *adj.*, quadratic; **квадратическое отклонение,** standard deviation; **квадратическое уклонение,** second order deviation
квадратично, *adv.*, quadratically, second-degree
квадратичный, *adj.*, square, quadratic, square-law; **квадратичный вычет,** quadratic residue; **широкополосный квадратичный усилитель,** wide-band square-law amplifier; **квадратичная ошибка,** squared error
квадратный, *adj.*, square, quadratic; **квадратный корень,** square root; **квадратный метр,** square meter; **квадратное уравнение,** quadratic equation; **квадратные дужки,** square brackets; **квадратные скобки,** square brackets, braces
квадратор, *m.*, squarer, square-law function generator
квадратура, *f.*, quadrature, squaring; **квадратура круга,** squaring the circle
квадратурный, *adj.*, quadrature, pertaining to quadrature

квадрика, *f.*, quadric
квадрируемость, *f.*, squarability, rectifiability
квадрируемый, *adj.*, squarable; rectifiable; **квадрируемая поверхность,** rectifiable surface, surface whose area can be determined, squarable surface
квадруполь, *m.*, quadrupole
квадрупольный, *adj.*, quadrupole
квази, *prefix*, quasi-, semi-
квазиалгебраический, *adj.*, quasi-algebraic
квазиалгеброидный, *adj.*, quasi-algebroidal
квазианалитический, *adj.*, quasi-analytic, pseudo-analytic
квазианалитичность, *f.*, quasi-analyticity, pseudo-analyticity
квазиасимптотический, *adj.*, quasi-asymptotic, semi-asymptotic
квазивнутренний, *adj.*, quasi-interior
квазивыпуклый, *adj.*, quasi-convex
квази-геодезическая, *f.*, quasi-geodesic
квази-геодезический, *adj.*, quasi-geodesic, quasi-geodetic
квазигеострофический, *adj.*, quasi-geostrophic
квазигомеоморфный, *adj.*, quasi-homeomorphic
квазигруппа, *f.*, quasi-group, semi-group
квазиделитель, *m.*, quasi-divisor
квазидецимал, *m.*, quasi-decimal
квазидиагональный, *adj.*, quasi-diagonal
квазидифференциальный, *adj.*, quasi-differential
квазидополнение, *n.*, quasi-complement; **структура с обобщенным квазидополнением,** quasi-complemented lattice
квазиединичный, *adj.*, quasi-unitary
квазизамкнутый, *adj.*, semi-closed, quasi-closed
квазиидемпотентность, *f.*, quasi-idempotency
квазиидемпотентный, *adj.*, quasi-idempotent
квазикватернионный, *adj.*, quasi-quaternionic
квазиклассический, *adj.*, semi-classical
квазикольцо, *n.*, semi-ring, quasi-ring
квазикомпактный, *adj.*, quasi-compact
квазикомплексность, *f.*, quasi-complexity, quasi-complex
квазикомплексный, *adj.*, quasi-complex
квазикомпонент, *m.*, quasi-component
квазикомпонента, *f.*, quasi-component
квазиконформность, *f.*, quasi-conformality
квазиконформный, *adj.*, quasi-conformal; **квазиконформное отображение,** quasi-conformal mapping
квазикоордината, *f.*, quasi-coordinate
квазикратный, *adj.*, quasi-factor, quasi-multiple
квазилимитирующий, *adj.*, quasi-limiting, weakly limiting
квазилинейный, *adj.*, quasi-linear
квази-метрический, *adj.*, quasi-metric
квазимономиальный, *adj.*, quasi-monomial
квазимонотонный, *adj.*, semi-monotonic, quasi-monotone
квазимонохроматичность, *f.*, semi-monochromaticity, quasi-monochromaticity
квазинезависимый, *adj.*, quasi-independent
квазинепрерывный, *adj.*, quasi-continuous, semi-continuous
квазинеразложимый, *adj.*, quasi-indecomposable
квазинильгруппа, *f.*, quasi-nilgroup
квазинормальность, *f.*, quasi-normality, weak normality
квазинормальный, *adj.*, quasi-normal, weakly normal
квазиобратный, *adj.*, quasi-inverse
квазиограниченный, *adj.*, quasi-bounded, weakly bounded
квазиоднородный, *adj.*, quasi-homogeneous
квазиоператорный, *adj.*, quasi-operator
квазиопределенный, *adj.*, quasi-definite, semi-definite
квази-ортогональный, *adj.*, quasi-orthogonal

квазиоткрытый, *adj.*, semi-open, quasi-open, half open
квазипаракомплексный, *adj.*, quasi-paracomplex
квазипараэрмитовый, *adj.*, quasi-parahermitian
квазиперенос, *m.*, quasi-translation
квазипериодический, *adj.*, quasi-periodic, almost periodic
квазиплоский, *adj.*, quasi-plane, quasi-planar
квазиполином, *m.*, quasi-polymonial
квазипростой (cf. **полупростой**), *adj.*, semi-simple, quasi-simple
квазиравномерно, *adv.*, semi-uniformly; **квазиравномерно непрерывный,** semi-uniformly continuous
квазиравномерность, *f.*, quasi-uniformity, semi-uniformity
квазиравномерный, *adj.*, quasi-uniform, semi-uniform
квазиранг, *m.*, semi-rank
квазирассеянный, *adj.*, quasi-dispersed, " quasi-clairsème "
квазирасстояние, *n.*, quasi-distance
квазирегулярность, *f.*, quasi-regularity, semi-regularity
квазирегулярный, *adj.*, quasi-regular, semi-regular, pseudo-regular
квазисвободный, *adj.*, quasi-free; **квазисвободный электрон,** quasi-free electron
квазистатический, *adj.*, quasi-static
квазистационарный, *adj.*, quasi-stationary, quasi-steady
квазистепенный, *adj.*, quasi-exponential
квазистохастический, *adj.*, quasi-stochastic
квазисубрешение, *n.*, semi-minorant
квазисуперрешение, *n.*, semi-majorant
квазисходимость, *f.*, quasi-, semi-convergence
квазисходящийся, *adj.*, quasi-, semi-convergent
квазиумножение, *n.*, quasi-multiplication, weak multiplication
квази-упорядоченность, *f.*, quasi-ordering, weak ordering, partial ordering
квазиупругий, *adj.*, quasi-elastic
квазифробениусовый, *adj.*, quasi-Frobenius
квази-хаусдорфовский, *adj.*, quasi-Hausdorff
квазицикличный, *adj.*, semi-cyclic, quasi-cyclic
квазиэлектростатический, *adj.*, quasi-electrostatic
квазиэрмитовый, *adj.*, quasi-Hermitian
квалификатор, *m.*, qualificator, qualifier
квалификационный, *adj.*, qualified, qualification
квалифицировать, *v.*, qualify
квалифицирующий, *adj.*, qualifying; **квалифицирующее число,** acceptance number
квант, *m.*, quantum; **квант света,** light quantum; **квант информации,** information bit
кванта, *f.*, quantum
квантиль, *m.*, quantile
квантильный, *adj.*, quantile, quantum
квантификация, *f.*, quantification, quantifying
квантование, *n.*, quantification, quantization
квантованный, *adj.*, quantified, quantized
квантовать, *v.*, quantize
квантовомеханический, *adj.*, quantum mechanical, pertaining to quantum mechanics
квантовый, *adj.*, quantum; **квантовая теория,** quantum theory; **квантовая механика,** quantum mechanics
квантор, *m.*, quantor, quantifier
квартал, *m.*, quarter, square, block
квартиль, *m.*, quartile; **нижний квартиль,** lower quartile; **верхний квартиль,** upper quartile
кварц, *m.*, quartz
кватернарный, *adj.*, quaternary
кватернион, *m.*, quaternion
кватернионный, *adj.*, quaternion
кверху, *adv.*, up, upwards
квинтик, *m.*, quintic

келеровый, *adj.*, Kählerian
керн, *m.*, kernel, core, center
кернфункция, *f.*, kernel function, kernel
кибернетика, *f.*, cybernetics
киловатт, *m.*, kilowatt; **киловатт-час,** kilowatt-hour
кинематика, *f.*, kinematics
кинематический, *adj.*, kinematic
кинескоп, *m.*, viewer; **электронный кинескоп,** electron microscope
кинетика, *f.*, kinetics
кинетико-, *prefix*, kinetic-, kinetically
кинетический, *adj.*, kinetic; **кинетическая энергия,** kinetic energy
кипение, *n.*, boiling; **точка кипения,** boiling point
кипячение, *n.*, boiling
кирпич, *m.*, brick, cube; **гильбертовый кирпич,** Hilbert cube
кислород, *m.*, oxygen
кислородный, *adj.*, oxygen
клавиатура, *f.*, keyboard
кладет (cf. **класть**), puts, lays
клан, *m.*, clan
клапан, *m.*, valve, gate; **клапан сложения,** add gate; **клапан переноса,** carry gate; **входной клапан,** in-gate; **выходной клапан,** out-gate
класс, *m.*, class, set; **класс вычета,** residue class; **класс информации,** information set
классификатор, *m.*, classifier
классификационный, *adj.*, classified, sorted, graded
классификация, *f.*, classification
классифицировать, *v.*, classify
классифицируемый, *adj.*, classified
классический, *adj.*, classical
классный, *adj.*, class, pertaining to class
классовый, *adj.*, class
класть, *v.*, put, place, lay, build
клеить, *v.*, glue, paste, identify
клейновский, *adj.*, pertaining to Klein, Klein
клетка, *f.*, cell, square, sector
клеточный, *adj.*, cell-like, cell, latticed; **клеточное разбиение,** complex
клин, *m.*, wedge; **конический клин,** conical wedge, conocuneus
клиновидный, *adj.*, wedge, wedge-shaped
клониться, *v.*, tend, incline, bend
клотоида, *f.*, clothoid, spiral of Cornu, spiral of Euler
клочковатый, *adj.*, ragged
ключ, *m.*, source, key
ключевой, *adj.*, key
книга, *f.*, book
книзу, *adv.*, down, downwards
кнопка, *f.*, push button, knob; **стартовая кнопка,** start button; **пусковая кнопка,** start button; load button; **остановочная кнопка,** stop button
кнут, *m.*, whip
ко (cf. **к**), *prep.*, to, towards
коаксиальный, *adj.*, coaxial
коалиционный, *adj.*, coalition, cooperative
коалиция, *f.*, coalition
ковариантно, *adv.*, from **ковариантный; ковариантно замкнутый,** *adj.*, co-closed; **ковариантно точный,** *adj.*, co-exact
ковариантность, *f.*, covariance, covariant property
ковариантный, *adj.*, covariant
ковариациальный, *adj.*, covariance
ковариационный, *adj.*, covariance
ковариация, *f.*, covariance
ковка, *f.*, forging
ковкость, *f.*, malleability, ductility
когда, *adv.*, when; *conj.*, when, while, as; **в тех случаях, когда,** where, when
когерента, *f.*, coherence
когерентно-инвариантный, *adj.*, coherence-invariant; **когерентно-инвариантное отображение,** coherence-invariant mapping
когерентность, *f.*, coherence
когерентный, *adj.*, coherence, coherent
когомологически, *adv.*, cohomologously
когомологический, *adj.*, cohomologous, cohomology
когомология, *f.*, cohomology

когомотопический, *adj.*, cohomotopic, cohomotopy
кoградиентно, *adv.*, cogradiently
когрaдиентный, *adj.*, cogradient
кoграница, *f.*, coboundary
кoграничный, *adj.*, abutting, coboundary
когредиентный, *adj.*, cogredient
код, *m.*, code; **прямой код,** true representation; **дополнительный код,** true complement; **код операции,** operation part, operation code
кодирование, *n.*, coding, encoding, **кодирование с относительными адресами,** relative coding; **система кодирования,** coding; **система ускоренного кодирования,** speed-coding system
кодированно-десятичный, *adj.*, coded decimal; **кодированно-десятичный сумматор,** coded decimal adder
кодировка, *f.*, coding, encoding
кодированный, *adj.*, coded
кодировать, *v.*, code
кодироваться, *v.*, be coded
кодирующий, *adj.*, coding; **кодирующая схема,** coding circuit; **кодирующая запасающая схема,** coding storage circuit
кодифференцирование, *n.*, codifferentiation
кодовый, *adj.*, code
кодопреобразователь, *m.*, code converter
кое-где, *adv.*, somewhere, here and there
кое-какой, *pron.*, some
козамкнутый, *adj.*, co-closed
коидеал, *m.*, co-ideal
коинициальный, *adj.*, co-initial
коинциндентность, *f.*, coincidence
коинциндентный, *adj.*, coincidence, coincident
кокатегория, *f.*, co-category
коконцевой, *adj.*, co-final, co-terminal
колебание, *n.*, oscillation, vibration, fluctuation, deviation; **неустановившееся колебание,** transient oscillation; **пилообразное колебание,** saw-tooth wave
колебательность, *f.*, variability, oscillation, variation
колебательный, *adj.*, oscillating, vibrating, oscillatory, wave; **колебательное уравнение,** wave equation
колебаться, *v.*, oscillate, hesitate
колеблемость, *f.*, variability, ability to oscillate
колеблющийся, *adj.*, oscillating, unsteady, uncertain
колейный, *adj.*, **колейная группа,** track group
колец, *gen. pl. of* **кольцо**
коли, *conj.*, if
количественный, *adj.*, quantitative, numerical; **выборочный контроль по количественному признаку,** sampling by variables
количество, *n.*, amount, quantity, number; **количество информации,** precision of information; **количество движения,** momentum; **вычисление с двойным количеством разрядов,** double-precision computation; **число с двойным количеством разрядов,** double-precision number; **момент количества движения,** moment of momentum, angular momentum
коллектив, *m.*, collective, association
коллективизированный, *adj.*, collective; **модель коллективизированных электронов,** collective electron model
коллективный, *adj.*, collective
коллекционирование, *n.*, collecting
коллекция, *f.*, collection
коллинеарность, *f.*, collinearity, collineation
коллинеарный, *adj.*, collinear
коллинеация, *f.*, collineation, projectivity
коллоидный, *adj.*, colloidal, colloid
коллоквиум, *m.*, colloquium
колода, *f.*, block, pack; **колода карт,** deck of cards, pack of cards
колоколообразный, *adj.*, bell-shaped
колонка, *f.*, column, core, core sample

колонна, *f.*, column, pillar
колориметрия, *f.*, colorimetry
коль (cf. **коли**), *conj.*; **коль скоро,** as soon as, as, whenever
кольцевой, *adj.*, annular, ring, pertaining to a ring; **кольцевое умножение,** ring multiplication; **кольцевая функция,** ring-function
кольцеобразный, *adj.*, ring-shaped, annular
кольцо, *n.*, ring, annulus
кольцоида, *f.*, ringoid
кома, *f.*, coma; **кома Зейделя,** Seidel coma
комаксимальный, *adj.*, co-maximal
команда, *f.*, command, order, instruction; **последовательность команд,** routine; **команда условного перехода,** conditional transfer; conditional transfer instruction
командный, *adj.*, pertaining to command order; team-
комбинаторика, *f.*, combinatorial analysis
комбинаторно, *adv.*, combinatorially
комбинаторный, *adj.*, combinatorial; **комбинаторная топология,** combinatorial topology
комбинационный, *adj.*, combinative; **сумматор комбинационного типа,** coincidence-type adder
комбинация, *f.*, combination
комбинирование, *n.*, combination
комбинированный, *adj.*, combined, composed, composed of
комбинировать, *v.*, combine, arrange
комиссия, *f.*, commission, committee
комитант, *m.* (**комитанта,** *f.*), concomitant, comitant
комкать, *v.*, crumple, bunch up
комментарий, *m.*, comment, commentary
коммерческий, *adj.*, commercial, business
коммутант, *m.*, commutator-group, commutant
коммутантный, *adj.*, commutator, commutator-group; **коммутантный изоморфизм,** commutator-group isomorphism
коммутативно, *adv.*, commutatively
коммутативность, *f.*, commutativity
коммутативный, *adj.*, commutative
коммутатор, *m.*, commutator
коммутаторный, *adj.*, commutator
коммутация, *f.*, commutation
коммутирование, *n.*, commutation
коммутированный, *adj.*, commuted
коммутировать, *v.*, commute, reverse, commutate
коммутирующий, *adj.*, commuting
комната, *f.*, room
комнатный, *adj.*, room, indoor; **комнатная температура,** room temperature
компакт, *m.*, compactum, bicompactum
компактификация, *f.*, compactification
компактифицировать, *v.*, compactify
компактно (from **компактный**), *adv.*; **компактно-открытая топология,** compact-open topology
компактность, *f.*, compactness
компактный, *adj.*, compact, dense, solid
компенсационный, *adj.*, compensating, compensation
компенсация, *f.*, compensation
компенсировать, *v.*, compensate, indemnify
компенсирующийся, *adj.*, compensating; **компенсирующаяся ошибка,** compensating error
компетенция, *f.*, competence
компиляция, *f.*, compilation
компланарность, *f.*, coplanarity
компланарный, *adj.*, coplanar
комплекс, *m.*, complex
комплексификация, *f.*, complexification
комплексно-аналитический, *adj.*, complex-analytic
комплекснозначный, *adj.*, complex-valued
комплексно-сопряженный, *adj.*, complex conjugate; **комплексно-сопряженная матрица,** adjoint matrix
комплексный, *adj.*, complex, complex-valued, composite; **комплексная мера,** complex-valued measure

комплект, *m.*, complete set, complete series, complex
комплектировать, *v.*, complete
комплектный, *adj.*, complete
комплектовать, *v.*, complete, replenish
композант, *m.*, compositor, component
композит, *m.*, aggregate, totality
композитный, *adj.*, composite
композиционный, *adj.*, composite, composed of, composition
композиция, *f.*, composition, grouping, convolution
компонент, *m.*, component, constituent
компонента, *f.*, component
компоновка, *f.*, arrangement, grouping
компромиссный, *adj.*, compromise
комптоновский, *adj.*, Compton
комптон-эффект, *m.*, Compton effect
конвексный, *adj.*, convex
конвективный, *adj.*, convective, convection
конвекционный, *adj.*, convection, convecting
конвекция, *f.*, convection
конвергенция, *f.*, convergence
конверсия, *f.*, conversion
конволюция, *f.*, convolution
конгресс, *m.*, congress
конгруэнтность, *f.*, congruence
конгруэнтный, *adj.*, congruent
конгруэнция, *f.*, congruence
конгруэнц-подгруппа, *f.*, congruence subgroup
конденсатор, *m.*, condenser, capacitor
конденсационный, *adj.*, condensation; **конденсационный аппарат,** condenser
конденсация, *f.*, condensation
конденсированный, *adj.*, condensed
конденсор, *m.*, condenser
кондиционирование, *n.*, conditioning; **кондиционирование воздуха,** air conditioning
кондуктор, *m.*, conductor
конец, *m.*, end; **в конце концов,** finally, in the last analysis; **простой конец,** prime end
конечно, *adv.*, finitely, of course, certainly; *pred.*, is finite; *prefix*, finite, finitely
конечно-аддитивный, *adj.*, finitely additive
конечно-ветвящийся, *adj.*, finitely branched, of finite branching
конечно-дифференцируемый, *adj.*, finitely differentiable
конечнозначный, *adj.*, finite-valued, finitely valued
конечнократный, *adj.*, finite-to-one, of finite multiplicity
конечнолистный, *adj.*, finite-sheeted
конечномерность, *f.*, finite dimensionality
конечномерный, *adj.*, finite-dimensional
конечноопределенный, *adj.*, finitely defined
конечно-разностный, *adj.*, finite difference, difference
конечносвязный, *adj.*, finitely connected, of finite connectivity
конечнострочный, *adj.*, finite-rowed
конечность, *f.*, finiteness
-конечный, *suffix*, -pointed; **пятиконечный,** five-pointed
конечный, *adj.*, final, finite, terminal; **в конечном итоге,** as the final result; **конечное приращение,** finite increment
коника, *f.*, conic
конический, *adj.*, conic, conal; **коническое сечение,** conic section
конкретизация, *f.*, concrete definition
конкретизировать, *v.*, render concrete, realize, define concretely
конкретно, *adv.*, concretely, specifically
конкретность, *f.*, concreteness
конкретный, *adj.*, concrete, particular, specific
конкурентный, *adj.*, competitive
конкуренция, *f.*, competition
конкурировать, *v.*, compete, compete with
конкурирующий, *adj.*, competing, competitive
конкурс, *m.*, contest, competition

коннекс, *m.*, connex
коноид, *m.*, conoid
консервативный, *adj.*, conservative
консистентный, *adj.*, consistent
консистенция, *f.*, consistence, consistency
консистометр, *m.*, consistometer
консолидация, *f.*, consolidation
консольный, *adj.*, cantilever, console
конспект, *m.*, summary, abstract
конспективный, *adj.*, concise, recapitulating
константа, *f.*, constant
константный, *adj.*, constant
констатировать, *v.*, state, certify, ascertain
констатироваться, *v.*, be stated
конституанта, *f.*, constituent, component
конституэнт, *m.*, constituent
конструирование, *n.*, construction, formation
конструировать, *v.*, construct, form
конструируемый, *adj.*, constructible
конструктивный, *adj.*, constructive
конструктор, *m.*, designer
конструкция, *f.*, construction, design
контакт, *m.*, contact
контактный, *adj.*, contact, tangent
контекст, *m.*, context
контингенциальный, *adj.*, contingent, contingency
контингенция, *f.*, contingency
континуальный, *adj.*, continual
континуант, *m.*, continuant (determinant)
континуум, *m.*, continuum
континуум-гипотеза, *f.*, continuum hypothesis
конторский, *adj.*, account, office
контравариантный, *adj.*, contravariant
контраградиентный, *adj.*, contragradient
контрагредиент, *m.*, contragredient
контрагредиентный, *adj.*, contragredient
контрадикторный, *adj.*, contradictory
контракомпактный, *adj.*, countercompact, contracompact
контракт, *m.*, contract, agreement
контрактированный, *adj.*, contracted, compressed, abridged
контрактованный, *adj.*, according to contract, contracted
контрапозиция, *f.*, contraposition, opposite viewpoint
контрарный, *adj.*, contrary
контраст, *m.*, contrast
контрастность, *f.*, visibility, contrast; **контрастность полос,** visibility of fringes; **контрастность изображения,** image contrast, image visibility
контрастный, *adj.*, contrasting
контролер, *m.*, controller, inspector
контролированный, *adj.*, inspected, controlled
контролировать, *v.*, inspect, control, check
контролируемый, *adj.*, check, control, controlled
контроллер, *m.*, controller, checker
контроль, *m.*, control, check; **контроль качества,** quality control; **профилактический контроль,** checking, checking procedure; **контроль "в две руки"**, duplication check
контрольный, *adj.*, check, control, regulating; **контрольный разряд,** check bit
контрпример, *m.*, counterexample
контур, *m.*, contour, boundary, outline, loop, circuit
контурный, *adj.*, contour, boundary
конус, *m.*, cone
конусность, *f.*, conicity, angle of taper
конусный, *adj.*, conic, conical
конусообразный, *adj.*, cone-shaped, conical
конференция, *f.*, conference
конфигурационный, *adj.*, configuration
конфигурация, *f.*, configuration, pattern
конфинальность, *f.*, co-finality
конфинальный, *adj.*, co-final
конфликт, *m.*, conflict
конфлюэнтный, *adj.*, confluent, confluence; **конфлюэнтный анализ,** confluence analysis

конфокальный, *adj.*, confocal
конформно, *adv.*, conformally; **конформно эквивалентный,** *adj.*, conformally equivalent
конформно-инвариантный, *adj.*, conformally invariant
конформно-плоский, *adj.*, conformally flat
конформно-эйнштейновый, *adj.*, conformally Einsteinian
конформность, *f.*, conformality
конформный, *adj.*, conformal; **конформное отображение,** conformal mapping; **конформный радиус,** mapping radius
конхоида, *f.*, conchoid
конхоидальный, *adj.*, conchoidal
концевой, *adj.*, final, terminal, end
концентрат, *m.*, concentrate
концентрация, *f.*, concentration
концентрирующий, *adj.*, concentrating
концентрически, *adv.*, concentrically
концентрический, *adj.*, concentric
концентричность, *f.*, concentricity
концептуальный, *adj.*, conceptual
концепция, *f.*, conception, idea, concept
кончать, *v.*, finish, end
кончаться, *v.*, end, end in, result
кончая, *adv. part.*, ending, terminating; *prep.*, until, ending with
конъюнктивный, *adj.*, conjunctive
конъюнкция, *f.*, conjunction
кообраз, *m.*, co-image
кооперативный, *adj.*, cooperative
кооперирование, *n.*, cooperation; **игра с двумя участниками и возможностью их кооперирования,** two-person cooperative game
координата, *f.*, coordinate
координатизация, *f.*, coordinatization
координатный, *adj.*, coordinate
координировать, *v.*, introduce coordinates, coordinate
копараллелизм, *m.*, coparallelism
копараллельный, *adj.*, coparallel
копировать, *v.*, copy, imitate
копия, *f.*, copy, replica, counterpart
корадикал, *m.*, co-radical
коразмерность, *f.*, co-dimension
корасслоение, *n.*, co-fibering, co-fibration
корень, *m.*, root, radical; **знак корня,** radical sign; **квадратный корень,** square root; **кубический корень,** cube root; **корень уравнения,** solution of an equation, root of an equation
кориолисовой, *adj.*, Coriolis; **кориолисовы силы,** Coriolis forces
корневой, *adj.*, pertaining to root, root, radical; **корневой годограф,** " Root locus " curve
коробка, *f.*, box
коробление, *n.*, warping, buckling
коромысло, *n.*, balance, beam, yoke
короткий, *adj.*, short; **короткая волна,** short wave; **короткое замыкание,** short circuit
коротко, *adv.*, briefly; *prefix*, short-
короткодействующий, *adj.*, short-range
короткоживущий, *adj.*, short-lived
короткопериодный, *adj.*, short-period, short-term
короче, *adv.*, briefly, more concisely
короче (*comp.* of **короткий),** shorter
корпоидальный, *adj.*, field, field-like
корпус, *m.*, field, body
корпускулярный, *adj.*, corpuscular
корректирование, *n.*, correcting, correction
корректировать, *v.*, correct
корректирующий, *adj.*, correcting
корректно, *adv.*, correctly, reasonably
корректность, *f.*, correctness, reasonableness
корректный, *adj.*, correct, proper, reasonable
коррекция, *f.*, correction
коррелированный, *adj.*, correlated; **коррелированные величины,** correlated variables
коррелограмма, *f.*, correlation table, correlogram
коррелятивность, *f.*, correlativity

коррелятивный, *adj.*, correlative
коррелятор, *m.*, correlator
корреляционный, *adj.*, correlative, correlation, cross-correlation; **корреляционное отношение,** correlation ratio
корреляция, *f.*, correlation; **порядковая корреляция,** rank correlation
корреспондирующий, *adj.*, corresponding
корригированный, *adj.*, corrected
кортеж, *m.*, procession, train, suite
коса, *f.*, braid, scythe
косвенно, *adv.*, indirectly
косвенный, *adj.*, indirect; **косвенное доказательство,** indirect proof
косвязность, *f.*, co-connectedness
косвязный, *adj.*, co-connected
косеканс, *m.*, cosecant
косеть, *f.*, co-net
косинус, *m.*, cosine
косинусный, *adj.*, cosine
косинусоида, *f.*, cosine curve
косинусоидальный, *adj.*, cosine
кослой, *m.*, co-fibre
космический, *adj.*, cosmic; **космические лучи,** cosmic rays
космогония, *f.*, cosmogony
космография, *f.*, cosmography
космологический, *adj.*, cosmological
космология, *f.*, cosmology
космос, *m.*, cosmos
коснуться (cf. **касаться**), touch, concern, relate, be tangent to
косой, *adj.*, oblique, slanting, skew; **косой угол,** oblique angle; **косое произведение,** fiber bundle; **косая производная,** directional derivative; **косая линейчатая поверхность,** non-developable ruled surface, scroll
кособоммутативный, *adj.*, skew commutative, anticommutative
кососимметрический, *adj.*, skew-symmetric
кососимметричность, *f.*, skew-symmetry, antisymmetry
кососимметричный, *adj.*, skew-symmetric, antisymmetric, alternating
косоугольный, *adj.*, scalene, oblique-angled, oblique
коспектр, *m.*, co-spectrum, co-net
косточка, *f.*, stone, counter, abacus ball, bead
кость, *f.*, bone; **игральная кость,** die
котангенс, *m.*, cotangent
котерминология, *f.*, coterminology
который, *pron.*, which, who, that
кофактор, *m.*, cofactor
кофинально, *adv.*, cofinally
кофинальный, *adj.*, cofinal
коцепь, *f.*, cochain
коцикл, *m.*, cocycle
коциклоид, *m.*, cocycloid
коэффициент, *m.*, coefficient; **коэффициент зацепления,** linking number, torsion coefficient; **коэффициент инцидентности,** incidence number; **коэффициент корреляции,** coefficient of correlation; **коэффициент усиления,** amplification factor; **коэффициент асимметрии,** coefficient of skewness; **коэффициент доверия,** confidence coefficient; **коэффициент изменчивости,** coefficient of variation; **полный коэффициент корреляции,** total coefficient of correlation; **сводный коэффициент корреляции,** multiple coefficient of correlation; **частный коэффициент корреляции,** partial coefficient of correlation; **коэффициент перехода,** conversion factor; **коэффициент полезного действия,** efficiency; **коэффициент разброса,** scatter coefficient; **коэффициент расхождения,** coefficient of divergence; **коэффициент регрессии,** coefficient of regression; **коэффициент эксцесса,** coefficient of excess; **коэффициент порядковой корреляции,** rank correlation coefficient; **коэффициент корреляции упорядоченности,** rank correlation coefficient
коядро, *n.*, co-kernel

краевой, *adj.*, boundary, edge, border; **краевая задача,** boundary value problem; **краевое значение,** boundary value

край, *m.*, edge, border, rim, extremity

крайне, *adv.*, highly, extremely, very

крайний, *adj.*, extreme, last; **по крайней мере,** at least, at any rate

крамерский, *adj.*, Cramér, pertaining to Cramér

красивый, *adj.*, beautiful

краска, *f.*, color; **задача четырех красок,** four-color problem

красный, *adj.*, red

краткий, *adj.*, brief, short

кратко, *adv.*, briefly

кратковременный, *adj.*, short-term, transitory, transient

краткосрочный, *adj.*, short-range, short term

краткость, *f.*, brevity, conciseness

кратно, *adv.*, multiply

кратное, *n.*, multiple; **общее наименьшее кратное,** least common multiple

кратно-круговой, *adj.*, multi-circular

кратно-кругообразный, *adj.*, of multi-circular type, multi-circular

кратно-периодический, *adj.*, multi-periodic

кратно-совершенный, *adj.*, multiperfect; **кратно-совершенное число,** multiperfect number

кратность, *f.*, multiplicity; **бесконечно большая кратность,** infinite multiplicity; **считается столько раз, какова его кратность,** is counted according to its multiplicity

кратноупорядоченный, *adj.*, multiply ordered

кратный, *adj.*, multiple, divisible; **кратное число,** multiple; **число кратное** 4, a number divisible by 4; **кратная последовательность,** multi-sequence

кратчайший (cf. **короткий**), *adj.*, shortest

крейцкопф, *m.*, cross-head

кремниевый, *adj.*, silicon; **кремниевый полупроводниковый триод,** silicon transistor

крен, *m.*, bank, list, heel; **угол крена,** angle of bank

крениться, *v.*, list, heel, bank

крепкий, *adj.*, firm, strong

крепление, *n.*, strengthening, bracing, fastening

крепость, *f.*, stability, strength

крест, *m.*, cross

крест-накрест, *adv.*, cross-wise, criss-cross

крестовый, *adj.*, cross

крестообразный, *adj.*, crosslike, cross-shaped

кривая, *f.*, curve; **кривая погони,** curve of pursuit; **кривая плотности** frequency curve; **кривая равных вероятностей,** equiprobability curve; **кривая роста,** curve of growth

кривизна, *f.*, curvature; **кривизна профиля,** camber

кривой, *adj.*, curved; **кривая линия,** curve, curved line

криволинейный, *adj.*, curvilinear; **криволинейный интеграл,** line integral

кривошип, *m.*, crank

криптанализ, *m.*, cryptanalysis

криптоанализ, *m.*, cryptanalysis

криптограмма, *f.*, cryptogram

кристалл, *m.*, crystal

кристаллический, *adj.*, crystalline, crystal; **кристаллический триод,** transistor

кристаллографический, *adj.*, crystallographic

кристаллография, *f.*, crystallography

кристаллооптика, *f.*, crystal optics

критерий, *m.*, criterion, test, testing; **критерий долговечности,** longevity testing; **критерий знаков,** sign test; **критерий значимости,** significance test; **критерий согласия,** goodness-of-fit test; **критерий устойчивости,** stability criterion; **наиболее мощный**

критерий, most powerful test; **равномерно наиболее мощный критерий,** uniformly most powerful test; **несмещенный критерий,** unbiased test; **критерий однородности,** test of homogeneity; **критерий смещения,** test of location; **критерий нормальности,** test of normality; **наилучший несмещенный критерий,** best unbiased test; **последовательный критерий отношений вероятностей,** sequential probability ratio test
критический, *adj.*, critical
кроить, *v.*, cut, cut out
кроме, *prep.*, except, besides; **кроме того,** besides, in addition
кромка, *f.*, edge, border, rim
крона, *f.*, crown, top
кронгласс, *m.*, crown glass
кронекеровский, *adj.*, Kronecker; **кронекеровское умножение,** Kronecker-product
кронекеровый, *adj.*, Kronecker
кронштейн, *m.*, bracket, holder, stand, support
кропотливый, *adj.*, laborious, tedious
крошечный, *adj.*, small, minute
круг, *m.*, circle, disk; **на круг,** on the average
круглосуточно, *adv.*, around the clock
круглосуточный, *adj.*, twenty-four-hour, around-the-clock
круглый, *adj.*, round, circular
круговой, *adj.*, circular, cyclic, circulatory, cyclotomic; **круговой полином,** cyclotomic polynomial; **круговой перенос,** end-around carry; **круговой сдвиг,** cyclic shift
кругом, *prep.*, around
кругообразность, *f.*, circularity
кругообразный, *adj.*, circular
кружок, *m.*, circle, society; **математический кружок,** mathematical circle for young students
кружковой, *adj.*, pertaining to **кружок**
кружковый, *adj.*, from **кружок**
крупинка, *f.*, grain, granule
крупномасштабный, *adj.*, large-scale
крупносортный, *adj.*, large, large size, coarse
крупный, *adj.*, large, large scale, coarse
крутизна, *f.*, steepness
крутильный, *adj.*, rotating, twisting, torsional
крутить, *v.*, twist, turn
крутой, *adj.*, steep; sudden, abrupt
крутящий, *adj.*, turning, twisting; **крутящий момент,** *m.*, torque
круче (крутой), *comp.*, steeper
кручение, *n.*, torsion, twisting; **группа без кручения,** torsion-free group; **группа с кручением,** torsion group
крученный, *adj.*, twisted
крученый, *adj.*, twisted
крыло, *n.*, wing, pinion, airfoil
крюк, *m.*, hook
кстати, *adv.*, apropos, incidentally
кто, *pron.*, who
кто-либо, *pron.*, someone, anyone
кто-нибудь, *pron.*, someone, anyone
куб, *m.*, cube
кубатура, *f.*, cubic content, volume
кубатурный, *adj.*, cubic
кубический, *adj.*, cubic
кубичный, *adj.*, cubic, cube; **кубичный корень,** cube root
кубовидный, *adj.*, cubical, cube-shaped
куда, *adv.*, where, where to, whither
кузов, *m.*, basket, body, hood
кулачковый, *adj.*, cam; **кулачковый вал,** camshaft
кулон, *m.*, Coulomb
кулоновский, *adj.*, pertaining to Coulomb, Coulomb
кульминационный, *adj.*, culminating; **кульминационный пункт,** culmination, apex
кульминация, *f.*, culmination, transit; **нижняя кульминация,** lower transit; **верхняя кульминация,** upper transit
кумулянт, *m.*, cumulant, accumulator, accumulant

кумулянтный, *adj.*, cumulant, accumulant, accumulator
кумулятивный, *adj.*, cumulative
курс, *m.*, course, policy, rate of exchange (of currency); **валютный курс,** exchange rate
курсант, *m.*, student
курсив, *m.*, italics; **печатать курсивом,** *v.*, print in italics, italicize
курсовой, *adj.*, course
курьез, *m.*, curiosity, oddity; **для курьеза,** for the interest of the thing
курьезность, *f.*, curiosity
курьезный, *adj.*, curious, strange, odd
кусок, *m.*, piece, bit
кусочно, *adv.*, piece-wise; sectionally
кусочно-гармонический, *adj.*, piecewise harmonic
кусочно-гладкий, *adj.*, piecewise smooth, sectionally smooth
кусочно-голоморфный, *adj.*, piecewise holomorphic, sectionally holomorphic
кусочно-квадратичный, *adj.*, piecewise quadratic
кусочно-конформный, *adj.*, piecewise conformal
кусочно-линейный, *adj.*, piecewise linear
кусочно-непрерывный, *adj.*, sectionally continuous, piecewise continuous
кусочно-постоянный, *adj.*, piecewise constant; **кусочно-постоянная функция,** step function
куча, *f.*, heap, pile; **выбор из кучи,** bulk sampling
Кэли, Cayley; **числа Кэли,** Cayley numbers
кюри, *m.*, curie (unit)

Л

лабиринт, *m.*, maze, labyrinth
лаборатория, *f.*, laboratory
лабораторный, *adj.*, laboratory
лава, *f.*, lava, clinker
лавина, *f.*, avalanche, snow slide; **электронно-фотонная лавина,** electro-photonic avalanche
лавинный, *adj.*, avalanche; **лавинная ионизация,** avalanche ionization
лавинообразный, *adj.*, avalanche, in the form of an avalanche
лагранжевый, *adj.*, Lagrangian, Lagrange
лагранжиан, *m.*, Lagrangian
ладья, *f.*, boat, castle, rook
лаконизм, *m.*, terseness, conciseness
лаконично, *adv.*, laconically, concisely
лаконичный, *adj.*, laconic, terse, concise
лакуна, *f.*, lacuna, void, gap; **теорема о лакунах,** gap theorem
лакунарность, *f.*, lacunarity
лакунарный, *adj.*, lacunary, gap; **лакунарный ряд,** gap series
лямбда, *f.*, lambda; **лямбда-определимость,** λ-definability
ламинарный, *adj.*, laminar
ламинировать, *v.*, laminate, press into sheets
лампа, *f.*, tube, lamp; **лампа-вентиль с тремя управляющими сетками,** triple-control-grid gate tube
лапласиан, *m.*, Laplacian
лапласовский, *adj.*, Laplacian, Laplace
латентный, *adj.*, latent; **латентная теплота,** latent heat
латинский, *adj.*, Latin; **латинский квартал,** Latin square
латунный, *adj.*, brass
лауреат, *m.*, laureate
лебеговый, *adj.*, Lebesgue; **лебегова мера,** Lebesgue measure
левоидеал, *m.*, left ideal
левоидеальный, *adj.*, left-ideal
левоинвариантный, *adj.*, left-invariant
левооднородный, *adj.*, left-homogeneous

леворазрешимый, *adj.*, left-solvable
левосторонний, *adj.*, left-side, left; **левосторонний смежный класс,** left co-set
левоуничтожающий, *adj.*, left-annihilating
левоупорядоченный, *adj.*, left-ordered
левый, *adj.*, left, left-hand; **левый идеал,** left ideal; **левая сторона,** left-hand side
легализировать, *v.*, legalize
легально, *adv.*, legally
легальность, *f.*, legality
легальный, *adj.*, legal
легкий, *adj.*, easy, light; **легко,** it is easy
легко, *adv.*, easily
легкость, *f.*, ease, readiness; **с большой легкостью,** very easily
лед, *m.*, ice
ледяной, *adj.*, icy, ice, glacial
лежать, *v.*, lie, be situated
лежащий, *adj.*, lying, horizontal, situated
лексика, *f.*, vocabulary
лексикографический, *adj.*, lexicographic, dictionary
лексикография, *f.*, lexicography
лексикон, *m.*, lexicon, dictionary
лекция, *f.*, lecture
лемма, *f.*, lemma
лемниската, *f.*, lemniscate
лента, *f.*, band, tape; **блок управления лентой,** tape control unit; **подача ленты,** tape feed; **протяжка ленты,** tape handling; **опознавание ленты,** tape identification; **останов ленты,** tape stopping; **устройство записи на ленту,** tape inscriber; **устройство для считывания с ленты,** tape reader; **перфоратор с вводом на ленте,** tape reading punch; **катушка с лентой,** tape reel; **повторная протяжка ленты,** tape rerun; **главная лента,** master tape; **система для обработки данных (записанных) на ленте,** tape data precessing system; **числовая лента,** data tape, number tape
лента-перемычка, *f.*, bridge band
лентопротяжный, *adj.*, tape-stretching, tape-drive, tape-feeding, tape-handling; **лентопротяжный механизм,** tape-drive mechanism, tape feed, tape transport, tape handler; **лентопротяжное устройство,** tape handler
ленточный, *adj.*, tape; **ленточный перфоратор,** tape perforator
лепестковый, *adj.*, leaved, leafed; **четырехлепестковая роза,** four-leaved rose
лет (from **лета**), years, age; **ему 50 лет,** he is 50 years old
летний, *adj.*, summer; **летнее солнцестояние,** summer solstice
лето, *n.*, summer; **лета,** *pl.*, years
летопись, *f.*, chronicle; *pl.*, annals
летучий, *adj.*, flying
лживость, *f.*, falsity
ли, *conj.*, whether, if; *untranslated particle indicating interrogative*
либо, *conj.*, or; **либо . . . или,** either . . . or; **либо . . . либо,** either . . . or
либрация, *f.*, libration
ливень, *m.*, shower; **каскадные ливни,** cascade showers
ливневый, *adj.*, shower; **ливневая функция в максимуме,** shower maximum
лидирующий, *adj.*, leading
лиевый, *adj.*, Lie, pertaining to Lie; **лиевая группа,** Lie group; **лиева группа,** Lie group
ликвидация, *f.*, removal, liquidation, elimination
ликвидироваться, *v.*, be eliminated, be removed
лимб, *m.*, limb
лимит, *m.*, limit
лимитировать, *v.*, limit
лимитирующий, *adj.*, limiting
лингвистика, *f.*, linguistics
лингвистический, *adj.*, linguistic
линеал, *m.*, line-element, lineal, linear manifold
линеаризация, *f.*, linearization

линеаризированный, *adj.*, linearized, linear

линеаризоваться, *v.*, be linearized

линейка, *f.*, ruler, straightedge; **логарифмическая линейка,** slide rule

линейно, *adv.*, linearly, linear, arcwise; **линейно независимый,** linearly independent; **линейно упорядоченный,** linearly ordered; **линейно связный**, arcwise connected

линейность, *f.*, linearity

линейный, *adj.*, linear, arcwise, one-dimensional, line, contour; **линейная зависимость,** linear dependence; **линейное семейство,** linear system, linear family; **линейная связность,** arcwise connectedness; **линейный интеграл,** line integral, contour integral; **линейное планирование,** linear programming; **линейное программирование,** linear programming

линейчато-геометрический, *adj.*, line-geometric

линейчатый, *adj.*, ruled, line, lined; **линейчатая поверхность,** ruled surface; **линейчатые координаты,** line coordinates

линза, *f.*, lens; **пространство линзы,** lens space

линзовый, *adj.*, lens

линзообразный, *adj.*, lenticular, lens-shaped

линиаризация, *f.*, linearization

линия, *f.*, line, curve; **линия временного типа,** time line; **линия тока,** streamline; **линия уровня,** level line, level curve

лист, *m.*, sheet, leaf; **лист мёбиуса,** Möbius band; **декартов лист,** folium of Descartes

-листный, *adj. suffix*, -sheeted; ***n*-листный,** *adj.*, *n*-sheeted

литература, *f.*, literature

литий, *m.*, lithium

литографированный, *adj.*, lithographed

литр, *m.*, liter

литцендрат, *m.*, litzendraht wire; r-f. cable

лицо, *n.*, face, person

лично, *adv.*, personally

личной, *adj.*, face

личность, *f.*, person, individuality, personality

личный, *adj.*, personal, individual

лишать, *v.*, deprive

лишенный, *adj.*, devoid of, deprived; **лишен основания,** baseless, groundless

лишний, *adj.*, superfluous, unnecessary

лишь, *adv.*, only; *conj.*, as soon as; **лишь только,** as soon as; **лишь тогда, когда,** if and only if

лобовой, *adj.*, frontal; **лобовое сопротивление,** drag, head resistance; **лобовое столкновение,** head-on collision

ловушка, *f.*, trap; **электронная ловушка,** electron trap; **дырочная ловушка,** hole trap

логарифм, *m.*, logarithm

логарифметика, *f.*, logarithmetics

логарифмирование, *n.*, taking the logarithm

логарифмировать, *v.*, take the logarithm; **логарифмировать обе части равенства (1),** take the logarithm of both sides of (1)

логарифмический, *adj.*, logarithmic; **логарифмическая линейка,** slide rule

логик, *m.*, logician

логика, *f.*, logic; **математическая логика,** mathematical logic

логистика, *f.*, logistics

логистический, *adj.*, pertaining to logistics, logistic

логический, *adj.*, logical, consequent, logistic; **логический сдвиг,** cyclic shift

логичный, *adj.*, logical, logistic

логнормальный, *adj.*, logarithmically normal

ложноклассический, *adj.*, pseudo-classical
ложность, *f.*, falsity
ложный, *adj.*, false; **ложный вывод,** false conclusion; **ложное срабатывание,** malfunctioning; **ложный сигнал,** spurious signal
ложь, *f.*, falsity, falsehood
локализация, *f.*, localization
локализированный, *adj.*, localized, local
локализировать, *v.*, localize
локализовать, *v.*, localize
локализуемый, *adj.*, local, localized
локалитет, *m.*, locality, spot
локально, *adv.*, locally
локально-аналитический, *adj.*, locally analytic
локально-бикомпактный, *adj.*, locally bicompact
локально-выпуклый, *adj.*, locally convex
локально-гомеоморфный, *adj.*, locally homeomorphic
локально-евклидовой, *adj.*, locally Euclidean
локально-компактный, *adj.*, locally compact
локально-нильпотентный, *adj.*, locally nilpotent
локальный, *adj.*, local
локон, *m.*, curl, ringlet; **локон Аньези,** witch of Agnesi
локсодрома, *f.*, loxodrome, rhumb (line)
локсодромический, *adj.*, loxodromic
локсодромия, *f.*, loxodromic curve, loxodrome
ломаная, *f.*, broken line, polygonal line, polygon
ломанный, *adj.*, broken; **ломанная линия,** polygonal path, open polygon
ломаный, *adj.*, broken; **ломаная линия,** broken line
ломать, *v.*, break
лопасть, *f.*, blade, fan, vane
лопатка, *f.*, blade; **во все лопатки,** at full speed
лоран, *m.*, Laurent; **ряд лорана,** Laurent series
лошадиный, *adj.*, horse; **лошадиная сила,** horse power
луна, *f.*, moon
лунно-солнечный, *adj.*, lunisolar
лунный, *adj.*, lunar
лунообразный, *adj.*, crescent-shaped
луночка, *f.*, crescent, lune
лупа, *f.*, magnifier, magnifying glass, loop; **алгебра лупы,** loop algebra
луч, *m.*, ray, beam; **испускать лучи,** *v.*, radiate
лучевой, *adj.*, pertaining to ray, ray, radial
лучеиспускаемость, *f.*, radiativity, emissivity
лучеиспускание, *n.*, radiation, emission
лучепреломление, *n.*, refraction
лучистый, *adj.*, pertaining to radiation, radiant, radiating; **лучистый перенос,** radiation transfer; **лучистая энергия,** radiant energy
лучше, *adj.*, better
лучший, *adj.*, better, best; **возможно лучший,** best possible
любитель, *m.*, amateur
любой, *adj.*, any, arbitrary
любопытный, *adj.*, curious, inquisitive
любопытство, *n.*, curiosity
люминесцентный, *adj.*, luminescent
люминесценция, *f.*, luminescence

M

магический, *adj.*, magic; **магические квадраты,** magic squares
магнетизм, *m.*, magnetism
магнетический, *adj.*, magnetic
магнетон, *m.*, magneton
магний, *m.*, magnesium
магнит, *m.*, magnet
магнитный, *adj.*, magnetic; **магнитное притяжение,** magnetic attraction; **магнитное поле,** magnetic field; **магнитный поток,** flux; **магнитный барабан,** drum, magnetic drum
магнитогидродинамика, *f.*, magneto-hydrodynamics
магнитокалорический, *adj.*, magneto-caloric
магнитооптика, *f.*, magneto-optics
магнитостатика, *f.*, magnetostatics
магнитостатический, *adj.*, magneto-static
магнитоэлектрический, *adj.*, magneto-electric, electromagnetic
мажор, *m.*, major
мажоранта, *f.*, majorant; **числовая мажоранта,** numerical majorant
мажорантный, *adj.*, majorizing, majorant
мажорирование, *n.*, majorization
мажорированный, *adj.*, majorized, dominated
мажорировать, *v.*, majorize, dominate
мажорируемый, *adj.*, majorized, dominated, majorizable
мажорирующий, *adj.*, majorizing, dominating, dominant
мажоритарный, *adj.*, majority; **мажоритарная игра,** majority game
мажорный, *adj.*, major
майорант, *m.*, majorant
майорантный, *adj.*, majorant
макет, *m.*, model, dummy
макро-, *prefix*, macro-
макроскопический, *adj.*, macroscopic
макрофизика, *f.*, macrophysics
макрочастица, *f.*, macroscopic particle
максвелл, *m.*, maxwell
максвелловский, *adj.*, Maxwell
максимальность, *f.*, maximality; **условие максимальности,** maximality condition, ascending chain condition
максимальный, *adj.*, maximum, maximal
максимизация, *f.*, maximization
максимизирование, *n.*, maximization
максимизированный, *adj.*, maximized
максимизировать, *v.*, maximize
максимизирующий, *adj.*, maximizing; **максимизирующая последовательность,** maximizing sequence
максимум, *m.*, maximum, peak; **резонансный максимум,** resonance peak
малая, (from **малый**), *f.*, small quantity; **бесконечно малая (величина),** *f.*, infinitesimal
маленький, *adj.*, small, little
мало, *adv.*, little; cf. **малый**
маловажный, *adj.*, insignificant, unimportant
маловероятный, *adj.*, low-probability, improbable, unlikely
малогабаритный, *adj.*, small, small-size
малоизвестный, *adj.*, little known
малоинерционный, *adj.*, low-inertia, quick-response
маломощный, *adj.*, low-power, low-duty
малопонятный, *adj.*, difficult to understand
малоразрядный, *adj.*, low-discharge
малость, *f.*, trifle, smallness
малосущественный, *adj.*, unimportant, not substantial
малый, *adj.*, small; **сколь бы мало ни было,** no matter how small; **в малом,** in the small; **малая скорость,** low speed; **самое малое,** the least; **малый цикл,** word time
мана, *f.*, polygon
маневренность, *f.*, maneuverability
маневрировать, *v.*, maneuver
манипуляция, *f.*, manipulation

манометр, *m.*, manometer, pressure gauge
манометрический, *adj.*, manometric, pressure
мантисса, *f.*, mantissa
маргинальный, *adj.*, marginal; **маргинальная стоимость,** marginal cost; **маргинальная цена,** marginal price
марка, *f.*, brand, sign, mark
маркерный, *adj.*, marker
марковость, *f.*, Markov property, Markov behavior
марковский, *adj.*, Markov
мартингал, *m.*, martingale
мартингал-процесс, *m.*, martingale process
маршрут, *m.*, route, itinerary, course
маскировка, *f.*, masking, camouflage
масса, *f.*, mass, bulk, lot; **молекулярная масса,** molecular mass; **масса покоя,** rest-mass
массивный, *adj.*, massive
массовый, *adj.*, mass
мастерство, *n.*, skill, mastery
масштаб, *m.*, scale, degree, measure; **истинный масштаб времени,** real-time; **работа в истинном масштабе времени,** real-time operation; **вычисления в истинном масштабе времени,** real-time computation, **изменять масштаб,** *v.*, scale, **приводить к масштабу,** *v.*, scale
масштабный, *adj.*, scale, scaled; **масштабный множитель,** scale factor; **масштабный параметр,** scale parameter
математик, *m.*, mathematician
математика, *f.*, mathematics
математический, *adj.*, mathematical
материал, *m.*, material
материалистический, *adj.*, materialistic
материальный, *adj.*, material, pecuniary, financial, mass; **материальная точка,** mass point, single mass point; **материальное тело,** mass
материнский, *adj.*, maternal; **материнский атом,** parent nucleus
матрица, *f.*, matrix, array; **матрица для двух переменных,** two-variable matrix; **матрица из магнитных сердечников,** array of cores
матрица-строка, *f.*, row matrix
матрица-функция, *f.*, matrix-function
матричнозначный, *adj.*, matrix-valued
матрично-степенный, *adj.*, pertaining to powers of matrix
матричный, *adj.*, matrix, matric
маховик, *m.*, flywheel
мачта, *f.*, mast, column, support
машина, *f.*, machine, engine, mechanism; **машина последовательного действия,** series machine; **машина параллельного действия,** parallel machine; **машина общего назначения,** general computer
машинка, *f.*, machine; **пишущая машинка,** typewriter; **печатать на машинке,** *v.*, type
маяк, *m.*, beacon, lighthouse
маятник, *m.*, pendulum
мгновение, *n.*, instant, moment
мгновенно, *adv.*, instantly
мгновенность, *f.*, instantaneity, instantaneousness
мгновенный, *adj.*, instantaneous, momentary; **мгновенное значение,** instantaneous value
мегаэлектронвольт (Мэв), *m.*, million-electron-volt (Mev)
медиана, *f.*, median
медиановый, *adj.*, median
медицинский, *adj.*, medical
медленно, *adv.*, slowly
медленнодействующий, *adj.*, slow, slow-acting
медленность, *f.*, slowness
медленный, *adj.*, slow, sluggish
медлительность, *f.*, sluggishness, tardiness
медлительный, *adj.*, sluggish, slow, tardy
медлить, *v.*, be slow, delay, linger, lag
меднение, *n.*, copper plating
медный, *adj.*, copper
медь, *f.*, copper

меж-, *prefix*, inter-
межатомный, *adj.*, interatomic
межгрупповой, *adj.*, intergroup, intragroup, between group(s)
между, *prep.*, between, among; **между тем как**, meanwhile; **отношение "между"**, relation of betweenness, betweenness relation; **между прочим**, among other things; **между собой**, among themselves
между-, *prefix*, inter-
междублочный, *adj.*, interblock
междузвездный, *adj.*, interstellar
международный, *adj.*, international
междуядерный, *adj.*, internuclear
межклассовый, *adj.*, interclass, intergroup, between class(es)
межконтинентальный, *adj.*, intercontinental
межмолекулярный, *adj.*, intermolecular
межъядерный, *adj.*, internuclear
мезоатом, *m.*, mesonic atom, meson
мезон, *m.*, meson
мезонный, *adj.*, meson
мелко, *adv.*, finely
мелководный, *adj.*, shallow
мелкость, *f.*, fineness, mesh; **мелкость покрытия**, mesh of a covering
мелкий, *adj.*, shallow, fine, small
мембрана, *f.*, membrane; diaphragm, film
мембранный, *adj.*, membrane; **мембранное равновесие**, membrane equilibrium
мемуар, *m.*, memoir; **мемуары**, *pl.*, memoirs
менее, *comp.*, less; **тем не менее**, nevertheless
мензула, *f.*, plane table
меновой, *adj.*, exchange; **меновая стоимость**, exchange value
меньше, *comp.*, smaller, less (than)
меньший, *comp.*, smaller, lesser
менять (поменять), *v.*, vary, change
меняться (поменяться), *v.*, change, vary
меняющийся, *adj.*, changing, varying, alternating
мера, *f.*, measure, degree; **мера независимости**, degree of independence; **чистая мера веса**, absolute estimate of the size; **по мере того**, as; **по мере возможности**, as far as possible; **по меньшей мере**, at least; **по крайней мере**, at least; **по большей мере**, at most; **в значительной мере**, to a considerable extent
мереология, *f.*, mereology, Lesniewski system
меридиан, *m.*, meridian
меридиональный, *adj.*, meridional, meridian
мерить, *v.*, measure
-мерный, *adj. suffix*, -dimensional; ***n*-мерный**, *n*-dimensional
мероморфизм, *m.*, meromorphism
мероморфность, *f.*, property of being meromorphic, meromorphy
мероморфный, *adj.*, meromorphic
мероопределение, *n.*, metric, measure, definition of measure, metrization, mensuration
мероприятие, *n.*, measure, action
мертвый, *adj.*, dead; **мертвый ход**, backlash; **мертвая точка**, dead center, standstill
местный, *adj.*, local
место, *n.*, place, locus, spot; **иметь место**, *v.*, occur, take place; hold; **стоять на месте**, *v.*, stand still; **геометрическое место**, locus; **асимптотическое место**, asymptotic spot; **задача с узким местом**, bottleneck problem
местонахождение, *n.*, occurrence, location, position; **определение местонахождения**, locating
местоположение, *n.*, location
месяц, *m.*, month, moon
месячный, *adj.*, monthly
метабелевый, *adj.*, metabelian; **метабелева группа**, metabelian group
метаболизирующий, *adj.*, metabolizing
метаболизм, *m.*, metabolism
метаболит, *m.*, metabolite

метаболический, *adj.*, metabolic
метагармонический, *adj.*, ultra-harmonic, metaharmonic
метакалорийный, *adj.*, metacaloric; *n*-**метакалорийная функция,** *n*-metacaloric function
металингвистический, *adj.*, metalinguistic
металл, *m.*, metal
металлический, *adj.*, metallic
металлопокрытый, *adj.*, plated, metal coated
металлургический, *adj.*, metallurgical
металлургия, *f.*, metallurgy
металогический, *adj.*, metalogical
метаматематика, *f.*, metamathematics
метаматематический, *adj.*, metamathematical
метаполный, *adj.*, meta-complete
метасистема, *f.*, meta-system
метастабильный, *adj.*, metastable
метательный, *adj.*, throwing, missile; **метательный снаряд,** *m.*, projectile, missile
метатеория, *f.*, metatheory
метафизический, *adj.*, metaphysical
метацентр, *m.*, metacenter
метацентрический, *adj.*, metacentric
метациклический, *adj.*, metacyclic; **метациклическая группа,** metacyclic group
метаязык, *m.*, metalanguage
метеорологический, *adj.*, meteorological
метеорология, *f.*, meteorology
метить, *v.*, aim, mark
метод, *m.*, method; **метод перевала,** saddle point method; **метод проб,** cut-and-try method
методика, *f.*, methods, procedures
методический, *adj.*, methodical, systematic; **методическая погрешность,** systematic error
методичный, *adj.*, methodical, systematic
методологический, *adj.*, methodological
методология, *f.*, methodology
метр, *m.*, meter
метризатор, *m.*, valuation, metrizer
метризационный, *adj.*, metrized, valuation; **метризационное кольцо,** valuation ring
метризация, *f.*, metrization, valuation
метризование, *n.*, metrization
метризованный, *adj.*, metrized, with metric, with a valuation; **метризованное поле,** field with a valuation
метризовать, *v.*, metrize
метризуемость, *f.*, metrizability
метризуемый, *adj.*, metrizable
метрика, *f.*, metric, distance function, valuation
метрически, *adv.*, metrically; **метрически плотный,** *adj.*, metrically dense
метрический, *adj.*, metric
метрически-чебышевский, *adj.*, metrically Chebysheff
метроном, *m.*, metronome
механизация, *f.*, mechanization
механизированный, *adj.*, mechanized
механизм, *m.*, mechanism
механика, *f.*, mechanics
механический, *adj.*, mechanical
меченый, *adj.*, marked, labelled; **меченые атомы,** radioactive tracers
мешать, *v.*, interfere with, hinder, mix
мешающий, *adj.*, interfering, interference, nuisance; **мешающий параметр,** nuisance parameter
миграция, *f.*, migration
микро-, *prefix*, micro-
микробиология, *f.*, microbiology
микроволна, *f.*, microwave
микроволновый, *adj.*, microwave
микрокосм, *m.*, microcosm
микрокосмический, *adj.*, microcosmic
микромир, *m.*, microcosmos, microworld
микрон, *m.*, micron
микроорганизм, *m.*, microorganism
микросекунда, *f.*, microsecond
микросистема, *f.*, microsystem
микроскопический, *adj.*, microscopic
микроскопия, *f.*, microscopy
микрофизика, *f.*, microphysics
микрофон, *m.*, microphone
микрочастица, *f.*, microparticle

миллиампер, *m.*, milliampere
миллиангстрем, *m.*, milliangstrom
миллиард, *m.*, milliard, billion (10^9)
миллибар, *m.*, millibar
милливольт, *m.*, millivolt
миллиграмм, *m.*, milligram
милликюри, *m.*, millicurie
миллиметр, *m.*, millimeter
миллимикрон, *m.*, millimicron
миллирентген, *m.*, milliroentgen
мимо, *adv.*, *prep.*, past, by
мимоходом, *adv.*, in passing, incidentally
миниатюризация, *f.*, miniaturization
миниатюрный, *adj.*, miniature
минимакс, *m.*, minimax
минимаксность, *f.*, minimaxity, minimax property
минимаксный, *adj.*, minimax
минимальность, *f.*, minimality; **условие минимальности,** minimality condition, descending chain condition
минимальный, *adj.*, minimum, minimal
минимизация, *f.*, minimization
минимизировать, *v.*, minimize
минимизирующий, *adj.*, minimizing; **минимизирующая последовательность,** minimizing sequence
минимировать, *v.*, minimize
минимум, *m.*, minimum
миновать, *v.*, pass, be over, omit, by-pass
минор, *m.*, minor
миноранта, *f.*, minorant
минута, *f.*, minute
минуть, *v.*, pass, by-pass, omit
минуя, *adv. part.*, omitting, by-passing, if we omit
мир, *m.*, world, universe, peace
мировой, *adj.*, world; **мировая точка,** world point
мироздание, *n.*, universe
мишенный, *adj.*, target
мишень, *f.*, target
мк-, *abbrev. prefix* **(микро-),** micro-
мкбар, *abbrev.*, microbar
мксек, *abbrev.*, microsecond
младенчество, *n.*, infancy
младший, *adj.*, lowest, lower, minor, youngest, junior; **младший член многочлена,** lowest term of a polynomial
мне, (cf. **я**) *pron.*, for me, to me; **мне пришлось,** I had to
мнемоника, *f.*, mnemonics
мнемонический, *adj.*, mnemonic; **мнемоническая схема,** mnemonic, mnemonic circuit, memory circuit
мнение, *n.*, opinion, judgement
мнимый, *adj.*, imaginary; **мнимая ось,** imaginary axis, conjugate axis (of hyperbola)
многие, *adj.* (*pl.*), many, a great many
много, *adv.*, much, plenty, many; *prefix*, multi-, poly-, many-
многоадресный, *adj.*, multi-address
многоатомный, *adj.*, polyatomic
многовалентный, *adj.*, multivalent
многовершинный, *adj.*, multimodal, multivertex, multipeak
многогранник, *m.*, polyhedron, polytope
многогранный, *adj.*, polyhedral
многозначность, *f.*, multivalence, multiformity; **группа многозначности,** monodromy group
многозначный, *adj.*, many-valued, multiform
многокомпонентный, *adj.*, multicomponent
многоконтактный, *adj.*, multicontact
многоконтурный, *adj.*, multiple loop, multicircuit
многокорневой, *adj.*, multi-rooted, with multiple roots, with many roots
многократно, *adv.*, repeatedly, multiply
многократность, *f.*, recurrence, repetition, multiplicity
многократный, *adj.*, multiple, repeated
многолистный, *adj.*, many-sheeted, multivalent, many-to-one
многомерный, *adj.*, many-dimensional, multivariate; **многомерное распределение,** multivariate distribution
многоместный, *adj.*, many-placed, many-place, multiple, polyadic

многонуклеонный, *adj.*, many-nucleon
многообмоточный, *adj.*, multi-wound; **многообмоточное реле,** multi-wound relay
многообразие, *n.*, manifold, variety
многообразный, *adj.*, manifold, multi-form
многоосный, *adj.*, multi-axis, poly-axis
многополюсник, *m.*, multipole, network, multiterminal network
многополюсный, *adj.*, multipole, multi-terminal; **многополюсный переключатель,** multipole switch
многосвязный, *adj.*, multiply connected
многосеточный, *adj.*, multigrid
многосложный, *adj.*, complex, poly-syllabic
многослойный, *adj.*, stratified, multi-layer
многостадийный, *adj.*, multistage
многостепенный, *adj.*, several-stage, multi-level, multi-grade
многосторонний, *adj.*, polygonal, multi-lateral, versatile
многосторонность, *f.*, polygonality, ver-satility
многоступенчатый, *adj.*, multi-stage, multi-step, multiphase
многотактный, *adj.*, multi-stage, mul-tiple
многоточие, *n.*, dots
многоугольник, *m.*, polygon
многоугольный, *adj.*, polygonal
многофазный, *adj.*, multi-phase, poly-phase
многофазовый, *adj.*, multiphase
многоцелевой, *adj.*, multipurpose
многочисленность, *f.*, multiplicity
многочисленный, *adj.*, numerous, multiple
многочлен, *m.*, polynomial
многочленный, *adj.*, polynomial
многошаговый, *adj.*, multistage, multi-step
множественность, *f.*, plurality, multi-plicity
множественный, *adj.*, multiple, multi-variate; **множественный анализ,** multivariate analysis; **множественная корреляция,** multiple cor-relation; **множественная регрессия,** multiple regression
множество, *n.*, set, aggregate, collection; **множество точек,** point set; **множество меры нуль,** null set, set of measure zero; **обратимое множество,** inverse set, pre-image
множество-произведение, *n.*, product set
множество-частное, *n.*, quotient set
множимое, *n.*, multiplicand
множитель, *m.*, factor, multiplier, co-efficient; **разложение на множители,** factorization
множительно-делительный, *adj.*, mul-tiplication-division; **множительно-делительный блок,** multiplication-division unit
множить, *v.*, multiply
моб, *m.*, mob
могут (from **мочь**), they can
могущий, *adj.*, capable
мода, *f.*, fashion, style, mode
модальность, *f.*, modality
модальный, *adj.*, modal
моделирование, *n.*, simulation, analogue
моделировать, *v.*, simulate, model, shape
моделирующий, *adj.*, simulating, ana-logue; **моделирующее устройство (на переменном токе),** (A.C.) ana-logue computer
модель, *f.*, model, pattern
модернизированный, *adj.*, modernized
модификатор, *m.*, modifier, transformer
модификация, *f.*, modification
модифицированный, *adj.*, modified
модифицировать, *v.*, modify
модный, *adj.*, fashionable
модулированный, *adj.*, modulated
модулировать, *v.*, modulate
модуль, *m.*, modulus, absolute value, module; **модуль вычета,** residue class module; **по модулю 2,** modulo 2

модульспектр, *m.*, spectrum modulus, spectral norm
модулярность, *f.*, modularity
модулярный, *adj.*, modular
модуляционный, *adj.*, modulation
модуляция, *f.*, modulation; **частотная модуляция,** frequency modulation
модус, *m.*, mode, modus
можем (from **мочь**), we can
может (from **мочь**), he can, it can, it might; **может быть,** maybe, it is possible, possibly; **может встретиться,** may be encountered, may happen; **может и не быть,** may not be, need not be
можно, *pred.*, it is possible
мозаика, *f.*, tesselation, mosaic
мозаичный, *adj.*, mosaic, tesselation
мозг, *m.*, brain
мой, *pron.*, my, mine
мокрота, *f.*, humidity
молекула, *f.*, molecule
молекулярный, *adj.*, molecular; **молекулярный вес,** molecular weight; **молекулярная сила,** molecular force
молча, *adv.*, tacitly, silently
моль, *f.*, mole, gram-molecule
мольный, *adj.*, molar
молярный, *adj.*, molar; **молярная удельная теплоемкость,** molar specific heat
момент, *m.*, moment, instant; **момент времени,** instant, time; **момент количества движения,** angular momentum, moment of momentum; **вращателный момент,** angular momentum; **момент вращения,** torque; **момент силы,** moment of force, torque; **абсолютный момент,** absolute moment; **групповой момент,** grouped moment, raw moment; **смешанный момент,** product moment, mixed moment; **факториальный момент,** factorial moment; **центральный момент,** central moment; **момент инерции,** moment of inertia; **момент съема,** sampling instant
моментный, *adj.*, moment; **моментная последовательность,** moment sequence
монарный, *adj.*, monic
монета, *f.*, coin
моноалфавитный, *adj.*, mono-alphabetic
моногенность, *f.*, monogeneity
моногенный, *adj.*, monogenic
монография, *f.*, monograph
монодромия, *f.*, monodromy
моноид, *m.*, monoid
моноидальный, *adj.*, monoidal
моноклинический, *adj.*, monocline
моноклинный, *adj.*, monocline
моном, *m.*, monomial
мономиальный, *adj.*, monomial
мономорфизм, *m.*, monomorphism
мономорфный, *adj.*, monomorphic
монополь, *m.*, monopole
монослой, *m.*, monolayer
монотип, *m.*, monotype
монотипный, *adj.*, monotype
монотонно, *adv.*, monotonically, steadily
монотонность, *f.*, monotonicity
монотонный, *adj.*, monotone, monotonic; **монотонная неубывающая функция,** monotone non-decreasing function; **монотонная невозрастающая функция,** monotone non-increasing function
монофокальный, *adj.*, monofocal
монохроматический, *adj.*, monochromatic, simple harmonic; **монохроматическая волна,** simple harmonic wave
монохроматичность, *f.*, monochromaticity
моноэнергетический, *adj.*, monoenergetic, monoenergy
монтаж, *m.*, assembly, mounting, installation
море, *n.*, sea
мореплавание, *n.*, navigation
мореплавательный, *adj.*, nautical, navigational
мореходство, *n.*, navigation
мороз, *m.*, frost; degree of frost

морской, *adj.*, sea
морфема, *f.*, morpheme
мост, *m.*, bridge; **задача семи мостов Калининграда,** problem of the seven bridges of Königsberg
мостик, *m.*, (little) bridge
мостиковый, *adj.*, pertaining to bridge, bridge, paved, covered; **мостиковая схема,** bridge circuit
мостовой, *adj.*, bridge; **мостовое число,** bridging number; **мостовая схема,** bridge circuit
мотивирование, *n.*, motivation, justification
мотивировка, *f.*, motivation, justification
мотор, *m.*, motor, engine
мочь, *f.*, power, might
мочь, *v.*, be able
мощность, *f.*, power, capacity, output, cardinality; **номинальная мощность нагрузки,** capacity; **функция мощности,** power function
мощный, *adj.*, powerful, high capacity
мощь, *f.*, power, might
мсек., *abbrev.* (**миллисекунда,** *f.*), millisecond
М-структура, *f.*, matroid lattice
мужчина, *m.*, man, male
мультивектор, *m.*, multivector
мультивибратор, *m.*, multivibrator
мультигруппа, *f.*, multigroup
мультидифференциальный, *adj.*, multidifferential
мультикогерентный, *adj.*, multicoherent
мультимодальный, *adj.*, multimodal; **мультимодальное распределение,** multimodal distribution
мультиномиальный, *adj.*, multinomial; **мультиномиальное распределение,** multinomial distribution
мультинормальный, *adj.*, multinormal
мультиотношение, *n.*, multirelation
мультиплет, *m.*, multiple, multiplet
мультиплетность, *f.*, multiplicity
мультиплетный, *adj.*, multiplet
мультипликативно-аддитивный, *adj.*, multiplicatively additive
мультипликативность, *f.*, multiplicativity
мультипликативный, *adj.*, multiplicative
мультипликатор, *m.*, multiplicator, multiplier
мультипликационный, *adj.*, multiplication
мультиполь, *m.*, multipole
мультипольный, *adj.*, multipolar, multipole
мультиструктура, *f.*, multi-lattice
мультисубъективный, *adj.*, multisubjective
муфта, *f.*, coupling, clutch, sleeve
мы, *pron.*, we
мыльный, *adj.*, soap, soapy
мысленно, *adv.*, mentally, conceptually, ideally
мысленный, *adj.*, mental, conceptual, ideal
мыслимый, *adj.*, conceivable
мыслительный, *adj.*, cogitative, reflective
мыслить, *v.*, think, conceive
мысль, *f.*, thought, idea; **наводить на мысль,** *v.*, suggest
мышление, *n.*, thinking, thought
мышца, *f.*, muscle
Мэв, *abbrev.* (**мегаэлектронвольт**), million-electron-volt, Mev
мяч, *m.*, ball

Н

на, *prep.*, on, onto, upon, in, to, towards, at; **на самом деле,** in reality, actually
набегающий, *adj.*, filling, accumulating
набивка, *f.*, printing, stuffing, filling
набирать (набрать), *v.*, gather, collect, compose
набла, *f.*, nabla, del
наблюдаемость, *f.*, observability
наблюдаемый, *adj.*, observed, observable
наблюдатель, *m.*, observer
наблюдательный, *adj.*, observational
наблюдать, *v.*, observe
наблюдение, *n.*, observation; **визуальное наблюдение,** visualization; **игра с единичным наблюдением числовой величины,** game with a numerical-valued single observation
наблюденный, *adj.*, observed
набор, *m.*, collection, set
наборный, *adj.*, plugged program, typesetting; **наборная программа,** *f.*, plugged program; **вычислительная машина с наборной программой,** plugged program computer
набранный, *adj.*, collected, gathered, printed
набрасывание, *n.*, sketch, outline
набрасывать (набросать), *v.*, sketch, outline, draft
набрасывать (набросить), *v.*, throw, throw on
набрать (cf. **набирать**), *v.*, collect, accumulate
набросок, *m.*, sketch, draft, outline
наведение, *n.* induction, guidance
наведенный, *adj.*, led, directed, guided
наверно, *adv.*, certainly, probably
наверняка, *adv.*, certainly, for sure
навертывать (навертеть), *v.*, twist, wind (around)
навертывать (навернуть), *v.*, screw, screw on
наверх, *adv.*, up, upward, on top
навести, cf. **наводить**
навешивание, *n.*, weighing; **навешивание кванторов,** quantification
навешивать (навешать), *v.*, weigh, weigh out; **навешивать кванторы,** *v.*, quantify
навиваться, *v.*, coil, reel in
навивающийся, *adj.*, coiling, reeling in
навигационный, *adj.*, navigational
наводить (навести), *v.*, direct, induce, aim (at), cover; **наводить на мысль,** *v.*, suggest
наводящий, *adj.*, directing, leading; **наводящее рассуждение,** heuristic consideration
навсегда, *adv.*, forever
навстречу, *adv.*, towards, from the opposite direction
навык, *m.*, practice, experience, habit
наглядно, *adv.*, obviously, graphically, visually, intuitively
наглядно-геометрический, *adj.*, descriptive-geometric, pertaining to descriptive geometry
наглядность, *f.*, obviousness, clearness, visualization
наглядный, *adj.*, descriptive, obvious, visual, intuitive
нагнетание, *n.*, forcing, supercharging
нагнетатель, *m.*, supercharger
нагнетательный, *adj.*, forcing, supercharging
нагнетать (нагнести), *v.*, force, press, supercharge
нагрев, *m.*, heat, heating
нагревание, *n.*, heating
нагревать, *v.*, heat, warm
нагревающий, *adj.*, heating, warming
нагретый, *adj.*, heated
нагромождать (нагромоздить), *v.*, heap up, pile up
нагружать (нагрузить), *v.*, load, charge
нагруженный, *adj.*, loaded, charged
нагрузка, *f.*, loading, load; **номинальная мощность нагрузки,** capacity

над, *prep.*, over, above, off
надвое, *adv.*, in two
наддиагональный, *adj.*, off-diagonal; **наддиагональные элементы (матрицы),** off-diagonal elements (of a matrix)
надежность, *f.*, reliability, dependability, safety, accuracy
надежный, *adj.*, reliable, dependable, accurate
наделение, *n.*, allotment
наделенный, *adj.*, allotted
наделять (наделить), *v.*, allot, provide
надеяться, *v.*, hope for, rely on
надир, *m.*, nadir, nadir point
надкольцо, *n.*, super-ring, extension ring
надкрылье, *n.*, wing sheath, upper wing
надлежать, *v.*, (*impersonal*); **надлежит,** it is necessary; **это надлежало бы сделать,** this ought to be done
надлежаще, *adv.*, suitably, properly
надлежащий, *adj.*, proper, suitable; **надлежащим образом,** properly
надлом, *m.*, fracture, break
надмножество, *n.*, superset
надмодель, *f.*, hyper-model
наднильпотентный, *adj.*, hyper-nilpotent
надо, (from **нужно**), it is necessary; **надо будет,** it will be necessary
надобность, *f.*, need, necessity; **(то) нет надобности**, it is not necessary
надобный, *adj.*, necessary, requisite
надолго, *adv.*, for a long time
надполе, *n.*, extension field, superfield
надрез, *m.*, cut
надсеть, *f.*, super-net(work)
надстраивать (надстроить), *v.*, raise, build over
надстроенный, *adj.*, built over
надстройка, *f.*, superstructure, suspension; **гомоморфизм надстройки,** suspension homomorphism
надфункция, *f.*, majorant
нажатие, *n.*, pressure
назад, *adv.*, back, backwards; **возвращаясь назад,** turning back, in retrospect; **тому назад,** ago
название, *n.*, name, title
названный, *adj.*, named, titled
назвать (cf. **называть**), *v.*, name, call
наземный, *adj.*, ground, surface
назначение, *n.*, purpose, assignment; **задача о назначениях,** assignment problem
назначенный, *adj.*, fixed, prescribed, set, designated, assigned
назовем (from **называть**), we shall call
называемый, *adj.*, named, so-called
называется (from **называться**), is called
называть (назвать), *v.*, call, name, designate
называться, *v.*, be called, be named
называющий, *adj.*, calling, naming; **называющая форма,** name-form
наи- (*prefix indicating superlative*), most
наиб. н. г., *abbrev.* **(наибольшая нижняя грань),** greatest lower bound
наиболее, *adv.*, most; **наиболее мощный критерий,** most powerful test
наибольший, *adj.*, greatest, largest; **общий наибольший делитель,** greatest common divisor
наивный, *adj.*, naive
наивыгоднейший, *adj.*, optimal, optimum
наивысший, *adj.*, highest
наизусть, *adv.*, by heart, by rote
наилучший, *adj.*, best; **наилучшим образом,** in the best way; **наилучшее приближение,** best approximation
наим. в. г., *abbrev.* **(наименьшая верхняя грань),** least upper bound
наименее, *adv.*, least
наименование, *n.*, name; denomination, designation
наименьший, *adj.*, least, smallest; **общее наименьшее кратное,** least common multiple; **наименьший неотрицательный вычет,** least non-negative residue; **метод наименьших квадратов,** method of least squares

наинизший, *adj.*, lowest
наискорейший, *adj.*, fastest, quickest; **метод наискорейшего спуска,** method of steepest descent
наискось, *adv.*, obliquely
наислабейший, *adj.*, weakest
наихудший, *adj.*, the worst
найдем (from **находить**), we (shall) find
найденный, *adj.*, obtained, found; **найденный элемент,** the element obtained
найдут (from **находить**), they (will) find
найти (cf. **находить**), *v.*, find; **найти себе применение,** have an application
найтись (cf. **находиться**), be, be found
накаливание, *n.*, heating, incandescence
накапливать, *v.*, accumulate
накапливаться, *v.*, be accumulated, accumulate
накапливающий, *adj.*, accumulating; **накапливающий сумматор,** accumulator, adder; **сумматор накапливающего типа,** counter-type adder
накладываемый, *adj.*, imposed on
накладывать, *v.*, superimpose, impose, lay on
накладываться, *v.*, be imposed upon, be laid on, be superimposed on
наклеивать (наклеить), *v.*, paste on
наклон, *m.*, inclination, slope, pitch
наклонение, *n.*, inclination
наклоненный, *adj.*, inclined, tilted
наклонно, *adv.*, obliquely, aslant
наклонность, *f.*, inclination
наклонный, *adj.*, sloping, inclined, slanting, oblique
наконец, *adv.*, at last; finally
наконечник, *m.*, tip, point
накопитель, *m.*, accumulator; **накопитель произведений,** product accumulator; **накопитель сумм,** sum accumulator
накопительный, *adj.*, accumulative, storage
накопление, *n.*, accumulation
накопленный, *adj.*, cumulative, accumulated
накоплять (накопить), *v*, accumulate
накопляющийся, *adj.*, accumulative, cumulative
накрест, *adv.*, cross, crosswise; **накрест лежащий,** *adj.*, opposite; **внутренние накрест лежащие углы,** opposite (alternate) interior angles
накрестлежащий, *adj.*, opposite; **накрестлежащие углы,** alternate angles
накрывать (накрыть), *v.*, cover
накрываться, *v.*, be covered
накрывающий, *adj.*, covering; **накрывающее пространство,** covering space
накрытие, *n.*, covering; **двулистное накрытие,** double covering
налагаемый, *adj.*, imposed
налагать, *v.*, impose, lay on
налагая, *adv. part.*, imposing, laying
налаживать (наладить), *v.*, put right, fix, adjust
налево, *adv.*, to the left
налегать, *v.*, overlap, overlie, lean on; **налегать друг на друга,** overlap
налегающий, *adj.*, leaning, overlying, straining, overlapping
налицо, *adv.*, present; **быть налицо,** be present
наличие, *n.*, presence, availability, existence; **при наличии,** in the presence of, involving
наличный, *adj.*, ready, at hand, cash; **наличные ресурсы,** cash resources
налог, *m.*, tax
наложение, *n.*, covering, superposition; **поверхность наложения,** covering surface; **универсальная поверхность наложения,** universal covering surface
наложенный, *adj.*, superimposed, covered
наложимость, *f.*, superposition, covering, applicability
наложимый, *adj.*, applicable; **наложимые поверхности,** applicable surfaces

наложить, *v.*, impose, superpose
намагничение, *n.*, magnetization
намагниченность, *f.*, magnetization; **остаточная намагниченность,** remanence
намагничивание, *n.*, magnetization
намагничивающий, *adj.*, magnetizing
наматывать, *v.*, wind, wind around
намек, *m.*, hint, allusion
намереваться, *v.*, intend to, be about to
намерен (cf. **намеренный**), intends to, is going to
намерение, *n.*, intention, purpose
намеренный, *adj.*, intentional, deliberate
намётка, *f.*, rough draft, first outline
намечать (наметить), *v.*, plan, project, outline
намечаться, *v.*, be possible, be planned
намеченный, *adj.*, marked, projected, planned, designated
намного, *adv.*, considerably, by far
намотанный, *adj.*, wound, coiled
намотать, *v.*, wind
нанесенный, *adj.*, marked, drawn, plotted
наносить (нанести), *v.*, plot, bring, cause; **наносить деления,** *v.*, graduate; **наносить по точкам,** *v.*, fit
наноситься, *v.*, be plotted, be drawn, be mapped
наоборот, *adv.*, conversely, back to front, vice versa, on the contrary
наперед, *adv.*, beforehand, in advance; **наперед заданный,** *adj.*, preassigned
напечатанный, *adj.*, printed, published
напечатать (cf. **печатать**), *v.*, print, publish
написанный, *adj.*, written
написать (cf. **писать**), write
напоминать (напомнить), *v.*, call to mind, remind
напоминающий, *adj.*, recalling, reminding
напор, *m.*, pressure; **скоростной напор,** pressure head
направить (cf. **направлять**), direct, send
направление, *n.*, direction, path; **производная по направлению,** (directional) derivative in the direction (of); **кривизна в двумерном направлении,** sectional curvature
направленность, *f.*, directedness, direction, trend
направленный, *adj.*, directed; **направленное множество,** directed set
направлять (направить), *v.*, direct, turn, send
направляющая, *f.*, directrix, guide
направляющий, *adj.*, directing, guiding, direction, directional; **направляющий коэффициент,** direction number; **направляющий косинус,** direction cosine; **направляющий конус,** director cone (of a ruled surface); **направляющая линия,** directrix
направо, *adv.*, to the right
напрасно, *adv.*, in vain; it is useless (*pred.*)
напрашиваться, *v.*, suggest itself
например, *parenthet.*, for example
напротив, *adv.*, conversely, on the contrary; *prep.*, opposite
напрягать, *v.*, strain
напряжение, *n.*, stress, strain, voltage, tension; **делитель напряжения,** potentiometer, bleeder; **снятие напряжения,** *n.*, dump; **снимать напряжение,** *v.*, dump; **падение напряжения,** *n.*, voltage drop; **местное напряжение сдвига,** local shear
напряженность, *f.*, strength; **напряженность электрического поля,** electric field strength
напряженный, *adj.*, stress, strain, strained, tense, taut
наравне, *adv.*, on a level with, equally
нарастание, *n.*, increase, growth, rise
наращивать (нарастить), *v.*, accumulate, raise, grow
нарезка, *f.*, thread, rifling
нарисовать, *v.*, draw
народ, *m.*, people, nation
народонаселение, *n.*, population
нарост, *m.*, growth
нарочито, *adv.*, expressly, deliberately, intentionally

нарочитый, *adj.*, deliberate, intentional
нарочно, *adv.*, purposely
наружный, *adj.*, external
наружу, *adv.*, outside
нарушать (нарушить), *v.*, break, violate, infringe, disturb
нарушаться, *v.*, be broken, be violated
нарушая, *adv. part.*, violating, disturbing, breaking; **не нарушая общности,** without losing generality
нарушение, *n.*, violation, infraction
нарушенный, *adj.*, violated, disturbed
нарушиться, *v.*, (cf. **нарушаться**)
наряду с, *prep.*, along with, side by side with, parallel with
население, *n.*, population
насколько, *adv.*, how much, to what extent, as far as; **насколько нам известно,** as far as we know
наследие, *n.*, inheritance, heritage
наследственно, *adv.*, hereditarily, inherently, completely
наследственно-нормальный, *adj.*, completely normal
наследственность, *f.*, heredity
наследственный, *adj.*, hereditary, full, complete; **наследственная нормальность,** complete normality
настаивать (настоять), *v.*, insist, persist, infuse
настолько, *adv.*, so, as much
настольный, *adj.*, table, desk; **настольная книга,** handbook, reference book; **настольная счетная машина,** desk computer
настоящий, *adj.*, present, real; **в настоящее время,** today, at present
наступать, *v.*, occur, appear, ensue
наступление, *n.*, advent, approach, coming; attack, offensive; **наступление события,** occurrence of an event
насчитываться, *v.*, number
насыпать, *v.*, put, fill, pour
насыщение, *n.*, saturation
насыщенность, *f.*, saturation
насыщенный, *adj.*, saturated
наталкиваться (натолкнуться), *v.*, meet, come across, strike
натуральный, *adj.*, natural; **натуральное число,** positive integer, natural number
натягивать, *v.*, stretch, span
натяжение, *n.*, tension, pull; **поверхностное натяжение,** surface tension
натянутый, *adj.*, tight, stretched, strained, spanned
натянуть (cf. **натягивать),** stretch, span
наугад, *adv.*, at random, by guess
наугольник, *m.*, T-square, bevel square
наудачу, *adv.*, at random
наука, *f.*, science, knowledge
научить, *v.*, teach
научиться, *v.*, learn
научно-исследовательский, *adj.*, research, pertaining to research
научный, *adj.*, scientific
находимый, *adj.*, determined, discovered
находить (найти), *v.*, discover, find, come across
находиться, *v.*, be, be found, be situated, belong
находя, *adv. part.*, finding, by finding, if we find
находящийся, *adj.*, situated, being, lying in
нахождение, *n.*, determination, location, discovery, finding
нацеливать (нацелить), *v.*, aim
нацело, *adv.*, evenly, without a remainder, totally
национальный, *adj.*, national; **национальный доход,** national income
начало, *n.*, beginning, origin, principle, basis, source; **начала Евклида,** Euclid's elements; **начало координат,** origin, origin of coordinates
начально, *adv.*, initially, at first; **начально-краевая задача,** initial boundary value problem
начальный, *adj.*, initial, first, elementary; **начальная точка,** starting point, initial point
начатый, *adj.*, started, begun

начать (cf. **начинать**), *v.*, begin
начертательный, *adj.*, descriptive, graphic; **начертательная геометрия,** descriptive geometry
начертить (cf. **чертить**), *v.*, draw, sketch
начерченный, *adj.*, drawn, traced, outlined
начинать (начать), *v.*, begin, start, commence
начинаться, *v.*, begin, start
начинающий, *adj.*, initial, beginning
начиная, *adv. part.*, beginning, starting; **начиная с**, *prep.*, beginning with
начинаясь, *prep.*, beginning (with)
начисляться, *v.*, be calculated, be compounded
начнем (from **начать**), we (shall) begin
наш, *pron.*, our
нащупывать, *v.*, grope, feel about, find by feeling
наэлектризованный, *adj.*, electrified
не, *negative part.*, not; **не (одна) только,** not only; **схема "не",** "not" circuit; *prefix*, un-, non-
неабелевый, *adj.*, non-Abelian
неавтономный, *adj.*, non-autonomous; **неавтономные системы,** non-autonomous systems
неаддитивность, *f.*, non-additivity
неадиабатический, *adj.*, non-adiabatic
неадэкватный, *adj.*, inadequate
неаксиоматизуемый, *adj.*, non-axiomatizable
неалгебраический, *adj.*, non-algebraic
неаналитический, *adj.*, non-analytic
неаналитичность, *f.*, non-analyticity
неапосиндетический, *adj.*, non-aposyndetic
неаристотелевый, *adj.*, non-Aristotelian
неархимедовость, *f.*, non-Archimedean case, non-Archimedean property
неархимедовски, *adv.*, in a non-Archimedean manner; non-Archimedean
неархимедовский, *adj.*, non-Archimedean
неархимедовый, *adj.*, non-Archimedean
неасимптотический, *adj.*, non-asymptotic
неассоциированный, *adj.*, non-associated
неасферичный, *adj.*, non-aspheric
неатомический, *adj.*, non-atomic
неатомичный, *adj.*, non-atomic
небезынтересно, *adv.*, not without interest
небесный, *adj.*, celestial
неблагоприятный, *adj.*, unfavorable, disadvantageous, adverse, unsuccessful; **неблагоприятный исход,** failure
небо, *n.*, sky
небольшой, *adj.*, not large, small
небрежно, *adv.*, carelessly, negligently
небрежный, *adj.*, careless, negligent
неванлинновый, *adj.*, Nevanlinna
невариационный, *adj.*, non-variational
невеликий, *adj.*, not too large, smallish
неверный, *adj.*, incorrect, false
невероятный, *adj.*, unlikely, improbable
невесомость, *f.*, imponderability, weightlessness
невесомый, *adj.*, imponderable, weightless
невещественный, *adj.*, non-real
невзаимодействие, *n.*, non-interaction
невзаимодействующий, *adj.*, non-interacting
невзвешенный, *adj.*, unweighted
невидимый, *adj.*, invisible
невозвратный, *adj.*, transient, irreversible, irrevocable
невозможно (from **невозможный**), it is impossible
невозможность, *f.*, impossibility
невозможный, *adj.*, impossible
невозмутимый, *adj.*, imperturbable
невозмущенный, *adj.*, non-perturbed
невозрастание, *n.*, lack of growth, lack of increase
невозрастающий, *adj.*, non-increasing; **монотонная невозрастающая функция,** monotone non-increasing function
невоспроизводимый, *adj.*, irreproducible
невральный, *adj.*, neural

невыводимый, *adj.*, non-deductive, not derivable
невыписанный, *adj.*, not written out, implicit
невыполнение, *n.*, omission, non-fulfilment
невыполнимость, *f.*, impracticability
невыполнимый, *adj.*, impracticable; **невыполнимое множество,** incompletable set
невыпуклый, *adj.*, non-convex
невыработка, *f.*, non-fulfilment
невыразимый, *adj.*, inexpressible, beyond expression
невыразительность, *f.*, inexpressiveness
невыразительный, *adj.*, inexpressive
невырождающийся, *adj.*, non-degenerate, not degenerating
невырожденность, *f.*, non-degeneracy, non-singularity; **мера невырожденности распределения,** degree of non-singularity of a distribution
невырожденный, *adj.*, non-degenerate, non-singular; **невырожденная матрица,** non-singular matrix
невычет, *m.*, non-residue
невязка, *f.*, discrepancy, disparity, residual
негармонический, *adj.*, non-harmonic; **негармонический ряд фурье,** non-harmonic Fourier series
негатив, *m.*, negative
негатон (негатрон), *m.*, negaton, negatron
негауссовский, *adj.*, non-Gaussian
негильбертовый, *adj.*, non-Hilbert, non-Hilbertian
неглавный, *adj.*, non-principal, subsidiary
негодный, *adj.*, unsuitable, unfit, defective
неголономный, *adj.*, non-holonomic
негомеоморфный, *adj.*, not homeomorphic
негомологичный, *adj.*, non-homologous, not homologous
негомотопный, *adj.*, non-homotopic, not homotopic
негофрированный, *adj.*, non-corrugated
недавний, *adj.*, recent, late
недавно, *adv.*, recently
недалеко, *adv.*, not far
недвусмысленный, *adj.*, unambiguous
недействительный, *adj.*, invalid, void; **делать недействительным,** *v.*, invalidate
неделимый, *adj.*, indivisible
неделя, *f.*, week
недетерминистический, *adj.*, non-deterministic
недиагональный, *adj.*, off-diagonal, non-diagonal; **недиагональный матричный элемент,** off-diagonal matrix element
недискретный, *adj.*, non-discrete
недистрибутивный, *adj.*, non-distributive
недифференцированный, *adj.*, undifferentiated
недифференцируемость, *f.*, non-differentiability
недифференцируемый, *adj.*, non-differentiable
недоброкачественность, *f.*, poor quality
недоброкачественный, *adj.*, low-grade, poor quality
недоказанность, *f.*, failure to prove
недоказанный, *adj.*, unproved, not proved
недоказательный, *adj.*, failing to prove, not serving as a proof
недоказуемость, *f.*, unprovability
недоказуемый, *adj.*, unprovable, indemonstrable
недолговечный, *adj.*, ephemeral, short-lived, transient
недоопределенный, *adj.*, sub-definite
недооценивать (недооценить), *v.*, underestimate, underrate
недопустимый, *adj.*, inadmissible
недоработанный, *adj.*, unfinished, unsolved
недоразумение, *n.*, misunderstanding, ambiguity
недосмотреть, *v.*, overlook, miss

недоставать (недостать), *v.*, be missing, lack

недостает (from **недоставать**), is missing, lacks

недостаток, *m.*, lack, shortage, deficiency

недостаточно, (from **недостаточный**), *adv.* insufficiently; *pred.*, it is insufficient

недостаточность, *f.*, insufficiency, inadequacy

недостаточный, *adj.*, insufficient, inadequate, defective

недостающий, *adj.*, missing, deficient

недостижимость, *f.*, inaccessibility, unattainability

недостижимый, *adj.*, unattainable, inaccessible

недостоверный, *adj.*, uncertain, doubtful

недоступность, *f.*, inaccessibility

недоступный, *adj.*, inaccessible

недосягаемость, *f.*, inaccessibility

недосягаемый, *adj.*, inaccessible

недоумевать, *v.*, be perplexed, be puzzled

недоумение, *n.*, perplexity, bewilderment

недохват, *m.* **(недохватка,** *f.*), shortage

недочет, *m.*, deficiency, defect, shortage

недра, *pl.*, interior, depths; womb

недуализируемость, *f.*, non-dualizability

нее (cf. **она**), *pron.*, her, it

неевклидовый, *adj.*, non-Euclidean

неединственность, *f.*, non-uniqueness

неединственный, *adj.*, non-unique, not unique

неестественный, *adj.*, unnatural

нежелание, *n.*, reluctance, unwillingness

нежелательность, *f.*, undesirability

нежелательный, *adj.*, undesirable, objectionable; **нежелательный сигнал,** noise

нежели, *conj.*, than

нежесткий, *adj.*, nonrigid

незавершенность, *f.*, incompleteness

независимо, *adv.*, independently, regardless

независимость, *f.*, independence

независимый, *adj.*, independent; **независимая величина,** independent variable; **независимое испытание,** independent trial; **независимое повторение,** independent repetition; **независимые события,** independent events; **линейно независимое решение,** linearly independent solution

независящий (от), *adj.*, independent (of)

незаконный, *adj.*, not valid

незамещенный, *adj.*, unreplaced, not substituted

незамкнутый, *adj.*, non-closed, non-isolated, open

незарегистрированный, *adj.*, non-registered, unrecorded

незатухающий, *adj.*, undamped

незаузленность, *f.*, unknottedness

незаузленный, *adj.*, unknotted

незацепляемость, *f.*, non-linkability

незачем, *adv.*, there is no need, it is useless

незаштрихованный, *adj.*, unshaded, unhatched

незнакомство, *n.*, non-acquaintance, ignorance

незнание, *n.*, ignorance, lack of knowledge; **априорное незнание,** a priori ignorance; **начальное незнание,** initial ignorance

незначительный, *adj.*, negligible, insignificant

неидеальный, *adj.*, imperfect, non-ideal

неидентичный, *adj.*, not identical, non-identical

неизбежно, *adv.*, inevitably, of necessity

неизбежность, *f.*, inevitability

неизбежный, *adj.*, unavoidable, inevitable

неизведанный, *adj.*, unknown, unexperienced, unexplored

неизвестно (from **неизвестный**), it is not known

неизвестность, *f.*, uncertainty, obscurity

неизвестное, *n.*, unknown quantity, unknown, indeterminate; **уравнение с двумя неизвестными,** equation in two unknowns

неизвестный, *adj.*, unknown, indeterminate
неизгибаемость, *f.*, rigidity
неизгибаемый, *adj.*, rigid
неизданный, *adj.*, unpublished
неизменность, *f.*, invariance, invariability
неизменный, *adj.*, invariable, fixed
неизменяемость, *f.*, invariability, immutability
неизменяемый, *adj.*, invariable
неизмеримый, *adj.*, non-measurable
неизначальный, non-initial
неизолированный, *adj.*, non-isolated
неизоморфность, *f.*, non-isomorphy
неизоморфный, *adj.*, non-isomorphic, not isomorphic
неизотропный, *adj.*, non-isotropic, anisotropic
неименованный, *adj.*, abstract, indeterminate, unnamed
неинерциальный, *adj.*, noninertial
неискаженный, *adj.*, unbiased, undisturbed; **неискаженная оценка,** unbiased estimate
неисключенный, *adj.*, non-excluded, nonexceptional
неискривленный, *adj.*, unbent, uncurved, undistorted
неисполнение, *n.*, violation, non-fulfillment
неисполненный, *adj.*, unfulfilled
неиспользованный, *adj.*, unused
неисправность, *f.*, inaccuracy, fault
неисчезающий, *adj.*, non-vanishing
неймановый, *adj.*, Neumann
нейроанатомия, *f.*, neuro-anatomy
нейрон, *m.*, neuron
нейрофизиология, *f.*, neurophysiology
нейроэлемент, *m.*, neuroelement
нейтрализованный, *adj.*, neutralized
нейтральность, *f.*, neutrality
нейтральный, *adj.*, neutral; **нейтральный элемент,** unit element
нейтрино, *n.*, neutrino
нейтрон, *m.*, neutron
некасательный, *adj.*, non-tangential; **по некасательным путям,** along a non-tangential path
неквадратичный, *adj.*, non-quadratic
неквантованный, *adj.*, not quantized, unquantified
некий, *adj.*, certain, some
неклассический, *adj.*, non-classical
некоалиционный, *adj.*, non-cooperative; **некоалиционная игра,** non-cooperative game
некогерентный, *adj.*, incoherent, non-coherent
неколебание, *n.*, stability, non-oscillation
некоммутативно, *adv.*, non-commutatively
некоммутативный, *adj.*, non-commutative, non-abelian
некоммутирующий, *adj.*, non-commuting
некомпактный, *adj.*, non-compact
некомпланарный, *adj.*, non-coplanar, not coplanar
некомплектный, *adj.*, incomplete
неконгруэнтный, *adj.*, incongruent, non-congruent
неконкурентный, *adj.*, non-competitive (compare **внеконкурентный**)
неконсервативный, *adj.*, nonconservative
неконструктивность, *f.*, non-constructivity
неконструктивный, *adj.*, non-constructive
неконтролируемый, *adj.*, uncontrollable
нeконциклический, *adj.*, non-concyclic
некооперативный, *adj.*, non-cooperative
некорректность, *f.*, incorrectness, unreasonableness
некорректный, *adj.*, incorrect, false, improper
некоррелированность, *f.*, non-correlatedness, lack of correlation
некоррелированный, *adj.*, uncorrelated
некоторый, *adj.*, certain, some; **до некоторой степени,** to some extent
некофинальный, *adj.*, non-cofinal

некруговой, *adj.*, non-circular
некубический, *adj.*, non-cubic
некуда, *adv.*, nowhere
нелепица, *f.*, absurdity
нелепость, *f.*, absurdity
нелепый, *adj.*, absurd
нелетучий, *adj.*, non-volatile
нелинейность, *f.*, non-linearity
нелинейный, *adj.*, non-linear
нелишний, *adj.*, useful, relevant
нелогичность, *f.*, illogicality, lack of logic
нелогичный, *adj.*, illogical
нельзя, *pred.*, one cannot, it is impossible
немагнитный, *adj.*, unmagnetized, non-magnetic
немало, *adv.*, much, many
немарковский, *adj.*, non-Markov
нематематически, *adv.*, non-mathematically, in a non-mathematical manner
немедленно, *adv.*, immediately, instantly
немедленный, *adj.*, immediate, instantaneous
неметризуемый, *adj.*, non-metrizable
неметрический, *adj.*, non-metric
неминуемость, *f.*, inevitability, unavoidability
неминуемый, *adj.*, inevitable, unavoidable
немногие, *pl.*, few, not many
немногий, *adj.*, a little, a few; **немногим больше,** a little larger; **в немногих словах,** in a few words
немного, *adv.*, a little, some, a few
немногочисленность, *f.*, sparsity
немногочисленный, *adj.*, sparse, not numerous
немой, *adj.*, mute; **немой индекс,** umbral index
немонотонный, *adj.*, not monotone, non-monotone
немощный, *adj.*, feeble, weak
немощь, *f.*, infirmity, weakness
немыслимый, *adj.*, inconceivable, unthinkable
ненадежность, *f.*, unreliability
ненадежный, *adj.*, unreliable
ненакопленный, *adj.*, non-cumulative
неналегающий, *adj.*, not leaning, not straining, non-overlapping
ненаправленный, *adj.*, undirected
неначерченный, *adj.*, untraced
ненила, *m.*, non-nil, non-zero; **ненила-идеал,** non-nil ideal
ненормальность, *f.*, abnormality, non-normality
ненормальный, *adj.*, abnormal, non-normal
ненулевой, *adj.*, non-zero, distinct from zero, non-trivial; **ненулевое решение,** non-trivial solution
необозримый, *adj.*, boundless, immense
необразцовый, *adj.*, not standard, unoriginal, non-exemplary
необратимость, *f.*, irreversibility
необратимый, *adj.*, irreversible
необходимо (from **необходимый**), *pred.*, it is necessary
необходимость, *f.*, necessity
необходимый, *adj.*, necessary
необыкновенно, *adv.*, unusually
необыкновенный, *adj.*, unusual
необычайный, *adj.*, unusual, extraordinary, exceptional
необычный, *adj.*, unusual
необязательно, *adv.*, optionally
необязательный, *adj.*, optional
неограниченно, *adv.*, indefinitely, with no limit, infinitely
неограниченность, *f.*, unboundedness, unrestrictedness
неограниченный, *adj.*, unlimited, unbounded, unrestricted
неодинаковый, *adj.*, not identical, unalike, unequal
неоднозначность, *f.*, ambiguity, lack of uniqueness
неоднозначный, *adj.*, ambiguous
неоднократный, *adj.*, repeated, reiterated
неоднолистность, *f.*, multivalence
неоднолистный, *adj.*, non-schlicht, multivalent; **неоднолистное отображение,** multivalent mapping, non-schlicht mapping

неоднородность, *f.*, non-homogeneity, heterogeneity, dissimilarity
неоднородный, *adj.*, not uniform, inhomogeneous, non-homogeneous; **неоднородная среда,** inhomogeneous medium
неодносвязный, *adj.*, not simply connected, multiply connected
неожиданно, *adv.*, unexpectedly, suddenly
неожиданный, *adj.*, unexpected, sudden
неокольцо, *n.*, neoring; **неокольцо без делителей нуля,** integral neodomain
неон, *m.*, neon
неоновый, *adj.*, neon; **неоновый вычислительный элемент,** neon computing element
неополе, *n.*, neofield
неопределенность, *f.*, indeterminacy, indetermination, indefiniteness, uncertainty; **точка неопределенности,** ambiguous point
неопределенный, *adj.*, indeterminate, indefinite, uncertain; undefined; **неопределенная форма,** indeterminate form; **неопределенное условие,** condition of uncertainty
неопределимый, *adj.*, indeterminable
неопределяемый, *adj.*, undefined, undefinable
неопровержимость, *f.*, irrefutability
неопровержимый, *adj.*, irrefutable, incontrovertible
неопубликованный, *adj.*, unpublished
неорганизованность, *f.*, disorganization
неорганический, *adj.*, inorganic
неориентированный, *adj.*, non-oriented, unoriented
неориентируемость, *f.*, non-orientability
неориентируемый, *adj.*, non-orientable
неособенный, *adj.*, non-singular, ordinary, non-exceptional
неособый, *adj.*, non-special, non-singular
неосуществимость, *f.*, impracticability, unrealizability
неосуществимый, *adj.*, impracticable, unrealizable
неосциллирующий, *adj.*, non-oscillatory, non-oscillating
неосцилляция, *f.*, non-oscillation
неотделимость, *f.*, inseparability, non-separability
неотделимый, *adj.*, inseparable, non-separable
неотклоненный, *adj.*, undeflected
неотличимость, *f.*, indistinguishability
неотличимый, *adj.*, indistinguishable
неотлучно, *adv.*, continually, constantly
неотмеченный, *adj.*, unmarked, unnoted
неотносительный, *adj.*, non-relative
неотрицательно, *adv.*, non-negatively; **неотрицательно определенный,** *adj.*, positive definite, positive semidefinite
неотрицательность, *f.*, non-negativity
неотрицательный, *adj.*, non-negative; **наименьший неотрицательный вычет,** least non-negative residue
неотчетливость, *f.*, vagueness, indistinctness
неотъемлемый, *adj.*, essential, integral, non-prescribable
неохотно, *adv.*, reluctantly
неоценимый, *adj.*, invaluable, inestimable
непараллельный, *adj.*, non-parallel
непараметрический, *adj.*, non-parametric, distribution-free; **непараметрический критерий согласия,** distribution-free test of fit
непарный, *adj.*, unpaired, odd, unmatched
неперекрываемость, *f.*, disjointness
неперекрывающийся, *adj.*, non-overlapping, disjoint
непересекать, *v.*, not intersect, not overlap
непересекающий (непересекающийся), *adj.*, non-overlapping, non-intersecting, non-crossing, disjoint
непифагоровый, *adj.*, non-pythagorean
неплоский, *adj.*, nonplanar; **неплоская кривая,** *f.*, twisted curve
неплотность, *f.*, thinness, non-compactness

неплотный, *adj.*, not compact, thin, non-dense; **нигде неплотный,** *adj.*, nowhere dense
неплохой, *adj.*, fairly good, quite good
неповрежденный, *adj.*, unimpaired, intact
неповторяющийся, *adj.*, non-recurrent, non-recurring
неповышение, *n.*, non-increasing (property); non-raising, non-enlargement
неподатливый, *adj.*, inflexible
неподвижность, *f.*, immovability, immobility
неподвижный, *adj.*, fixed, stationary, immovable; **неподвижная точка,** fixed point
неподготовленный, *adj.*, unprepared
неподобие, *n.*, dissimilarity
неподобный, *adj.*, dissimilar
непокрытый, *adj.*, uncovered
неполно, *adv.*, partially; **неполно упорядоченный,** *adj.*, partially ordered
неполнота, *f.*, incompleteness
неполный, *adj.*, incomplete, partial
неположительность, *f.*, non-positivity
неположительный, *adj.*, non-positive
неполупростой, *adj.*, non-semi-simple, not semi-simple
неполучение, *n.*, inability to receive, non-receipt
неполяризованный, *adj.*, unpolarized
непонятный, *adj.*, incomprehensible, unintelligible
непонятый, *adj.*, misunderstood, not properly understood
непополнимость, *f.*, non-completability
непополнимый, *adj.*, incapable of completion
непоследовательность, *f.*, inconsistency
непосредственно, *adv.*, directly, immediately
непосредственность, *f.*, spontaneity, directness
непосредственный, *adj.*, immediate, direct, spontaneous
непостоянный, *adj.*, not constant, non-constant
непостоянство, *n.*, variability; **непостоянство массы,** mass-variability
неправильно, *adv.*, improperly, falsely, incorrectly
неправильный, *adj.*, improper, irregular; **неправильная дробь,** improper fraction
непредвиденно, *adv.*, unexpectedly
непредвиденность, *f.*, unexpectedness
непредвиденный, *adj.*, unforeseen, unexpected
непредвосхищающий, *adj.*, non-anticipating
непредикативный, *adj.*, impredicative, non-predicative
непредположительный, *adj.*, non-presumable, non-conjectural
непременно, *adv.*, without fail, certainly
непременный, *adj.*, indispensable, necessary
непрерывно, *adv.*, continuously, uninterruptedly
непрерывно-дифференцируемый, *adj.*, continuously differentiable
непрерывность, *f.*, continuity
непрерывный, *adj.*, continuous, uninterrupted; **непрерывная дробь,** continued fraction; **непрерывный по упорядочению,** *adj.*, order-continuous; **непрерывный спектр,** continuous spectrum
неприводимо, *adv.*, irreducibly
неприводимость, *f.*, irreducibility
неприводимый, *adj.*, non-reducible, irreducible, indecomposable; **неприводимый полином,** irreducible polynomial, prime polynomial
непригодный, *adj.*, unfit, ineligible
неприменимость, *f.*, inapplicability, non-applicability
неприменимый, *adj.*, inapplicable, non-applicable
непроводник, *m.*, non-conductor
непроводящий, *adj.*, non-conducting
непродолжаемость, *f.*, non-extensibility, non-continuability

непродолжаемый, *adj.*, non-continuable, inextensible
непрозрачность, *f.*, opacity
непрозрачный, *adj.*, opaque
непроизводительный, *adj.*, unproductive
непроницаемость, *f.*, impenetrability, impermeability
непроницаемый, *adj.*, impenetrable, impermeable
непропорциональность, *f.*, disproportion
непропорциональный, *adj.*, not proportional, disproportionate
непростой, *adj.*, not prime, not simple
непротиворечивость, *f.*, consistency
непротиворечивый, *adj.*, consistent, non-contradictory
непусто (from **непустой**), is not empty
непустой, *adj.*, non-empty, non-vacuous; **непустое подмножество,** non-empty subset
непрямой, *adj.*, indirect
неравенство, *n.*, inequality; **неравенство Буняковского,** Cauchy-Schwarz-Buniakowski inequality
неравновесный, *adj.*, not in equilibrium
неравномерно, *adv.*, non-uniformly, irregularly
неравномерность, *f.*, non-uniformity, irregularity
неравномерный, *adj.*, non-uniform, irregular
неравноотстоящий, *adj.*, unequally spaced, not equidistant
неравноправность, *f.*, disparity
неравноправный, *adj.*, disparate
неравносильность, *f.*, non-equivalence
неравносильный, *adj.*, non-equivalent
неравносторонний, *adj.*, scalene
неравноточный, *adj.*, of varying accuracy, of unequal accuracy
неравный, *adj.*, unequal
нерадиантный, *adj.*, non-radiant
неразвертывающийся, *adj.*, non-developable; **линейная неразвертывающаяся поверхность,** warped surface
неразветвленный, *adj.*, non-ramified, unramified, unbranched
неразветвляемый, *adj.*, non-ramifiable
неразделимый, *adj.*, non-separable, inseparable, indivisible
неразделительный, *adj.*, non-exclusive, inclusive; **неразделительная дизъюнкция,** inclusive disjunction
неразличимый, *adj.*, indistinguishable
неразличный, *adj.*, non-distinct
неразложимость, *f.*, indivisibility, indecomposability, irresolvability
неразложимый, *adj.*, irresolvable, indecomposable, non-factorable
неразработанный, *adj.*, undeveloped, unsolved
неразрезной, *adj.*, continuous-solid
неразрешенный, *adj.*, unsolved; **неразрешенные вопросы,** unresolved problems
неразрешимость, *f.*, insolubility, unsolvability, undecidability
неразрешимый, *adj.*, unsolvable, insoluble, undecidable
неразрывность, *f.*, continuity, indissolubility, non-separability; **уравнение неразрывности,** equation of continuity
неразрывный, *adj.*, non-separable
нерандомизированный, *adj.*, non-randomized
нераспадающийся, *adj.*, irreducible, indecomposable
нерастворимый, *adj.*, insoluble
нерасторжимость, *f.*, indissolubility
нерастягивающий, *adj.*, non-expanding
нерв, *m.*, nerve; **нерв покрытия,** nerve of a covering
нервный, *adj.*, pertaining to nerve, nerve, nervous, neural
нервюра, *f.*, wing rib, rib
нереальный, *adj.*, unreal, non-real, ideal
нерегулярность, *f.*, irregularity, non-regularity
нерегулярный, *adj.*, irregular, non-regular
нередкий, *adj.*, frequent, ordinary

нередко, *adv.*, not infrequently
нерекурсивный, *adj.*, non-recursive
нерелятивистский, *adj.*, non-relativistic
нерентабельный, *adj.*, unprofitable
нерефлексивность, *f.*, non-reflexiveness, irreflexivity
нерефлексивный, *adj.*, irreflexive, non-reflexive
нерешенный, *adj.*, unsolved
нержавеющий, *adj.*, rust-resistant, stainless, non-corrosive
неровность, *f.*, irregularity, unevenness
неровный, *adj.*, irregular
несамосопряженный, *adj.*, not self-conjugate, not self-adjoint
несбалансированный, *adj.*, unbalanced
несверхпроводящий, *adj.*, nonsuperconducting
несводимый, *adj.*, irreducible; **несводимое доказательство,** irreducible proof
несвойственный, *adj.*, unusual, unnatural
несвязанность, *f.*, disconnectedness
несвязанный, *adj.*, disconnected
несвязность, *f.*, disconnectedness, disconnection; **локальная несвязность,** local disconnection
несвязный, *adj.*, incoherent, disconnected; **вполне несвязный,** *adj.*, totally disconnected
несепарабельный, *adj.*, non-separable
несерый, *adj.*, non-gray; **несерое вещество**, non-gray material
несет (from **нести**), carries, bears
несжимаемость, *f.*, incompressibility
несжимаемый, *adj.*, incompressible
несимметрический, *adj.*, unsymmetric, non-symmetric, asymmetric
несимметричный, *adj.*, asymmetric
несингулярный, *adj.*, non-singular
несинхронный, *adj.*, non-synchronous
нескалярный, *adj.*, non-scalar
несколько, *adv.*, rather, somewhat; *num.*, several, some, a few
нескомпенсированный, *adj.*, uncompensated
несложный, *adj.*, not complicated, simple
неслучайность, *f.*, non-randomness
неслучайный, *adj.*, non-random, assignable
несмежный, *adj.*, non-adjacent
несмешанный, *adj.*, unmixed, pure
несмешиваемость, *f.*, immiscibility
несмешиваемый, *adj.*, immiscible, nonmiscible
несмещенность, *f.*, unbiasedness, non-bias
несмещенный, *adj.*, unbiased, non-skew; **несмещенная оценка,** unbiased estimate
несмотря, *prep.*, in spite of; **несмотря на то, что,** in spite of the fact that
несобственный, *adj.*, improper, nonintrinsic, ideal, singular; **несобственная точка,** ideal point; **несобственное нормальное распределение,** singular normal distribution; **несобственная прямая,** ideal (straight) line
несовершенный, *adj.*, incomplete, imperfect; **несовершенное поле,** quasifield
несовершенство, *n.*, imperfection
несовместимость, *f.*, incompatibility, inconsistency
несовместимый, *adj.*, incompatible, inconsistent, disjoint
несовместный, *adj.*, disjoint, incompatible, inconsistent
несовпадение, *n.*, discrepancy, noncoincidence, divergence, disagreement
несогласие, *n.*, variance, discord, disagreement
несоединенный, *adj.*, disconnected
несоизмеримо, *adv.*, incommensurably
несоизмеримость, *f.*, incommensurability
несоизмеримый, *adj.*, incommensurable
несократимость, *f.*, irreducibility
несократимый, *adj.*, irreducible
несомненно, *adv.*, undoubtedly
несомненность, *f.*, certainty
несомненный, *adj.*, certain, definite; **практически несомненный,** practically certain

несостоятельность, *f.*, inconsistency
несостоятельный, *adj.*, inconsistent, insolvent, untenable
несотканный, *adj.*, webless
неспециальный, *adj.*, non-special
неспособность, *f.*, inability
несрабатывание, *n.*, malfunctioning
несравненно, *adv.*, by far, incomparably
несравненный, *adj.*, incongruent, noncomparable, incommensurable
несравнимо, *adv.*, incomparably, incommensurably
несравнимый, *adj.*, incomparable, noncomparable, incommensurable, unrelated
нестандартный, *adj.*, non-standard, abnormal, atypical
нестационарный, *adj.*, non-stationary, unstable
нести, *v.*, carry, bear; **нести с собой,** *v.*, imply
неструктурный, *adj.*, non-structural, non-lattice
несуммируемость, *f.*, non-summability
несуммируемый, *adj.*, non-summable
несущественный, *adj.*, unessential, immaterial, incidental
несуществование, *n.*, non-existence
несуществующий, *adj.*, non-existent
несущий, *adj.*, carrying, supporting, carrier; **несущее пространство,** carrier (space); **несущее множество,** carrier (set)
несходство, *n.*, dissimilarity, difference, discrepancy
несходящийся, *adj.*, non-convergent, divergent
несчастный, *adj.*, unlucky, unfortunate; **несчастный случай,** accident
несчетно, *adv.*, uncountably, non-denumerably
несчетно-бесконечный, *adj.*, uncountably infinite, non-denumerably infinite
несчетный, *adj.*, non-denumerable, uncountable
нет, *particle*, no, not; there is no
нетеревой, *adj.*, Noether, pertaining to Noether; **нетерова группа,** Noether group; **нетеровы кольца,** Noether rings
нетождественно, *adv.*, not identically
неточно, *adv.*, not exactly, inaccurately
неточность, *f.*, inaccuracy, discrepancy, error
неточный, *adj.*, inexact, incorrect, inaccurate
нетранзитивный, *adj.*, intransitive, nontransitive
нетриангулируемый, *adj.*, non-triangulable
нетривиальный, *adj.*, non-trivial
нетронутый, *adj.*, untouched; **нетронутая переменная,** *f.*, variable held constant
нетрудно, *adv.*, easily; *pred.*, it is not difficult
неубедительный, *adj.*, unconvincing, inconclusive
неубывающий, *adj.*, non-decreasing; **монотонная неубывающая функция,** monotone non-decreasing function
неуверенность, *f.*, uncertainty
неудача, *f.*, failure
неудачный, *adj.*, unsuccessful
неудобный, *adj.*, inconvenient, awkward
неудобство, *n.*, inconvenience
неудовлетворительный, *adj.*, unsatisfactory, inadequate
неуклюжий, *adj.*, clumsy, awkward
неулучшаемость, *f.*, unimprovability
неулучшаемый, *adj.*, unimprovable
неуменьшающий, *adj.*, non-decreasing
неуместный, *adj.*, inappropriate, misplaced, irrelevant
неуниформизируемый, *adj.*, non-uniformizable
неупорядоченный, *adj.*, unregulated, unordered
неупругий, *adj.*, inelastic, rigid
неуравновешенный, *adj.*, unstable; **неуравновешенный момент,** unstable moment

неусеченный, *adj.*, non-truncated
неустановившийся, *adj.*, unsteady, irregular, transient, unstable
неустойчивость, *f.*, instability, unsteadiness
неустойчивый, *adj.*, unstable, unsteady, uncertain
неустранимый, *adj.*, unremovable, inherent
неферромагнитный, *adj.*, non-ferromagnetic
нефинитный, *adj.*, non-finite, infinite
неформализованный, *adj.*, non-formalized
неформальный, *adj.*, informal
нефть, *f.*, oil, petroleum
нефундаментальный, *adj.*, non-fundamental, secondary
нехарактеристика, *f.*, noncharacteristic; **проблема двух нехарактеристик,** the two noncharacteristic problem
нехарактеристический, *adj.*, non-characteristic
нехватать (нехватить), [*usually* **не хватать**], *v.*, be insufficient
нецелое, *n.*, non-integral, non-integer
нецелочисленный, *adj.*, non-integral, fractional
нецелый, *adj.*, non-integral
нецентральный, *adj.*, non-central
нециклический, *adj.*, acyclic, non-cyclic
нечет, *m.*, odd number; **чет и нечет,** odd and even
нечеткий, *adj.*, illegible, difficult
нечеткость, *f.*, illegibility, carelessness
нечетнократный, *adj.*, odd-multiple
нечетномерный, *adj.*, odd-measured, odd-dimensional
нечетность, *f.*, property of being odd, oddness
нечетный, *adj.*, odd
нечто, *pron.*, something
нечувствительность, *f.*, inertness, non-sensitivity; **зона нечувствительности,** dead zone, inert zone
нечуствительный, *adj.*, insensitive
неэвклидовый, *adj.*, non-Euclidean; **неэвклидова геометрия,** non-Euclidean geometry
неэквивалентность, *f.*, non-equivalence
неэквивалентный, *adj.*, non-equivalent
неэкранированный, *adj.*, unscreened
неэкспоненциальный, *adj.*, non-exponential
неэлектролит, *m.*, nonelectrolyte
неэлектромагнитный, *adj.*, nonelectromagnetic, nonelectrodynamic
неэлементарный, *adj.*, non-elementary
неэрмитовый, *adj.*, non-Hermitian
неэффективность, *f.*, inefficiency, ineffectiveness
неэффективный, *adj.*, ineffective, inefficient
неявно, *adv.*, implicitly, tacitly
неявный, *adj.*, implicit; **неявная функция,** implicit function; **теорема о неявных функциях,** implicit function theorem
неясность, *f.*, vagueness, obscurity, ambiguity
неясный, *adj.*, vague, obscure
ни, *conj.*, **ни . . . ни,** neither . . . nor; *part.*, no, not; **сколь бы мало ни было,** no matter how small
нигде, *adv.*, nowhere; **нигде не плотный,** *adj.*, nowhere dense
ниже, *adv.*, lower, below
нижележащий, *adj.*, underlying
нижеопределенный, *adj.*, defined below
нижеперечисленный, *adj.*, enumerated below, stated below
нижепоименованный, *adj.*, named below
нижеприведенный, *adj.*, stated below, mentioned below
нижеследующий, *adj.*, following
нижеуказанный, *adj.*, stated below
нижний, *adj.*, lower; **нижняя грань,** lower bound, greatest lower bound
низ, *m.*, bottom
низкий, *adj.*, low
низко, *adv.*, low
низкочастотный, *adj.*, low-frequency
низший, *adj.*, lower, lowest

никак, *adv.*, in no way
никакой, *adj.*, no, none
никогда, *adv.*, never
никто, *pron.*, no one, nobody
ниль, *m.*, nil, null, zero
нильгруппа, *f.*, nil-group
нилькольцо, *n.*, nil-ring
нильпотентность, *f.*, nilpotency
нильпотентный, *adj.*, nilpotent
нильрадикал, *m.*, nil-radical, null-radical
нильряд, *m.*, nil-series, null-series
нильстепенный, *adj.*, nilpotent
нильэлемент, *m.*, nil-element
ним, *m.*, Nim
нисколько, *adv.*, not at all; *pron.*, none at all
нисходящий, *adj.*, descending
нитка, *f.*, thread, fiber
нить, *f.*, thread, filament; **нить накала,** filament
ничего (from **ничто**), nothing
ничей, *pron.*, no one's, nobody's
ничем (from **ничто**), by nothing, with nothing
ничто, *pron.*, nothing
ничтожный, *adj.*, insignificant, negligible
ничуть, *adv.*, not at all, by no means
ничья (from **ничей**), *f.*, tie, draw, drawn game
но, *conj.*, but
новейший, *adj.*, newest, latest
новорожденный, *adj.*, newly-born
новый, *adj.*, new, modern, fresh
ноль (= **нуль**), zero, null
номенклатура, *f.*, nomenclature
номер, *m.*, number, issue
номинал, *m.*, nominal (value), face value
номинализм, *m.*, nominalism
номиналист, *m.*, nominalist
номиналистический, *adj.*, nominalistic
номинальный, *adj.*, nominal, rated; **номинальная мощность нагрузки,** capacity
номограмма, *f.*, nomogram
номографирование, *n.*, nomograph(y), nomographic representation
номографировать, *v.*, nomograph, represent nomographically
номографируемость, *f.*, nomographic representability, nomographability
номографируемый, *adj.*, nomographable, nomographically representable
номографический, *adj.*, nomographic
номография, *f.*, nomography
норма, *f.*, norm, standard, rate, quota, bound, valuation; **теория норм,** theory of valuations
нормализатор, *m.*, normalizer
нормализация, *f.*, normalization, standardization
нормализованный, *adj.*, normalized
нормализировать, *v.*, normalize
нормаль, *f.*, normal
нормально, *adv.*, normally
нормальность, *f.*, normality
нормальный, *adj.*, normal, standard; **нормальный делитель,** normal divisor; **импульс нормальной величины,** full-sized pulse; **целая функция нормального типа,** entire function of mean type
норменный, *adj.*, normed, norm; **норменная форма,** normed form
нормирование, *n.*, normalization, valuation
нормированный, *adj.*, standardized, standard, normalized, normed; **нормированная величина,** standardized variable; **нормированное кольцо,** Banach algebra, normed ring
нормировать, *v.*, norm, normalize, standardize
нормировка, *f.*, normalization
нормируемость, *f.*, normability
нормирующий, *adj.*, normalizing
носимый, *adj.*, carried; **носимое множество,** carried set
носитель, *m.*, carrier, vehicle, medium; **носитель записи,** recording medium
носительница, *f.*, carrier, medium
носить, *v.*, carry, bear
носовой, *adj.*, nose, bow, fore part

нужда, *f.*, need, necessity; **без нужды,** needlessly
нуждаться, *v.*, need, require
нужно (from **нужный**), it is necessary; **нужно было,** it was necessary; **нужно будет,** it will be necessary
нужный (нужна, нужно), *adj.*, necessary, needed
нуклеарный, *adj.*, nuclear
нуклон, *m.*, nucleon
нулевой, *adj.*, zero, pertaining to zero, null; **нулевой корень,** zero root; **нулевой порядок,** (of) order zero; **нулевое решение,** trivial solution, zero solution; **нулевая точка,** origin; **нулевая гипотеза,** null hypothesis
нуль, *m.*, zero, origin; **обратиться в нуль,** *v.*, become zero, vanish
нульарный, *adj.*, null, 0-ary
нульмерность, *f.*, zero-dimensionality
нульмерный, *adj.*, of zero measure, zero-dimensional
нуль-многообразие, *n.*, zero variety; **теорема Сильвестра о нуль-многообразиях,** Sylvester's law of nullity
нуль-множество, *n.*, null-set, empty set
нуль-полугруппа, *f.*, zero semigroup
нуль-последовательность, *f.*, null-sequence, zero-sequence
нульстабильный, *adj.*, nilstable
нульформа, *f.*, null-form
нульэлемент, *m.*, zero element
нумер, *m.*, number, issue, copy
нумерация, *f.*, indexing, numbering, enumeration
нумерический, *adj.*, numerical
нумерование *n.*, enumeration, numbering, indexing
нумерованный, *adj.*, numbered, indexed, enumerated
нутация, *f.*, nutation
ныне, *adv.*, now, at present
ньютон, *m.*, newton (unit)
ньютоновский, *adj.*, Newtonian

О

о, об, *prep.*, about, on, of
оба, *pron.*, both; **непрерывный в обе стороны,** *adj.*, bicontinuous; **равномерный в обе стороны,** *adj.*, bi-uniform
обведенный, *adj.*, enclosed, encircled, outlined, surrounding
обвертывать, *v.*, wrap up, cover, envelop
обводить (обвести), *v.*, encircle, surround, outline
обволакивать, *v.*, envelop, cover
обдуманно, *adv.*, deliberately
обе (from **оба**), both
обегающий, *adj.*, running, running around
обертон, *m.*, overtone
обертывать (обернуть), *v.*, wrap up, cover, turn, envelop
обертывающий, *adj.*, enveloping; **универсальная обертывающая алгебра,** universal enveloping algebra
обеспечение, *n.*, security, guarantee
обеспеченный, *adj.*, secure, ensured
обеспечивать, *v.*, ensure, guarantee, provide
обеспечивающий, *adj.*, ensuring, providing, guaranteeing
обещать, *v.*, promise
обещающий, *adj.*, promising
обжимка, *f.*, pressing, squeezing
обзор, *m.*, survey, review
обзорный, *adj.*, review, survey
обилие, *n.*, abundance, plenty
обильность, *f.*, abundance
обильный, *adj.*, abundant, plentiful, copious, ample
обиход, *m.*, custom, use

обладать, *v.*, have, possess
обладающий, *adj.*, possessing, having
облако, *n.*, cloud
область, *f.*, domain, region, range, scope, system; **область главных идеалов,** principal ideal domain; **область коэффициентов,** coefficient domain; **область определения,** domain of definition; **область рациональности,** domain of rationality, field; **область целостностй,** integral domain; **как угодно малая область,** arbitrarily small domain, **область значений,** range of values; **область импримитивности,** system of imprimitivity; **область транзитивности,** transitivity set
облегчать (облегчить), *v.*, facilitate
облегчающий, *adj.*, facilitating
облегчение, *n.*, facilitation, lightening
облегченный, *adj.*, relieved, facilitated
обледенение, *n.*, icing, ice formation
обложение, *n.*, taxation, tax
облучение, *n.*, exposure, irradiation
облученность, *f.*, exposure, irradiation
обманывать (обмануть), *v.*, deceive, trick
обмен, *m.*, exchange, interchange
обменный, *adj.*, exchange
обменивать (обменять, обменить), *v.*, interchange, exchange
обмер, *m.*, measurement
обмотка, *f.*, winding, armature winding
обнадеживающий, *adj.*, reassuring, encouraging
обнаружение, *n.*, detection, discovery; **устройство для обнаружения ошибки,** error detecting facility
обнаруженный, *adj.*, discovered, uncovered, exposed
обнаруживаемый, *adj.*, detectable
обнаруживать (обнаружить), *v.*, discover, detect, reveal, find, show
обнаруживаться, *v.*, emerge, appear, be discovered
обобщать (обобщить), *v.*, generalize, extend
обобщение, *n.*, generalization, extension
обобщенно (from **обобщенный**), *adv.*, generalized
обобщенно-непрерывный, *adj.*, continuous in the extended sense
обобщенный, *adj.*, generalized, extended
обобщить (cf. **обобщать**), *v.*, generalize, extend
обогащение, *n.*, enrichment, concentration; **метод обогащения данных,** data enrichment method
обогнуть, cf. **огивать**
обод, *m.*, rim, hoop
обозначать (обозначить), *v.*, designate, denote
обозначение, *n.*, designation, notation
обозначенный, *adj.*, denoted, designated
обозначимый, *adj.*, assignable
обозреватель, *m.*, reviewer
обозревать (обозреть), *v.*, survey, review
обозрение, *n.*, review, survey
обозримость, *f.*, visibility
обозримый, *adj.*, visible
обойдемся (from **обходиться**), we shall manage (with)
обойти (cf. **обходить**), *v.*, go around, by-pass
обойтись (cf. **обходиться**), *v.*, manage, get along
оболочка, *f.*, envelope, casing, cover, hull, shell; **выпуклая оболочка,** convex hull; **линейная оболочка,** linear span; **оболочка голоморфности,** envelope of holomorphy
оболочный, *adj.*, hull, envelope
оборвать (cf. **обрывать**), *v.*, break, cut off
оборона, *f.*, defence; **задача обороны,** defence problem
оборот, *m.*, turn, revolution, rotation
оборотный, *adj.*, reverse, back; **оборотная сторона,** reverse side
оборудование, *n.*, equipment, outfit, arrangement, circuit; **вложение оборудования,** equipment investment
оборудовать, *v.*, equip, arrange
обоснование, *n.*, proof, basis, ground

обоснованный, *adj.*, justified, proved, valid
обосновывать (обосновать), *v.*, justify, substantiate
обособлять (обособить), *v.*, isolate
обостренный, *adj.*, tightened, strained
обошлись (from **обходиться**), got along, managed
обоюдно, *adv.*, mutually
обоюдный, *adj.*, mutual, reciprocal
обрабатывать (обработать), *v.*, treat, develop, process
обрабатываться, *v.*, be operated on
обработка, *f.*, processing, treatment, handling; **обработка данных,** data processing
образ, *m.*, image, form, manner, transform; **главным образом,** mainly; **таким образом,** in this way, thus; **разумным образом,** in a reasonable way
образец, *m.*, model, pattern, type, sample, specimen; **образец наибольшего риска,** maximum risk pattern
образный, *adj.*, figurative, descriptive, shaped; ***S*-образный,** *adj.*, *S*-shaped
образование, *n.*, formation, education; **образование групп чисел,** number grouping
образовывать (образовать), *v.*, form, make up, organize; **образовывать дополнение,** *v.*, complement
образуемый, *adj.*, formed, formed by
образующая, *f.*, generator, generatrix, element (of cylinder), ruling
образуя, *adv. part.*, forming, by forming, if we form
образцовый, *adj.*, key, exemplary, model
образчик, *m.*, sample, specimen
обрамлять, *v.*, frame
обратимость, *f.*, reversibility, reciprocity
обратимый, *adj.*, reversible, convertible, inverse, invertible
обратить (cf. **обращать**), *v.*, convert, turn into, transform
обратиться (cf. **обращаться**), *v.*, become, turn into; **обратиться в нуль,** *v.*, become zero, vanish
обратно, *adv.*, conversely, inversely, back, backwards; **обратно пропорциональный,** *adj.*, inversely proportional; **обратно двойственный,** *adj.*, dual
обратное, *n.*, inverse; **левое обратное,** left-inverse; **правое обратное,** right-inverse
обратно-разностный, *adj.*, backward-difference
обратный, *adj.*, inverse, converse, reverse, back, reciprocal, opposite; **обратная двойственность,** duality; **обратная связь,** feedback; **обратное преобразование,** reconversion; **обратное сопротивление,** back-resistance; **обратная матрица,** reciprocal matrix; **в обратном порядке,** in reverse order
обращать (обратить), *v.*, convert, turn into, transform, invert
обращаться, *v.*, reduce to, revert, turn into, circulate, become; **обращаться в нуль,** *v.*, vanish; **обращаться с,** *v.*, handle, use
обращающий, *adj.*, reversing, inverting, converting, transforming; **обращающий ориентацию,** *adj.*, orientation-reversing; **обращающая схема,** *f.*, inverter circuit
обращающийся, *adj.*, becoming, reducing to; **(не) обращающийся в нуль,** *adj.*, (non-)vanishing
обращение, *n.*, conversion, inversion, converse, circulation, reversion; **формула обращения,** inversion formula; **время обращения к запоминающему устройству,** storage access; **уисло обращений между регенерациями,** read-around ratio; **малое время обращения,** quick access, rapid access; **обращение вероятности,** inverse probability
обращенный, *adj.*, conversion

обрезывать (обрезать), *v.*, cut off
обременение, *n.*, overloading, burdening
обременительный, *adj.*, burdensome, heavy, overloaded
обременять (обременить), *v.*, burden, overload
обретать (обрести), *v.*, find, discover
обретение, *n.*, finding, discovery
обретенный, *adj.*, found, discovered
обрисовывать (обрисовать), *v.*, outline, delineate
обрыв, *m.*, break, cut-off, discontinuity, gap; **условие обрыва цепей,** chain condition; **условие обрыва возрастающей (убывающей) цепочки,** ascending (descending) chain condition
обрывание, *n.*, breaking, tearing
обрывать (оборвать), *v.*, break, tear, cut off
обрываться, *v.*, terminate, stop
обрывающийся, *adj.*, terminating, breaking, cutting off
обследование, *n.*, investigation, inspection; **выборочное обследование,** sample survey
обследовать, *v.*, inspect, examine, investigate
обследуемый, *adj.*, investigated
обслуживаемый, *adj.*, served, serviced
обслуживание, *n.*, service, attention, maintenance, care; **профилактическое обслуживание,** preventive maintenance; **задача в линиях обслуживания,** queueing problem
обслуживающий, *adj.*, auxiliary, servicing
обстановка, *f.*, circumstances, arrangement, conditions, situation
обстоит (from **обстоять**), is; **дело обстоит,** the situation is
обстоятельство, *n.*, case, circumstance, property
обстоять, *v.*, be, get on
обсуждать (обсудить), *v.*, consider, discuss, argue
обсуждение, *n.*, discussion, argument
обтекаемость, *f.*, streamlining
обтекаемый, *adj.*, streamlined
обтекание, *n.*, streamline, flow
обтекать, *v.*, flow around, circulate
обтекающий, *adj.*, circulating, flowing around; **скорость обтекающего потока,** ambient velocity
обточка, *f.*, turning, rounding off
обуславливать, cf. **обусловливать**
обусловить (cf. **обусловивать**), *v.*, stipulate
обусловленность, *f.*, condition, stipulation, conditionality
обусловленный, *adj.*, agreed upon, stipulated
обусловливать (обусловить), *v.*, stipulate, make conditions
обусловливаться, *v.*, depend on, be stipulated by
обучать, *v.*, teach, train
обучение, *n.*, instruction, training
обученный, *adj.*, trained
обхват, *m.*, girth
обход, *m.*, circuit, by-pass; **порядок обхода,** index
обходить (обойти), *v.*, go around, turn, avoid, by-pass
обходиться (обойтись), *v.*, treat, manage, make, do; **обходиться без,** *v.*, do without, dispense with
обширность, *f.*, extensiveness, magnitude
обширный, *adj.*, extensive
общезначимость, *f.*, general meaning, general validity
общезначимый, *adj.*, valid, generally valid
общеизвестный, *adj.*, commonly known, well known
общелогический, *adj.*, general-logical
общеобразовательный, *adj.*, (of) general education; (of) general form or shape
общеопределенность, *f.*, general determination, general definition
общепризнанный, *adj.*, universally recognized
общеприменимый, *adj.*, generally applicable

общепринятый, *adj.*, generally accepted, conventional

общерекурсивный, *adj.*, general recursive

общественный, *adj.*, community, social, public; **кривая общественного безразличия,** community indifference curve

общество, *n.*, society

общетеоретический, *adj.*, general-theoretical

общеупотребительный, *adj.*, current, in general usage

общий, *adj.*, common, general, total; **общее число,** general number; **общая сумма,** sum total; **общий закон взаимности,** general reciprocity law; **общее наименьшее кратное,** least common multiple; **общий наибольший делитель,** greatest common divisor; **общий пучок,** generic pencil; **общая точка,** generic point; **точный в общем,** *adj.*, generically exact; **общий доход,** aggregate profit; **общее решение однородного уравнения,** complementary function, general solution (of the homogeneous equation)

община, *f.*, community

общность, *f.*, generality, community

объединение, *n.*, union, join, combination, unification; **гомоморфизм по объединению,** *m.*, join-homomorphism; **гомоморфный по объединениям,** *adj.*, join-homomorphic; **неразложимый в объединение,** *adj.*, join-irreducible

объединенный, *adj.*, joined, united, amalgamated

объединяемый, *adj.*, joined, united, joinable

объединять (объединить), *v.*, join, unite, combine, consolidate, connect

объединяющий, *adj.*, joining, uniting, connecting, combining

объект, *m.*, object, item, entity, unit, target; **движущийся объект,** moving object, moving target

объективный, *adj.*, objective

объектно-эквивалентный, *adj.*, objectively equivalent

объем, *m.*, volume, size, extent, extension; **объем выборки,** sample size; **объем запоминающего устройства,** storage space

объемистый, *adj.*, voluminous, bulky

объемно-центрированный, *adj.*, body-centered

объемность, *f.*, volume, capacity

объемный, *adj.*, solid, volume, volumetric, extensional (log.); **объемная гармоника,** solid harmonic

объявлять (объявить), *v.*, announce, declare

объяснение, *n.*, explanation, cause

объясненный, *adj.*, explained

объяснительный, *adj.*, explanatory

объяснять (объяснить), *v.*, explain

объясняться (объясниться), *v.*, be explained, stem from

объять, *v.*, envelop

обыденный, *adj.*, common, ordinary

обыкновенно, *adv.*, ordinarily, usually

обыкновенный, *adj.*, ordinary, usual, normal, regular; **обыкновенная точка (линии),** regular point (of a line)

обычно, *adv.*, usually, generally, ordinarily

обычный, *adj.*, usual, ordinary

обязательно, *adv.*, without fail, necessarily

обязательный, *adj.*, obligatory, compulsory

обязательство, *n.*, obligation, commitment

обязывать (обязать), *v.*, bind, oblige

овал, *m.*, oval

овалоид, *m.*, ovaloid

овальный, *adj.*, oval

овладевать (овладеть), *v.*, seize, master

огибать (обогнуть), *v.*, bend, envelop, fit

огибающая, *f.*, envelope

огибающий, *adj.*, enveloping

огива, *f.*, ogive

оглядываться, *v.*, look back; **оглядываясь назад,** in retrospect

огнестрельный, *adj.*, firing
оговаривать (оговорить), *v.*, stipulate, specify, state explicitly
оговоренный, *adj.*, mentioned, stipulated; **если противное не оговорено,** unless otherwise stipulated
оговориться, *v.*, agree on conditions, stipulate
оговорка, *f.*, stipulation, reservation
ограничение, *n.*, restriction, limitation, restraint, constraint; **игра с ограничениями,** constrained game
ограниченно, *adv.*, restrictedly, boundedly, bounded; **ограниченно сходящийся,** *adj.*, boundedly convergent; **ограниченно-слабый,** *adj.*, bounded-weak
ограниченность, *f.*, boundedness
ограниченный, *adj.*, bounded, limited, restricted; **ограниченный сверху,** *adj.*, bounded above; **ограниченный снизу,** *adj.*, bounded below; **ограниченный по упорядоченности,** *adj.*, order-bounded
ограничивать (ограничить), *v.*, bound, restrict, limit, confine
ограничиваться (ограничиться), *v.*, restrict oneself (to), be restricted (to)
ограничивающий, *adj.*, limiting, bounding; **ограничивающий диод,** clamping diode
ограничитель, *m.*, stopping device, catch
ограничительный, *adj.*, limiting, restrictive, limitative
ограничить (cf. **ограничивать**), *v.*, limit, confine, restrict
ограничиться, *v.*, confine oneself to
огромный, *adj.*, vast, immense
одеяние, *n.*, attire
один, *num.*, one, some, certain, alone
одинаково, *adv.*, equally; **одинаково удаленный,** *adj.*, equidistant
одинаковость, *f.*, uniformity, identity, equality
одинаковый, *adj.*, equal, identical, the same, common; **одинаковый знаменатель,** common denominator
одинарный, *adj.*, single, unary, unitary
одиннадцать, *num.*, eleven
одиночный, *adj.*, single
одна (cf. **один**), one, some
однажды, *adv.*, once
однако (однако же), *conj.*, but, however
одно (cf. **один**), one, some; **одно и то же,** one and the same, the same
одно-, *prefix*, one-, single-, mono-, uni-
одноадресный, *adj.*, one-address, single-address
одноатомный, *adj.*, monoatomic, monatomic
однобережный, *adj.*, simple, taken once
одновалентный, *adj.*, univalent, one-valent
одновершинный, *adj.*, one-vertex, having one maximum
одновидовой, *adj.*, one-way; **одновидовая классификация,** one-way classification
одновременно, *adv.*, simultaneously
одновременность, *f.*, simultaneity
одновременный, *adj.*, simultaneous, synchronous; **одновременное множительное устройство,** simultaneous multiplier
одного (from **один**), (of) one
однодифференцируемый, *adj.*, once differentiable
однозначно, *adv.*, identically, uniquely; **взаимно однозначно,** *adv.*, one-to-one
однозначность, *f.*, uniqueness, single-valuedness; **теорема однозначности,** uniqueness theorem
однозначный, *adj.*, univalent, one-valued, single-valued; **взаимно однозначный,** *adj.*, one-to-one
одноидемпотентный, *adj.*, one-idempotent
одноименный, *adj.*, having the same name
одноиндексный, *adj.*, of index one, single-index
однокаскадный, *adj.*, single-stage
однокомпонентный, *adj.*, one-component

одноконтактный, *adj.*, single-contact
одноконтурный, *adj.*, single-circuit
однократный, *adj.*, single; **однократное выполнение программы**, run (on computer)
однолистно, *adv.*, univalently, in a one-to-one way
однолистность, *f.*, univalence, consisting of one sheet
однолистный, *adj.*, schlicht, one-sheeted; **подобно однолистный**, *adj.*, schlichtartig
одномерный, *adj.*, one-dimensional, univariate
одноместный, *adj.*, one-place
однообразный, *adj.*, uniform, monotone
одно-однозначный, *adj.*, one-to-one; **одно-однозначное соответствие**, one-to-one correspondence
одноосный, *adj.*, single axis, monoaxial, uniaxial
однопараметрический, *adj.*, one-parameter
однопериодический, *adj.*, singly-periodic
однополостный, *adj.*, of one sheet, of one nappe; **однополостный гиперболоид**, hyperboloid of one sheet
однополюсный, *adj.*, unipolar
однопотенциальный, *adj.*, unipotential
одноразовый, *adj.*, single, one-time, one-shot; **одноразовый счетник**, start-stop counter
одноразрядный, *adj.*, single-order, single-digit, single-discharge; **одноразрядное устройство**, single-order unit; **одноразрядное вычитающее устройство**, single-order subtractor; **одноразрядный сумматор**, single-digit adder, one-column adder
однородность, *f.*, homogeneity, uniformity, similarity
однородный, *adj.*, homogeneous, uniform, similar
однорядный, *adj.*, uniserial; **обобщенно однорядная алгебра**, generalized uniserial algebra
односвязность, *f.*, simple-connectedness, simple connectivity
односвязный, *adj.*, simply connected, 1-connected
однослойный, *adj.*, one-sheeted, one-layer, single-layer
одностадийный, *adj.*, single-stage
одностолбцовый, *adj.*, one-column, of one column
односторонний, *adj.*, one-sided, unilateral, single; **односторонняя поверхность**, one-sided surface
однострочечный, *adj.*, one-row, of one row
одноступенчатый, *adj.*, single-stage, single-step
однотипный, *adj.*, of the same type, one-type, single-type
одноточечный, *adj.*, single-point, one-point; **одноточечное компактное расширение**, one-point compactification
однофазный, *adj.*, one-phase, single-phase
одночлен, *m.*, monomial
одночленный, *adj.*, monomial, one-term
одношаговый, *adj.*, one-step
одношпунтовый, *adj.*, one-channel, single-channel
одноэлектронный, *adj.*, one-electron, single-electron
одноэлементный, *adj.*, one-element, consisting of a single element
оживальный, *adj.*, ogival
ожидаемый, *adj.*, expected; **ожидаемая частота**, expected frequency
ожидание, *n.*, expectation; **время ожидания**, latency, latency period, delay; **математическое ожидание**, mathematical expectation, mean value
ожидать, *v.*, expect, wait
озабочиваться (озаботиться), *v.*, see (to), attend (to), take care (of)
ознакомление, *n.*, acquaintance
ознакомлять (ознакомить), *v.*, acquaint
означать, *v.*, mean, denote, signify
оказать (cf. **оказывать**), *v.*, render, show; **оказать влияние**, *v.*, influence

оказывать (оказать), *v.*, render, show
оказываться (оказаться), *v.*, prove to be, turn out to be, be found
оказывающий, *adj.*, rendering, contributory
окаймление, *n.*, bordering, edging
окаймленный, *adj.*, edged, bordered
окаймлять (окаймить), *v.*, border, edge
окаймляющий, *adj.*, bordering, bounding; **окаймляющая грань,** boundary face
оканчивать (окончить), *v.*, finish, end
оканчивающийся, *adj.*, terminating
океан, *m.*, ocean
океанография, *f.*, oceanography
океанология, *f.*, oceanology
окисел, *m.*, oxide
окисление, *n.*, oxidation
окись, *f.*, oxide
окклюзия, *f.*, occlusion
оккультный, *adj.*, occult
около, *prep.*, near, about, by, close to, around
околозвуковой, *adj.*, transonic
окольный, *adj.*, roundabout
окомплексивание, *n.*, complexification
оконечный, *adj.*, final, end
окончание, *n.*, termination, end
окончательно, *adv.*, finally
окончательный, *adj.*, final, definitive, best possible, terminal; **функция окончательных решений,** terminal-decision function; **окончательное выражение,** resultant expression
окончить (cf. **оканчивать**), *v.*, finish, end, terminate
окрашенный, *adj.*, colored, tinted
окрестностный, *adj.*, neighborhood
окрестность, *f.*, neighborhood, vicinity
окрестный, *adj.*, neighboring, neighborhood
округление, *n.*, approximation, rounding off; **ошибка округления,** round-off error; **точка округления,** umbilical point
округленный, *adj.*, rounded, rounded off, approximated, umbilical
округлять (округлить), *v.*, round off, approximate
окружать (окружить), *v.*, enclose, surround
окружающий, *adj.*, enclosing, surrounding, encircling, ambient; **окружающая сфера,** environment
окружение, *n.*, enclosing, encirclement, environment
окруженный, *adj.*, surrounded, enclosed
окружность, *f.*, circumference, circle, periphery; **поле деления окружности,** cyclotomic field
окружный, *adj.*, peripheral, circumferential; **окружная скорость,** peripheral velocity
октава, *f.*, octave
октавный, *adj.*, octave
октанион, *m.*, octonion
октант, *m.*, octant
октаэдр, *m.*, octahedron
октаэдральный, *adj.*, octahedral
октиль, *m.*, octile
октупольный, *adj.*, octopole
олимпиада, *f.*, olympiad; **математическая олимпиада,** mathematical competition in schools
ом, *m.*, ohm (unit)
омбилический, *adj.*, umbilical
омега, *f.*, omega
омега-непротиворечивость, *f.*, omega-consistency
омега-полнота, *f.*, omega-completeness
омический, *adj.*, ohm, ohmic; **омическое сопротивление,** ohmic resistance
он, *pron. m.*, he, it
она, *pron. f.*, she, it
они, *pron. pl.*, they
оно, *pron. n.*, it
онтологический, *adj.*, ontological
онтология, *f.*, ontology
опасение, *n.*, fear, misgiving
опасность, *f.*, risk, hazard, danger
опасный, *adj.*, dangerous, risky
операнд, *m.*, operand
оператив, *m.*, operative

оперативный, *adj.*, operating, operative, operational

оператор, *m.*, operator; **оператор взятия границы,** boundary operator; **оператор вложения,** embedding operator; **оператор-гомоморфизм,** operator homomorphism; **оператор-изоморфизм,** operator isomorphism; **оператор осреднения,** averaging operator; **оператор переноса,** translation operator; **оператор у пульта управления,** console operator

операторно, *adv.*, operationally, by means of an operator; **операторно-гомоморфный,** *adj.*, operator-homomorphic; **операторно-изоморфный,** *adj.*, operator-isomorphic

операторный, *adj.*, operator, operational

операциональный, *adj.*, operational

операционно, *adv.*, operationally; **операционно связанный,** *adj.*, operationally related

операционный, *adj.*, operational

операция, *f.*, operation; **код операции,** operation part; **компонента операции,** operand

опереться (cf. **опираться**), *v.*, be based on, be guided by

оперирование, *n.*, operation

оперировать, *v.*, operate, use

опертый, *adj.*, supported, supported by, depending (on)

опечатка, *f.*, misprint

опираться (опереться), *v.*, rely on, use, be based on, rest on

опирающийся (на), *adj.*, based (on)

опираясь (на), *adv. part.*, relying (on), basing (on)

описание, *n.*, description

описанный, *adj.*, circumscribed

описательно, *adv.*, descriptively

описательный, *adj.*, descriptive

описать (cf. **описывать**), *v.*, circumscribe, describe, write

описаться, *v.*, be characterized, be circumscribed

описка, *f.*, error

описываемый, *adj.*, described, describable

описывать (описать), *v.*, describe, circumscribe, write

опознавательный, *adj.*, identification, authentication

опознание, *n.*, identification

опора, *f.*, support

опорный, *adj.*, supporting, support, bearing; **опорная плоскость,** plane of support; **опорная функция,** support function

оправдание, *n.*, justification

оправданный, *adj.*, justified

оправдывать (оправдать), *v.*, justify, warrant

определение, *n.*, definition, determination; **определение по индукции,** definition by induction; **по определению,** by definition; **определение местонахождения,** locating

определенно-отрицательный, *adj.*, negative definite

определенно-положительный, *adj.*, positive definite

определенность, *f.*, definiteness, determination

определенный, *adj.*, definite, specific, defined, well-defined, determinate, determined; **определенное событие,** specific event

определимость, *f.*, definability

определимый, *adj.*, definable

определитель, *f.*, determinant

определяемый, *adj.*, defined, definable, determined; **определяемое (выражение),** *n.*, definiendum (log.)

определять (определить), *v.*, define, determine, evaluate; **определять место,** *v.*, locate, allocate

определяться, *v.*, be defined, be determined

определяющий, *adj.*, defining, determining; **цифра, определяющая знак,** sign digit; **определяющее (выражение),** *n.*, definiens (log.)

опробование, *n.*, sampling, testing

опровергать (опровергнуть), *v.*, refute, disprove, contradict
опровергающий, *adj.*, disproving, rejected
опровергнутый, *adj.*, disproved, rejected
опровержение, *n.*, refutation, disproof, denial, contradiction
опровержимый, *adj.*, refutable
опрокидывающий, *adj.*, tipping, tilting
опрос, *m.*, inquiry, questionnaire, question
оптика, *f.*, optics
оптимальный, *adj.*, optimum, optimal, good; **оптимальная стратегия,** optimal strategy, good strategy
оптимизация, *f.*, optimization
оптимистический, *adj.*, optimistic
оптимум, *m.*, optimum
оптический, *adj.*, optical; **оптический обман,** optical illusion
оптовый, *adj.*, wholesale
опубликование, *n.*, publication
опубликованный, *adj.*, published
опубликовывать, *v.*, publish
опускаемый, *adj.*, lowered, dropped, omitted; **опускаемое значение,** omitted value, exceptional value
опускание, *n.*, lowering
опускать (опустить), *v.*, lower, drop, omit; **опустить перпендикуляр,** *v.*, drop a perpendicular
опускаться, *v.*, be dropped, relax
опустошение, *n.*, destruction
опущение, *n.*, omission
опущенный, *adj.*, omitted, dropped
опыт, *m.*, attempt, trial, experiment
опытный, *adj.*, experimental, empirical
опять, *adv.*, again; **опять же,** besides
опять-таки, *adv.*, but again, besides
орбита, *f.*, orbit
орбитальный, *adj.*, orbital
орган, *m.*, device, organ, body, agency
организационный, *adj.*, organizational
организация, *f.*, organization; **организация тыла,** logistics
организм, *m.*, organism
организовать, *v.*, organize
органический, *adj.*, organic, integral
ординал, *m.*, ordinal
ординальный, *adj.*, ordinal; **ординальное число,** ordinal number, ordinal
ординарность, *f.*, ordinariness
ординарный, *adj.*, ordinary, common
ордината, *f.*, ordinate
оригинал, *m.*, original, pre-image
оригинальный, *adj.*, original
ориентация, *f.*, orientation
ориентированный, *adj.*, oriented, directed
ориентировать, *v.*, orient, direct
ориентироваться, *v.*, be oriented, be guided (by)
ориентировка, *f.*, alignment, orientation
ориентировочный, *adj.*, approximate, tentative, orientation
ориентируемость, *f.*, orientability
ориентируемый, *adj.*, orientable
орицикл, *m.*, oricycle
орт, *m.*, basis vector, unit vector
ортант, *m.*, orthant; **негативный ортант,** negative orthant
ортогонализация, *f.*, orthogonalization
ортогонализировать, *v.*, orthogonalize
ортогонально-ассоциированный, *adj.*, orthogonally associated
ортогональность, *f.*, orthogonality
ортогональный, *adj.*, orthogonal
ортодоксальный, *adj.*, orthodox
ортодополнение, *n.*, orthocomplementation, orthocomplement, orthogonal complement
ортоморфизм, *m.*, orthomorphism
ортонормализация, *f.*, orthonormalization
ортонормальный, *adj.*, orthonormal
ортонормирование, *n.*, orthonormalization
ортонормированный, *adj.*, orthonormalized, normalized, orthonormal
ортоповерхность, *f.*, orthosurface
ортосимметрический, *adj.*, orthosymmetric
ортотропный, *adj.*, orthotropic
ортоцентр, *m.*, orthocenter
ортоцентрический, *adj.*, orthocentric

орудие, *n.*, tool, instrument, device
осадок, *m.*, sediment, deposit
осаждаться, *v.*, settle, deposit, be precipitated, fall, fall out
осваивание, *n.*, mastering, assimilation
осваивать (освоить), *v.*, master, assimilate
осведомление, *n.*, information, notification
осведомленный, *adj.*, informed
осведомлять, *v.*, inform (of)
освежать, *v.*, renew, regenerate, refresh
осветительный, *adj.*, lighting, illuminating
освещать (осветить), *v.*, illuminate, throw light (on)
освещение, *n.*, illumination, lighting, elucidation
освещенный, *adj.*, elucidated, illuminated
освободиться, *v.*, get rid of, eliminate, become free
освобождать (освободить), *v.*, liberate, release, set free
освобождение, *n.*, release, discharge, liberation
освоение, *n.*, mastering, assimilation
осевой, *adj.*, axial
оседание, *n.*, settling, yielding, precipitation
осесимметрический, *adj.*, axially symmetric
осесимметричный, *adj.*, axially symmetric
осечка, *f.*, misfire
осколок, *m.*, splinter, fragment
оскулаторный, *adj.*, osculatory; **обратная оскулаторная интерполяция,** inverse osculatory interpolation
оскулирование, *n.*, osculation
оскулировать, *v.*, touch, osculate
оскулирующий, *adj.*, touching, osculating
оскуляционный, *adj.*, osculatory
оскуляция, *f.*, osculation
ослабление, *n.*, weakening, slackening, reduction, relaxation, attenuation
ослабленный, *adj.*, weakened, relaxed
ослаблять (ослабить), *v.*, loosen, relax, weaken
осложнение, *n.*, complication
осложнять (осложнить), *v.*, complicate
осматривать (осмотреть), *v.*, examine, inspect, scan, look over
осмос, *m.*, osmosis
осмотический, *adj.*, osmotic
осмысленный, *adj.*, intelligent, sensible
осмыслять (осмыслить), *v.*, give meaning to, comprehend, interpret
оснащать (оснастить), *v.*, equip
оснащение, *n.*, equipment
оснащенный, *adj.*, equipped
основа, *f.*, base, basis, foundation; **на основе,** because of, on the basis of
основание, *n.*, base, reason, basis, foundation, ground; **на основании,** on the basis of, because of; **основание (системы счисления),** radix; **вычислительная машина с основанием два,** radix two computer; **основание (перпендикуляра),** foot (of a perpendicular)
основанный, *adj.*, established, based on; **основанный на постулатах,** *adj.*, postulational
основательно, *adv.*, fully, thoroughly
основательный, *adj.*, solid, substantial, thorough
основать (cf. **основывать**), *v.*, base, lay the foundation
основной, *adj.*, basic, basis, fundamental, principal; **основной вектор,** basis vector, unit vector; **основная линия,** base line; **основное значение,** basic meaning; **основной период,** fundamental period; **во всем основном,** on the whole; **основное поле,** ground field, base field
основоглавный, *adj.*, dominant
основополагать, *v.*, establish, found
основополагающий, *adj.*, basic, initial
основоположение, *n.*, basic foundation
основоположник, *m.*, initiator, founder
основоположный, *adj.*, fundamental, original, basic
основывать (основать), *v.*, base, found, lay the foundation

основываться, *v.*, be based, be based on
особенно, *adv.*, particularly, especially
особенность, *f.*, singularity, peculiarity, exception; **особенность типа диполя,** dipole singularity; **функция особенности,** singularity function, singular function
особенный, *adj.*, singular, particular, special
особо, *adv.*, separately, particularly, explicitly
особый, *adj.*, singular, particular, peculiar, critical; **особая точка,** singular point
осознавать (осознать), *v.*, realize
оспаривать (оспорить), *v.*, dispute, question
осреднение, *n.*, average, averaging
осредненный, *adj.*, average, averaged
оставаться (остаться), *v.*, remain
оставить (cf. **оставлять),** *v.*, leave
оставлять (оставить), *v.*, leave; **оставлять на месте,** *v.*, leave fixed; **оставить без внимания,** *v.*, disregard
оставляющий, *adj.*, leaving
остается (cf. **остаться**), it remains
остальной, *adj.*, the other, the rest, remaining
останавливать (остановить), *v.*, stop, discontinue, shut down
останавливаться, *v.*, stop, come to a stop, dwell on, go into
остановка, *f.*, stop, stopping, halt
остаток, *m.*, remainder, residue, residual; **нормальный остаток,** normal residual
остаточный, *adj.*, residual, remainder; **остаточный член,** remainder term; **остаточная дисперсия,** residual variance; **остаточная намагниченность,** remanence
остаться (cf. **оставаться**), *v.*, remain
остающийся, *adj.*, residual, remaining; *m.*, remainder; **остающаяся стратегия,** remaining strategy
остерегаться (остеречь), *v.*, avoid, be careful of
остов, *m.*, frame, framework, skeleton; **одномерный остов,** 1-skeleton
осторожно, *adv.*, carefully, cautiously
осторожность, *f.*, care, caution
осторожный, *adj.*, cautious, careful, delicate
острие, *n.*, point, spike, edge, cusp
островершинность, *f.*, pointedness, peakedness
Остроградский, *m.*, Ostrogradskii; **теорема Остроградского,** Gauss divergence theorem
остроконечность, *f.*, pointedness, peakedness
острота, *f.*, sharpness, delicacy
остроугольный, *adj.*, acute, acute-angled
острый, *adj.*, acute, sharp, spike; **острый угол,** acute angle; **острый импульс,** spike pulse
осуществимость, *f.*, realizability, practicability, feasibility, admissibility
осуществимый, *adj.*, realizable, practicable, feasible, admissible
осуществить (cf. **осуществлять),** *v.*, realize, effect, bring about
осуществление, *n.*, realization
осуществляемый, *adj.*, realized, effected, induced, defined
осуществлять (осуществить), *v.*, realize, effect, bring about
осуществляться, *v.*, be realized, be effected, come about
осуществляющий, *adj.*, realizing, effecting
осуществляя, *adv. part.*, effecting, realizing, making
осциллировать, *v.*, oscillate
осциллирующий, *adj.*, oscillating, oscillatory
осциллограмма, *f.*, oscillogram
осциллограф, *m.*, oscillograph
осциллятор, *m.*, oscillator
осцилляционность, *f.*, oscillation, oscillatory character
осцилляционный, *adj.*, oscillation, oscillatory
осцилляция, *f.*, oscillation

ось, *f.*, axis, axle; **главная ось,** principal axis, major axis
осями (from **ось**), (by the) axes
от, *prep.*, from, away from, of
отбирать (отобрать), *v.*, select, choose, take away
отбор, *m.*, selection
отборный, *adj.*, choice, selected
отбрасываемый, *adj.*, rejecting, rejected
отбрасывание, *n.*, rejection; **область отбрасывания,** rejection region; **ошибка при отбрасывании (членов),** truncation error
отбрасывать (отбросить), *v.*, reject, discard, throw off; **отбрасывать тень,** *v.*, shadow, cast a shadow
отброшенный, *adj.*, rejected, discarded
отвергать (отвергнуть), *v.*, reject, discard
отвергаться, *v.*, be rejected, be discarded
отвергнутый, *adj.*, rejected, discarded
отверстие, *n.*, perforation, opening, aperture, hole; **пробивать отверстие,** *v.*, punch
отвес, *m.*, plumb-line; **по отвесу,** perpendicularly
отвесный, *adj.*, plumb, sheer; **отвесная линия,** plumb-line
ответ, *m.*, answer, reply, response; **функция-ответ,** response function
ответвление, *n.*, branch, off-shoot, derivation
ответный, *adj.*, reciprocal, response
отвечать (ответить), *v.*, answer, reply, respond
отвечающий, *adj.*, responding (to), corresponding (to)
отвлекать (отвлечь), *v.*, abstract, divert, digress
отвлекаться, *v.*, be distracted, abstract
отвлечение, *n.*, abstraction
отвлеченность, *f.*, abstractness
отвлеченный, *adj.*, abstract
отвлечься, cf. **отвлекаться**
отвод, *m.*, branch, outlet
отдавать (отдать), *v.*, return, give back
отдаваться (отдаться), *v.*, be devoted to
отдача, *f.*, response, output, efficiency
отделение, *n.*, separation, isolation
отделенный, *adj.*, separated, detached, isolated
отделимость, *f.*, separability, separation, isolation; **аксиома отделимости,** separability axiom
отделимый, *adj.*, separable, separated
отделитель, *m.*, separator, eliminator
отделить (cf. **отделять**), *v.*, separate
отделка, *f.*, finishing, trimming, smoothing
отдельно, *adv.*, separately
отдельность, *f.*, individuality, singularity; **в отдельности,** individually, separately
отдельный, *adj.*, separate, individual, isolated; **отдельная точка,** isolated point
отделять (отделить), *v.*, separate, isolate
отделяющий, *adj.*, separating, isolating; **отделяющее множество,** separating set
отзыв, *m.*, opinion, reference
отказ, *m.*, refusal, denial, rejection
отказывать (отказать), *v.*, refuse, reject, deny
отказываться (отказаться), *v.*, waive, relinquish
откидной, *adj.*, reversible, collapsible
откидывать (откинуть), *v.*, throw off, discard
откладывание, *n.*, postponement
откладывать (отложить), *v.*, put aside, postpone
откладывая, *adv. part.*, postponing, putting aside
отклонение, *n.*, deviation, divergence, deflection, error
отклоненный, *adj.*, deviating, divergent, deflected
отклоняемость, *f.*, deviation
отклоняться, *v.*, deviate, diverge
отклоняющий, *adj.*, deflection, deflective, deflecting; **отклоняющая система,** deflection field, deflection system; **отклоняющее отображение,** perturbation, perturbation mapping

откос, *m.*, slope, side slope, inclination
открывать (открыть), *v.*, open, discover
открывающий, *adj.*, opening; **открывающее множество,** opening set, opener
открытие, *n.*, opening; discovery
открыто-замкнутый, *adj.*, open-closed
открытость, *f.*, openness
открытый, *adj.*, open, opened, discovered; **открытое отображение,** interior mapping, open mapping
открыть (cf. **открывать**), *v.*, open, discover
откуда, *adv.*, whence, from which
отлагать (= **откладывать**)
отлив, *m.*, low-tide, ebb
отличать (отличить), *v.*, distinguish
отличаться, *v.*, differ, differ from, be distinguished
отличающийся, *adj.*, differing
отличие, *n.*, difference, distinction; **в отличие от,** unlike, in contrast to, as opposed to
отличимость, *f.*, distinguishability
отличимый, *adj.*, distinguishable
отличительный, *adj.*, distinctive
отлично, *adv.*, differently, excellently, perfectly well
отличный, *adj.*, different, different from, distinct, distinctive
отложить (*perf.* of **откладывать, отлагать**), lay aside, postpone
отмена, *f.*, cancellation (of a command or signal)
отметина, *f.*, mark, marking, star
отметить (cf. **отмечать**), *v.*, single out, note, mark, mark off; **следует отметить что,** it should be noted that
отметка, *f.*, note, mark
отмечать (отметить), *v.*, mark, note
отмеченный, *adj.*, marked, noted, recorded, distinguished; **отмеченный для отличия,** *adj.*, distinguished; **отмеченный идеал,** distinguished ideal; **отмеченный граф,** signed graph
отнесение, *n.*, reference; **точка отнесения,** reference point
отнести (cf. **относить**), *v.*, refer, associate, attribute, put
отнимать (отнять), *v.*, take away, substract
относительно, *adv.*, relatively, with respect to; *prep.*, concerning, relative to, with respect to, over; **относительно инвариантный,** *adj.*, relatively invariant; **относительно обратный,** *adj.*, relative inverse; **алгебраический относительно,** *adj.*, algebraic over; **конечный относительно,** *adj.*, finite over
относительность, *f.*, relativity; **теория относительности,** theory of relativity
относительный, *adj.*, relative; **относительное произведение,** relative bundle; **относительный минимум,** relative minimum; **кодирование с относительными адресами,** relative coding; **относительное удлинение,** aspect ratio; **относительное число,** algebraic number
относить (отнести), *v.*, refer, relate, put
относиться, *v.*, be, be to, be relative to, relate; **три относится к четырем как шесть к восьми,** three is to four as six is to eight
относя, *adv. part.*, relating, referring, related (to)
относящийся, *adj.*, involving, relating to
отношение, *n.*, ratio, quotient, relation; **в этом отношении,** in this respect; **по отношению к,** with respect to; **отношение эквивалентности,** equivalence relation; **поле отношений,** quotient field; **кольцо отношений,** quotient ring; **последовательный критерий отношений вероятностей,** sequential probability ratio test; **отношение предпочтений,** preference relation, preference pattern; **двойное отношение,** cross-ratio; **двоичное отношение,** binary relation; **простое отношение,** affine ratio (of three points)

отныне, *adv.*, henceforth
отнюдь, *adv.*, by no means, not at all
отнять (cf. **отнимать**), *v.*, take away, subtract
отображать (отобразить), *v.*, map, reflect, represent, transform; **отображать в,** *v.*, map into; **отображать на,** *v.*, map onto
отображающий, *adj.*, mapping, transforming, representing
отображение, *n.*, mapping, representation, transformation; **отображение в целом,** global mapping, mapping in the large; **отображение в (себя),** into mapping; **отображение на (себя),** onto mapping; **отображение произведений,** bundle map
отображенный, *adj.*, represented, mapped
отобразимый, *adj.*, resolvable; **отобразимый предикат,** resolvable predicate
отобразить (cf. **отображать**), *v.*, map, represent, transform
отобранный, *adj.*, selected
отобрать (cf. **отбирать**), *v.*, select
отождествитель, *m.*, identifier
отождествление, *n.*, identification, identifying
отождествленный, *adj.*, identified
отождествлять (отождествить), *v.*, identify
отождествляться, *v.*, be identified
отопление, *n.*, heating
оторвать (cf. **отрывать**), *v.*, remove, tear off, separate, isolate
отослать (cf. **отсылать**), *v.*, refer to
отпадать (отпасть), *v.*, drop out, be eliminated
отправлять (отправить), *v.*, transmit, dispatch
отправляться, *v.*, start, go
отправной, *adj.*, starting; **отправная точка, отправной пункт,** starting point, origin
отпускание, *n.*, release, freeing
отработать, *v.*, complete, finish off
отражаемый, *adj.*, mapped, image; **отражаемая кривая,** image curve
отражатель, *m.*, reflector, deflector, ejector
отражательный, *adj.*, reflecting, reflective; **отражательная способность,** reflectance
отражать (отразить), *v.*, reflect, repulse, repel, map
отражаться, *v.*, be reflected, be mapped; **отражается в нуль,** vanishes
отражение, *n.*, reflection, image; **принцип отражения,** reflection principle
отраженный, *adj.*, reflected
отразить (cf. **отражать**), *v.*, reflect
отрасль, *f.*, branch
отрезок, *m.*, segment, (closed) interval; **отрезок, отсекаемый на оси (прямой линей),** intercept (of a straight line)
отрезочный, *adj.*, segment, pert. to segment; **отрезочный комплекс,** complex of segments
отрицание, *n.*, negation, denial
отрицательный, *adj.*, negative; **отрицательная обратная связь,** negative feedback
отрицать, *v.*, deny, contradict
отрицаться, *v.*, be negated, be denied, be contradicted
отрыв, *m.*, separation, isolation; **точка отрыва,** separation
отрывать (оторвать), *v.*, separate, isolate, tear off, interrupt
отрывок, *m.*, fragment
отрывочный, *adj.*, fragmentary
отсеивание, *n.*, elimination, screening, sifting
отсеивать (also **отсевать**), *v.*, sift, screen, eliminate
отсекаемьй, *adj.*, cut off, intercepted; **отрезок, отсекаемый на оси** *X*, intercept on the *X*-axis (*see also* **отрезок**)
отсекать (отсечь), *v.*, cut off, sever
отсеченный, *adj.*, cut off
отсечка, *f.*, cut-off
отсеять, cf. **отсеивать**
отставать (отстать), *v.*, lag, lag behind, fall back

отстаивать (отстоять), *v.*, defend, advocate
отстающий, *adj.*, lagging
отстоять, *v.*, be distant, be apart
отстоящий, *adj.*, distant
отступление, *n.*, digression, deviation
отсутствие, *n.*, absence, lack; **отсутствие сигнала,** no signal; **отсутствие импульса (сигнала),** gap (in a signal)
отсутствовать, *v.*, be lacking, be absent, be missing
отсутствующий, *adj.*, missing, absent
отсчет, *m.*, reading, reference; **ось отсчета,** axis of reference; **система отсчета,** frame of reference
отсчитывать (отсчитать), *v.*, count, reckon, count off
отсылать (отослать), *v.*, refer to
отсюда, *adv.*, from here, hence
отталкивание, *n.*, repulsion
отталкивать (оттолкнуть), *v.*, repel, repulse
отталкивающий, *adj.*, repelling, repellent, repulsing
оттачивать (отточить), *v.*, sharpen, perfect
оттенок, *m.*, nuance, inflection
оттенять (оттенить), *v.*, shade, tint, graduate
оттолкнуть, cf. **отталкивать**
оттуда, *adv.*, from there
оттянутый, *adj.*, plucked, delayed, drawn out; **оттянутая струна,** plucked string
отфильтровывать, *v.*, filter, filter out
отход, *m.*, removal, withdrawal, deviation, departure
отцепляемый, *adj.*, split off, segregated, splittable; **отцепляемая алгебра,** segregated algebra
отчасти, *adv.*, partly, partially
отчет, *m.*, report, account
отчетливо, *adv.*, clearly, distinctly
отчетливый, *adj.*, clear, distinct, sharp
отчетный, *adj.*, current, account, report; **отчетный период,** accounting period
отщепление, *n.*, splitting off, detaching, removal
отщепляться, *v.*, split off, detach
отъюстированный, *adj.*, adjusted
отыскание, *n.*, determination, discovery, estimation
отыскивание, *n.*, search
отыскивать (отыскать), *v.*, find out, search, discover
отягчать, *v.*, aggravate
охарактеризованный, *adj.*, characterized
охарактеризовать, *v.*, describe, characterize
охват, *m.*, scope, envelopment, inclusion
охватывать (охватить), *v.*, envelope, contain, involve, cover, include
охватываться, *v.*, be covered, be spanned
охватывающий, *adj.*, enveloping, overlapping, covering, containing
охваченный, *adj.*, included, spanned
охладевать (охладеть), *v.*, cool, grow cold
охлаждать (охладить), *v.*, cool, cool off; **охлаждать пар,** condense, condense steam
охлаждаться, *v.*, cool, cool down
охлаждающий, *adj.*, cooling
охлаждение, *n.*, cooling
охлажденный, *adj.*, cooled
оцененный, *adj.*, estimated, evaluated
оцениваемый, *adj.*, (being) evaluated, (being) estimated
оценивать (оценить), *v.*, consider, evaluate, estimate, bound
оценивающий, *adj.*, evaluating, estimating, assigning values
оценить (cf. **оценивать**), *v.*, estimate, evaluate, bound
оценка, *f.*, bound, estimate, evaluation, valuation, estimation; **оценка сверху,** upper bound; **оценка снизу,** lower bound; **асимптотически-эффективная оценка,** asymptotically efficient estimate; **достаточная оценка,** sufficient estimate; **оценка максимального правдоподобия,** maximum likelihood

estimate; **несмещенная оценка,** unbiased estimate; **состоятельная оценка,** consistent estimate; **эффективная оценка,** efficient estimate; **случай регулярной оценки,** regular estimation case; **совместно-достаточная оценка,** joint sufficient estimate; **совместно-эффективная оценка,** joint efficient estimate; **регулярная оценка,** regular estimate; **кольцо (дискретной) оценки,** (discrete) valuation ring

оценочный, *adj.*, evaluating, valuating, estimating; **оценочная функция,** estimator

очаг, *m.*, seat, center; **очаг землетрясения,** seismic center, seismic focus

очевидно (from **очевидный**), it is evident, it is obvious (that)

очевидно, *adv.*, evidently, obviously

очевидность, *f.*, clearness, obviousness

очевидный, *adj.*, obvious, evident, trivial

очень, *adv.*, very, very much

очередной, *adj.*, next, recurrent

очередность, *f.*, regular succession, order of priority, sequence

очередь, *f.*, turn, line, queue; **на очереди,** next in turn; **в первую очередь,** in the first place; **в свою очередь,** in turn; **теория очередей,** theory of queues, queueing theory

очерк, *m.*, outline, sketch

очерчивать (очертить), *v.*, outline, trace, draw around

очко, *n.*, point

ошибаться (ошибиться), *v.*, make a mistake, err

ошибка, *f.*, error, mistake; **ошибка округления,** round-off error; **ошибка при отбрасывании (членов),** truncation error; **распределение ошибок,** error distribution; **стандартная ошибка,** standard error; **время работы машины без ошибок,** good time; **устройство для обнаружения ошибки,** error detecting facility; **время работы с ошибками,** down time; **интеграл ошибок,** error integral, error function

ошибочно, *adv.*, by mistake, erroneously

ошибочность, *f.*, inaccuracy, error

ошибочный, *adj.*, erroneous

ощелачивание, *n.*, alkalization, alkalizing

ощелачивать, *v.*, alkalize

ощупание, *n.*, feeling, probing, sounding

ощупывать, *v.*, feel, probe, sound

ощупь, *f.*, touch

ощутимый, *adj.*, perceptible, tangible

ощутительно, *adv.*, perceptibly, appreciably, tangibly

ощутительность, *f.*, perceptibility, tangibility

ощутительный, *adj.*, tangible, perceptible, appreciable

ощущаемый, *adj.*, (being) felt, (being) perceived

ощущать (ощутить), *v.*, feel, sense, perceive

ощущение, *n.*, sensation, perception, sense

П

падать (пасть, упасть), *v.*, fall, drop

падающий, *adj.*, incident, falling, dropping

падение, *n.*, fall, drop, incidence; **угол падения,** angle of incidence; **падение напряжения,** voltage drop

пайка, *f.*, soldering

паз, *m.*, slot, groove

палец, *m.*, finger; **счет по пальцам,** finger counting

палиндромический, *adj.*, palindromic

палуба, *f.*, deck; **полетная палуба,** flight deck
память, *f.*, memory; **емкость памяти,** memory capacity, storage capacity
пангеодезический, *adj.*, pangeodesic
пандиагональный, *adj.*, pandiagonal
панель, *f.*, panel; **коммутационная панель,** keysets
пантограф, *m.*, pantograph
пар, *m.*, steam, vapor; **перегретый пар,** superheated steam
пара, *f.*, pair, couple; **пара сил,** couple, force couple; **задача о составлении пар,** matching problem
параабелевый, *adj.*, para-abelian
пароаналитический, *adj.*, para-analytic, hyperanalytic
парааналитичность, *f.*, para-analyticity
парабола, *f.*, parabola
параболический, *adj.*, parabolic
параболоид, *m.*, paraboloid
паравыпуклый, *adj.*, paraconvex
параграф, *m.*, paragraph, section
парадокс, *m.*, paradox
парадоксально, *adv.*, paradoxically
парадоксальность, *f.*, paradoxicality
парадоксальный, *adj.*, paradoxical
паразитический, *adj.*, parasitic
паразитный, *adj.*, parasite, parasitic; **паразитный сигнал,** spurious signal
паракомпактность, *f.*, paracompactness, compactness
паракомпактный, *adj.*, paracompact, compact
паракомплексный, *adj.*, para-complex
параксиальный, *adj.*, paraxial; **параксиальные лучи,** paraxial rays
параллакс, *m.*, parallax
параллактический, *adj.*, parallax
параллелепипед, *m.*, parallelepiped
параллелизм, *m.*, parallelism
параллелизуемость, *f.*, parallelizibility
параллелизуемый, *adj.*, parallelizable
параллелограмм, *m.*, parallelogram
параллелотоп, *m.*, parallelotope
параллель, *f.*, parallel; **проводить параллель,** *v.*, draw a parallel
параллельно, *adv.*, in a parallel way, in parallels; *pred.*, (it) is parallel
параллельно-аффинный, *adj.*, parallel-affine
параллельно-последовательный, *adj.*, parallel-serial; **параллельно-последовательный метод выполнения операций,** parallel-serial mode
параллельностный, *adj.*, parallel; **параллельностное распределение в целом,** parallel distribution in the large
параллельность, *f.*, parallelism
параллельный, *adj.*, parallel; **метод параллельного действия,** parallel mode
парамагнетизм, *m.*, paramagnetism
парамагнитный, *adj.*, paramagnetic
параметр, *m.*, parameter; **параметр положения,** location parameter; **параметр разброса,** scale parameter, dispersion index; **предварительно введенный параметр,** preset parameter
параметризация, *f.*, parametrization
параметрический, *adj.*, parametric
паранорма, *f.*, paranorm
паранормированный, *adj.*, paranormed, with a paranorm
параслед, *m.*, paratrace
парасфера, *f.*, parasphere
параунитарный, *adj.*, para-unitary
парафин, *m.*, paraffin
паритет, *m.*, parity, equality
паритетный, *adj.*, parity
парный, *adj.*, conjugate, twin, pair, dual
паровой, *adj.*, steam
пароход, *m.*, steamboat, steamship
парсек, *m.*, parsec (3.26 light years)
партиция, *f.*, partition
партия, *f.*, party, group, set, batch, lot, game
партнер, *m.*, partner
парциальный, *adj.*, partial
паскалевый, *adj.*, Pascal, pertaining to Pascal
пасовать (спасовать), *v.*, pass (at cards, in a game), no bid

пассивный, *adj.*, passive
пасть, cf. **падать**
патологический, *adj.*, pathological
патология, *f.*, pathology
пеановский, *adj.*, Peano, pertaining to Peano
педагогический, *adj.*, pedagogical
педантизм, *m.*, pedantry
педантичность, *f.*, pedantry
пентагон, *m.*, pentagon
пентагональный, *adj.*, pentagonal
пентаэдр, *m.*, pentahedron
пентод, *m.*, pentode
первично, *adv.*, primarily, initially
первичный, *adj.*, primary, initial, prime
первобытный, *adj.*, primitive
первоначально, *adv.*, originally, initially
первоначальный, *adj.*, original, initial, prime, primary, elementary, primitive; **первоначальные данные,** raw data
первообраз, *m.*, prototype, pre-image, primitive
первообразная, *f.*, primitive, antiderivative
первообразный, *adj.*, original, primitive; **первообразные корни,** primitive roots; **первообразная функция,** primitive, antiderivative
первооснова, *f.*, fundamental principle
первостепенный, *adj.*, primary, paramount
первый, *adj.*, first, former, **во первых,** in the first place; **первое слагаемое,** augend, addend, first term
перебирать (перебрать), *v.*, sort out, look over, reset
перебрасывание, *n.*, transfer, throwing over
переброс, *m.*, transfer, throwing over
переброска, *f.*, transfer, throwing over
перевал, *m.*, saddle-point, crossing, passing; **метод перевала,** saddle-point method
переваливать (перевалить), *v.*, cross, pass, load, exceed
перевалка, *f.*, transfer
перевалочный, *adj.*, transfer; **перевалочный пункт,** transfer point
переведенный, *adj.*, translated
перевернутый, *adj.*, inverted, reverse
перевертывать (перевернуть), *v.*, invert, turn over
перевести (cf. **переводить),** *v.*, translate, transfer
перевод, *m.*, translation, transfer, conversion; **таблица перевода,** conversion table
переводить (перевести), *v.*, translate, transfer
переводчик, *m.*, translator, interpreter; change-lever
переводящий, *adj.*, translating, transferring, transforming, sending
перевозка, *f.*, transport, conveyance, transportation
перегиб, *m.*, inflection, bend, twist; **точка перегиба,** point of inflection
переговоры, *pl.*, talks, negotiations
перегородка, *f.*, partition
перегрев, *m.*, superheating, overheating
перегревание, *n.*, superheating
перегревать (перегреть), *v.*, superheat, overheat
перегретый, *adj.*, superheated; **перегретый пар,** superheated steam
перегрузка, *f.*, overload
перегруппирование, *n.*, rearrangement, regrouping
перегруппированный, *adj.*, rearranged, regrouped
перегруппировка, *f.*, regrouping
перед, *prep.*, before, in front of, to, compared to
передаваемый, *adj.*, transmitted
передавать (передать), *v.*, transmit, pass, give
переданный, *adj.*, transmitted
передаточный, *adj.*, transmitting, transmission, transfer; **передаточная функция,** transfer function; **передаточное число,** ratio
передатчик, *m.*, transmitter
передача, *f.*, transmission, drive, broadcast; **передача управления по команде безусловного перехода,**

unconditional transfer; **сквозная передача,** rippling through

передающий, *adj.*, transmitting, transmission

передвигать (передвинуть), *v.*, move, shift

передвигаться (передвинуться), *v.*, move, change one's position

передвижение, *n.*, movement

переделка, *f.*, translation, conversion, alteration

передний, *adj.*, front, leading, fore; **передняя кромка,** leading edge

передоказывать (передоказать), *v.*, prove again, reprove

переиздавать (переиздать), *v.*, reprint, republish

переизлучать, *v.*, reradiate

переизлученный, *adj.*, reradiated

переизмерять (переизмерить), *v.*, remeasure

переименование, *n.*, renaming, rewriting

переименовывать (переименовать), *v.*, rename, rewrite

перейти (cf. **переходить**), *v.*, pass

перекидывать (перекидать), *v.*, span

переключатель, *m.*, switch; **переключатель с выборкой по напряжению,** voltage-selector switch

переключательный, *adj.*, switch, switching; **переключательная схема,** switching circuit

переключать (переключить), *v.*, switch, switch over

переключающий, *adj.*, switching; **переключающая схема,** switching circuit

переключение, *n.*, switching

перекрестный, *adj.*, cross, crossed, switch-back

перекрещивание, *n.*, crossing, intersection

перекрещивающийся, *adj.*, crossing, intersecting, criss-cross

перекрывать (перекрыть), *v.*, superimpose, overlap, cover

перекрываться, *v.*, overlap, be covered

перекрывающий, *adj.*, overlapping, covering

перекрывающийся, *adj.*, overlapping, covering, covered

перекрытие, *n.*, overlapping, covering, intersection, duplication

перекрытый, *adj.*, covered, spanned

перематывание, *n.*, rewinding

перемежаемость, *f.*, alternation

перемежать, *v.*, alternate

перемежающийся, *adj.*, alternate, alternating, intermittent

перемена, *f.*, interchange, change, alternation

переменить (cf. **переменять**), *v.*, change, vary

переменная, *f.*, variable, argument

переменный, *adj.*, variable; **переменный ток,** alternating current; **переменное основание системы счисления,** variable radix

переменять (переменить), *v.*, change, vary

переместительность, *f.*, commutativity

переместительный, *adj.*, commutative

переместить (cf. **перемещать**), *v.*, transpose, relocate, commute

перемешанный, *adj.*, mixed; **перемешанные числа,** shuffled numbers

перемешивание, *n.*, intermixing, confusion

перемешивающий, *adj.*, intermixing

перемещать (переместить), *v.*, transpose, transfer, commute

перемещение, *n.*, permutation, transfer, interchange, displacement, moving; **цена перемещения,** cost of moving; **обратное перемещение,** backspacing

перемещенный, *adj.*, displaced, permuted

перемножать (перемножить), *v.*, multiply, multiply out

перемножение, *n.*, multiplication, multiplying out

перемычка, *f.*, cross connection, jumper, bridge

перенапряженный, *adj.*, overstrained

перенесение, *n.*, transference, transportation, displacement

перенести (cf. **переносить**), *v.*, transfer, carry over

перенoмерование, *n.*, enumeration

перенормированный, *adj.*, renormalized

перенормировка, *f.*, renormalization, normalization

перенос, *m.*, transfer, translation, transport, carry, carry-over; **каскадный перенос,** step-by-step carry; **перенос из предыдущего разряда,** previous carry; **сквозной перенос,** ripple-through carry; **перенос переполнения,** overflow; **круговой перенос,** end-around carry; **сложный перенос,** accumulative carry; **циклический перенос,** end-around carry; **предыдущий перенос,** previous carry; **схема переноса,** carry circuit, **цепь переноса,** carry circuit

переносимый, *adj.*, transferable, endurable

переносить (перенести), *v.*, transfer, carry over

переносный, *adj.*, portable, figurative, transfer, transport

переносчик, *m.*, carrier

перенумерация, *f.*, renumbering, enumeration, numbering

перенумерование, *n.*, enumeration, numbering

перенумерованный, *adj.*, renumbered, enumerated

перенумеровать, *v.*, index, enumerate, number, renumber

переопределение, *n.*, overdetermination

переопределенный, *adj.*, overdetermined

переоценивать (переоценить), *v.*, overestimate, overrate

переоценка, *f.*, overestimation

переохладить, *v.*, supercool

переохлаждение, *n.*, supercooling

перепад, *m.*, overfall

переписка, *f.*, correspondence, copying

переписывание, *n.*, rewriting, copying

переписывать (переписать), *v.*, rewrite, copy, write over, make a census of, sample

переписывающий, *adj.*, rewriting, copying

перепись, *f.*, census

переплетение, *n.*, interlacing, linkage, linking; **группа переплетений,** link group

переплет, *m.*, interlacing

переполнение, *n.*, overfilling; **разряд переполнения,** redundancy bit, extra order; **перенос переполнения,** overflow

перепонка, *f.*, membrane

перепрыгивать, *v.*, skip, jump, jump over

перерабатывать (переработать), *v.*, process, remake, alter, revise, transform

переработанный, *adj.*, worked over, treated, revised, altered, transformed

переработать (cf. **перерабатывать**), *v.*, revise, alter, work over, change, transform

переработка, *f.*, processing, revision

перерасположение, *n.*, rearrangement

перераспределение, *n.*, redistribution

перераспределять (перераспределить), *v.*, redistribute

перерасчет, *m.*, re-computation

перерезать, *v.*, intersect, intercept

перерезывающий, *adj.*, intersecting, crosscutting

перерыв, *m.*, interruption, break

пересекать (пересечь), *v.*, intersect, cut, cross

пересекаться, *v.*, intersect; **попарно не пересекаться,** *v.*, be mutually disjoint; **взаимно не пересекаться,** *v.*, be mutually disjoint

пересекающийся, *adj.*, intersecting, crossing; **пересекающиеся линии,** intersecting lines; **пересекающая линия,** secant (line)

пересечение, *n.*, intersection, meet; **точка пересечения,** point of intersection; **гомоморфизм по пересечению,** *m.*, meet-homomorphism; **неразложимый в пересечение,** *adj.*, meet-irreducible

пересечься (cf. **пересекаться**), *v.*, intersect
перескакивать (перескочить), *v.*, skip, omit, jump over
пересматривать (пересмотреть), *v.*, revise, reconsider, look over
переставать (перестать), *v.*, cease, stop
переставлять (переставить), *v.*, rearrange, transpose, move, change the position of; **переставить порядок суммирований**, invert the order of summation
перестановка, *f.*, permutation, rearrangement, transposition
перестановочность, *f.*, permutability
перестановочный, *adj.*, permutation, permutational, commutative
перестать (cf. **переставать**), *v.*, cease, stop
пересчет, *m.*, recalculation, recount, enumeration
пересчитывать (пересчитать), *v.*, enumerate, count over
перетасовка, *f.*, shuffle, shift
перетасовывание, *n.*, reshuffling, reshuffle
перетягивать, *v.*, outweigh, overbalance, contract
переустройство, *n.*, reorganization, reconstruction
переформулирование, *n.*, reformulation, restatement
переформулировать, *v.*, reformulate, restate
перефразированный, *adj.*, rephrased
перефразировать, *v.*, rephrase, paraphrase
перефразировка, *f.*, rephrasing
перехватывать (перехватить), *v.*, intercept
переход, *m.*, passage, transfer, transition, jump, conversion; **условный переход**, branch, conditional jump, "jump if not"; **операция условного перехода**, "jump if not" operation; **команда условного перехода**, "jump if not" instruction; **коэффициент перехода** conversion factor
переходить, *v.*, pass, turn, cross, get over, turn (into)
переходный, *adj.*, transitional, transition; transient; **переходный процесс (явление)**, transient; **переходное состояние**, transient state
переходя, *adv. part.*, going over, passing on to; **переходя к общему случаю**, going over to the general case, if we go over to the general case
переходящий, *adj.*, transferring, translating, carrying
перечень, *m.*, enumeration, list
перечеркивать (перечеркнуть), *v.*, cross out, cancel
перечерчивание, *n.*, replotting, redrawing
перечисление, *n.*, enumeration, transfer
перечисленный, *adj.*, enumerated
перечислимость, *f.*, denumerability
перечислимый, *adj.*, denumerable, countable; **рекурсивно перечислимый**, *adj.*, recursively enumerable
перечислять (перечислить), *v.*, enumerate, transfer
перешеек, *m.* (*gen.* **перешейка**), isthmus, connection, neck
перешеечный, *adj.*, isthmus, connection, connective
перешейка (= **перешеек**), *f.*; **узкая перешейка**, narrow passage
перешел (перешла, перешло, перешли), (from **переходить**), passed
перигей, *m.*, perigee
перигелий, *m.*, perihelion
периметр, *m.*, perimeter
период, *m.*, period; **по периоду**, periodically
периодический, *adj.*, periodic, recurrent, alternating, torsion; **периодическая дробь**, repeating decimal
периодичность, *f.*, periodicity
периодичный, *adj.*, periodic
периодограмма, *f.*, periodogram
периферийный, *adj.*, peripheral
периферический, *adj.*, peripheral, periphery, rim

периферия, *f.*, periphery, circumference
перманентность, *f.*, permanence
пермнентный, *adj.*, permanent
перпендикуляр, *m.*, perpendicular
перпендикулярность, *f.*, perpendicularity
перпендикулярный, *adj.*, perpendicular
персистентный, *adj.*, persistent, persistence; **персистентная модель,** persistence model
перспектива, *f.*, perspective, view
перспективитет, *m.*, perspectivity
перспективно-аффинный, *adj.*, perspectively affine
перспективный, *adj.*, perspective
пертурбационный, *adj.*, perturbation
пертурбация, *f.*, perturbation
перфокарта, *f.*, punch card
перфолента, *f.*, tape, perforated tape, punch tape
перфоратор, *m.*, perforator, punch; **перфоратор с вводом на ленте,** tape-reading punch
перфорационный, *adj.*, perforated, punched, punch
перцентиль, *m.*, percentile
перцепция, *f.*, perception
песок, *m.*, sand
петель, cf. **петля**
петлевание, *n.*, looping
петлевидный, *adj.*, loop
петление, *n.*, looping
петля, *f.*, loop; **конструкция, позволяющая вычислять гомологии пространства петель,** cobar construction; **делание петли (петель),** *n.*, looping; **делать петлю,** *v.*, loop
печатать, *v.*, print, type
печатающий, *adj.*, printing
печатный, *adj.*, printed, published; **печатная схема,** printed circuit
печать, *f.*, imprint, seal, stamp
пик, *m.*, peak
пикаровый, *adj.*, Picard
пиковершинность, *f.*, peakedness
пиковый, *adj.*, peak, spades (cards)
пиктограмма, *f.*, pictogram
пилообразный, *adj.*, saw-tooth
пилот, *m.*, pilot
пирамида, *f.*, pyramid
пирамидальный, *adj.*, pyramidal
пироэлектрический, *adj.*, pyroelectric
пироэлектричество, *n.*, pyroelectricity
пирсоновский, *adj.*, Pearson, pertaining to Pearson
пируэт, *m.*, pirouette
писать (написать), *v.*, write
письменный, *adj.*, written
письмо, *n.*, letter
питание, *n.*, feed, feeding
питать, *v.*, feed, nourish
питающийся, *adj.*, fed, being fed
пифагорейский, *adj.*, Pythagorean
пифагоровый, *adj.*, Pythagorean
пишут (from **писать**), (they) write
пишущий, *adj.*, writing; **пишущая машинка,** typewriter
пища, *f.*, food, nourishment
плавание, *n.*, navigation
плавать, *v.*, drift, navigate
плавающий, *adj.*, floating, drifting, navigating; **плавающий адрес,** symbolic address, floating address; **плавающая запятая,** floating point; **система с плавающей запятой,** floating-point system
плавить, *v.*, melt
плавка, *f.*, melting, fusion, fuse
плавление, *n.*, melting, fusion
плавность, *f.*, smoothness, fluency
плавный, *adj.*, smooth
плавучесть, *f.*, buoyancy
плазма, *f.*, plasm, plasma
пламень, *n.*, flame, fire
пламя, *n.*, flame, fire
план, *m.*, plan, setting, scheme, map, design; **план с неполными блоками,** incomplete block design
планета, *f.*, planet; **малая планета,** asteroid
планиметр, *m.*, planimeter
планиметрирование, *n.*, planimetry
планиметрический, *adj.*, planimetric

планиметрия, *f.*, planimetry, plane geometry

планирование, *n.*, glide, gliding, planning, designing, programming; **линейное планирование,** linear programming; **планирование экспериментов,** design of experiments

планировка, *f.*, design, planning; **планировка экспериментов,** design of experiments; **планировка опыта,** design of an experiment

планковский, *adj.*, Planck

планомерный, *adj.*, systematic, regular, planned

планшет, *m.*, plane table, drawing board

пласт, *m.*, layer, stratum

пластика, *f.*, plastics

пластина, *f.*, plate, membrane, disk

пластинка, *f.*, plate, disk

пластинчатый, *adj.*, plate-like, sheet-like, lamellate

пластический, *adj.*, plastic

пластичность, *f.*, plasticity

пластичный, *adj.*, plastic

пластмасса, *f.*, plastic, composition material; **синтетическая пластмасса,** synthetic resin

плата, *f.*, charge, payment, fee, price

Плато, *m.*, Plateau; **задача Плато,** Plateau's problem

платеж, *m.*, payoff, payment

пленарный, *adj.*, plenary

пленка, *f.*, film, recording

плетение, *n.*, network, lattice, braiding

плечо, *n.*, arm

плита, *f.*, plate, slab

пловучесть, *f.*, buoyancy

пловучий, *adj.*, buoyant

плодородие, *n.*, productivity, fertility

плодотворный, *adj.*, fruitful

плоский, *adj.*, plane, planar, flat, horizontal; **плоское деформированное состояние,** state of plane deformation; **плоское напряженное состояние,** state of plane stress

плоскопараллельный, *adj.*, plane-parallel

плоскополяризованный, *adj.*, plane-polarized

плоскостной, *adj.*, planar, flat

плоскостность, *f.*, flatness

плоскость, *f.*, plane, surface, flat; **плоскости** (*pl.*) flats; **направляющая плоскость,** control surface; **расширенная плоскость,** extended plane; **плоскость диафрагмы,** aperture plane; **плоскость изображения,** image plane; **плоскость средней квадратической регрессии,** mean square regression plane

плотина, *f.*, dam

плотно, *adv.*, densely, compactly

плотность, *f.*, density, compactness; **плотность печати,** printing capacity; **запись с высокой плотностью,** high density recording; **плотность тока,** current density; **плотность вероятности,** probability density; **кривая плотности,** frequency curve; **функция плотности,** frequency function, density function

плотный, *adj.*, dense, compact; **плотный в себе,** *adj.*, dense in itself; **всюду плотный,** *adj.*, everywhere dense; **метрически плотный,** *adj.*, metrically dense; **нигде не плотный,** *adj.*, nowhere dense

плохо, *adv.*, badly, poorly

плохой, *adj.*, bad

плохообусловленный, *adj.*, improperly stipulated, poorly worded

площадка, *f.*, area element, small area, platform, ground

площадный, *adj.*, areal, area; **площадная производная,** *f.*, areolar derivative

площадочный, *adj.*, area, areal

площадь, *f.*, area, space

плюривариантный, *adj.*, multivariable, multivariate

плюри-дифференцирование, *n.*, pluri-differentiation

плюрижанр, *m.*, pluri-genus, multiple genus

плюри-производная, *f.*, pluri-derivative
плюрисубгармонический, *adj.*, plurisubharmonic
плюрисубгармоничность, *f.*, plurisubharmonicity
плюс, *m.*, plus, advantage
пневматический, *adj.*, pneumatic
по, *prep.*, along, by; with respect to, according to; on, over, in, at
поблизости, *adv.*, nearby
побочный, *adj.*, collateral, accessory, auxiliary
побуждать (побудить), *v.*, compel, induce, stimulate
поведение, *n.*, conduct, behavior; **асимптотическое поведение,** asymptotic behavior
поведенческий, *adj.*, behavioral
поверить (cf. **поверять**), *v.*, believe, check
поверка, *f.*, checking, verfication, proof
повернуть (cf. **поворачивать**), *v.*, turn
повернутый, *adj.*, turned, turned around, changed
поверочный, *adj.*, checking, verifying
поверх, *prep.*, over, above, on top of
поверхностный, *adj.*, pertaining to surface, surface, superficial; **поверхностная зональная функция,** surface zonal harmonic
поверхность, *f.*, surface, face, surface area; **поверхность раздела**, interface, boundary surface; **поверхность регрессии**, regression surface; **поверхность Клейна,** Klein bottle
поверять (поверить), *v.*, check, verify, inspect, trust
повесить (cf. **вешать**), *v.*, hang, hang up
по-видимому, *adv.*, apparently
повиноваться, *v.*, obey, comply with
повлечь (повлечь за собой), *v.*, imply, entail, involve
повлиять (cf. **влиять**), *v.*, influence, affect
повод, *m.*, cause, reason, pretext
поворачивание, *n.*, turning, swinging, rotation
поворачивать (повернуть), *v.*, turn, rotate, swing
поворачиваться, *v.*, turn, rotate, swing
поворот, *m.*, turn, rotation, bend, twist
поворотить, *v.*, turn
поворотный, *adj.*, rotary
повреждать (повредить), *v.*, damage, injure
повреждение, *n.*, damage
поврежденный, *adj.*, defective, damaged
повседневный, *adj.*, daily, everyday; **в повседневной речи,** in everyday language
повсюду, *adv.*, everywhere
повторение, *n.*, repetition, reiteration, recurrence, iteration; **матрица без повторения,** non-recurrent matrix
повторитель, *m.*, repeater, follower; **эмиттерный повторитель,** emitter follower; **катодный повторитель,** cathode follower
повторительный, *adj.*, reiterative, repetitive, repeating
повторить (cf. **повторять**), *v.*, repeat
повторно, *adv.*, repeatedly
повторный, *adj.*, repeated, reiterated, iterated; **повторный интеграл,** iterated integral; **повторная проверка,** recheck, reinspection
повторяемость, *f.*, recurrence, repetition, reiteration
повторять (повторить), *v.*, repeat, iterate, reiterate
повторяться, *v.*, be repeated
повторяющийся, *adj.*, recurring, repeating
повторяя, *adv. part.*, repeating, iterating, by repeating
повышать (повысить), *v.*, raise, enlarge; **повышать размерности,** raise the dimension
повышающий, *adj.*, raising, elevating
повышение, *n.*, rise, raising, increase, increment
повышенный, *adj.*, raised, advanced, increased, excited

погадать (cf. **гадать**), *v.*, guess, conjecture
погашать (погасить), *v.*, merge with, cancel, liquidate, amortize
погашение, *n.*, paying-off, amortization, discharge, cancellation
погибать (погибнуть), *v.*, perish, be lost
поглотитель, *m.*, absorber
поглощаемый, *adj.*, absorbent
поглощать (поглотить), *v.*, swallow, absorb, take up
поглощающий, *adj.*, absorbing, absorbent
поглощение, *n.*, absorption, consumption, input
поглощенный, *adj.*, absorbed
погода, *f.*, weather
погоня, *f.*, pursuit, chase
пограничный, *adj.*, boundary; **пограничный слой,** boundary layer
погрешность, *f.*, error, mistake
погружаемость, *f.*, imbeddability, imbeddedness
погружать (погрузить), *v.*, immerse, imbed
погружение, *n.*, immersion, imbedding, submersion
погруженный, *adj.*, imbedded, submerged, immersed
погрузить (cf. **погружать**), *v.*, immerse, imbed
под, *prep.*, under, beneath
под-, *pref.*, sub-, under-
подаваемый, *adj.*, given, being given, fed, supplied
подавать (подать), *v.*, give, supply, feed, serve; **подавать смещение,** *v.*, bias
подавить (cf. **подавлять**), *v.*, suppress, damp
подавление, *n.*, suppression, repression, damping
подавлять (подавить), *v.*, suppress, repress, damp
подавляющий, *adj.*, suppressing, repressing, damping
подавно, *adv.*, a fortiori, so much the more
подавтомат, *m.*, semi-automatic machine, subautomation
подалгебра, *f.*, sub-algebra
податливость, *f.*, pliability
податливый, *adj.*, pliable
подача, *f.*, feed, supply, feeding, input; **механизм подачи магнитной ленты,** magnetic tape transport; **подача энергии,** power supply
подбазис, *m.*, sub-basis
подбирать (подобрать), *v.*, select, assort, sort out, fit
подбор, *m.*, selection, choice, fitting, fit; **решение подбором,** solution by inspection
подбрав, *adv. part.*, having chosen, having taken
подбрасывание, *n.*, tossing, flipping (of coin)
подведение, *n.*, rendering; **подведение итога,** *n.*, tally
подвергаемый, *adj.*, subject to, being subjected to
подвергать (подвергнуть), *v.*, subject, subject to
подвергаться, *v.*, undergo, be subjected to
подвергающийся, *adj.*, undergoing, subject to
подвергнутый, *adj.*, subjected
подверженный, *adj.*, subjected to, open to
подвешенный, *adj.*, suspended
подвешивать (подвесить), *v.*, suspend, hang up
подвигать (подвинуть), *v.*, move, push
подвижной (= подвижный)
подвижность, *f.*, mobility
подвижный, *adj.*, mobile, moving, sliding, travelling, non-stationary; **подвижный адрес,** floating address; **подвижная шкала,** sliding scale; **задача с подвижной границей,** moving boundary problem
подвинуть (cf. **подвигать**), *v.*, move
подводить (подвести), *v.*, bring, bring to, place; **подводить итоги,** *v.*, summarize, tally; **подводить баланс,** *v.*, balance

подводный, *adj.*, underwater, submarine
подглядывание, *n.*, spying; **неполное подглядывание,** imperfect spying
подгонка, *f.*, trimming, matching, adjustment
подгонять (подогнать), *v.*, adjust, fit, drive on
подготавливать (подготовить), *v.*, prepare, prepare for
подготовительный, *adj.*, preparatory; **подготовительная теорема,** lemma, preparation theorem
подготовиться, *v.*, prepare, get ready
подготовка, *f.*, preparation, training
подготовленный, *adj.*, prepared
подграф, *m.*, subgraph
подгруппа, *f.*, subgroup
подгруппоид, *m.*, subgroupoid
поддаваться (поддаться), *v.*, yield, lend itself
поддающийся, *adj.*, yielding, subject to, lending itself to
поддерживать (поддержать), *v.*, support, hold up, maintain
поддерживаться, *v.*, be maintained, be supported
поддерживающий, *adj.*, supporting, carrying, maintaining
поддержка, *f.*, support, backing
подзаголовок, *m.*, subtitle, subhead
подидеал, *m.*, sub-ideal
подидемпотентный, *adj.*, subidempotent
подинтегральный, *adj.*, integrand
подинтегральный, *m.*, integrand
подинтервал, *m.*, subinterval
подиспытание, *n.*, subexperiment
подкасательная, *f.*, subtangent
подкласс, *m.*, subclass, subset
подклеивать (подклеить), *v.*, glue, paste, associate
подкольцо, *n.*, sub-ring
подкомплекс, *m.*, subcomplex
подконтинуум, *m.*, subcontinuum
подкоренная, *f.*, radicand
подкоренной, *adj.*, subradical, under the radical sign; **подкоренная величина,** radicand
подкрепленный, *adj.*, supported, confirmed
подкреплять (подкрепить), *v.*, substantiate, confirm
подкрученный, *adj.*, twisted; **подкрученная степень,** twisted degree
подле, *prep.*, next to, beside
подлежать, *v.*, be subject to
подлежащее, *n.*, subject
подлежащий, *adj.*, subject to
подлинник, *m.*, original
подлинно, *adv.*, in truth, really
подлинность, *f.*, authenticity
подлинный, *adj.*, true, real, genuine
подлупа, *f.*, subloop
подматрица, *f.*, submatrix
подмашина, *f.*, submachine
подмногообразие, *n.*, submanifold, subvariety
подмножество, *n.*, subset
подмодель, *f.*, submodel
подмодуль, *m.*, submodule
поднимать (поднять), *v.*, lift, raise
подниматься, *v.*, rise
поднормаль, *f.*, subnormal
поднормальный, *adj.*, subnormal
поднятие, *n.*, raising, lifting, rise, elevation
поднять, cf. **поднимать**
подняться (cf. **подниматься**), *v.*, rise
подобие, *n.*, similarity, similitude
подобласть, *f.*, subregion, subdomain
подобно, *adv.*, like, similarly; **подобно однолистный,** *adj.*, schlichtartig
подобно-изоморфный, *adj.*, order-isomorphic
подобно-однолистный, *adj.*, schlichtartig
подобный, *adj.*, similar, similar to, similariy, homothetic; **подобным образом,** in a similar way, similarly; **подобное преобразование,** similitude, dilation
подобранный, *adj.*, selected, chosen
подобрать (cf. **подбирать**), *v.*, select, pick out
подозревать, *v.*, suspect

подозрение, *n.*, suspicion
подойти (cf. **подходить**), *v.*, arrive at, approach
подокрестность, *f.*, subneighborhood
подоплека, *f.*, actual situation, background
подошва, *f.*, base, foot, underside
подошли (past of **подходить**)
подпирать (подпереть), *v.*, support, sustain
подпирающий, *adj.*, supporting
подписной, *adj.*, subscription, subscript
подписывать (подписать), *v.*, sign, add to, subscribe
подпись, *f.*, subscript, signature, subscription
подподпоследовательность, *f.*, subsubsequence, subsequence
подпокрытие, *n.*, subcovering
подполугруппа, *f.*, sub-semigroup
подполе, *n.*, subfield
подпоследовательность, *f.*, subsequence
подпочти-кольцо, *n.*, subsemiring
подпрограмма, *f.*, subroutine
подпроизведение, *n.*, subproduct, subbundle
подпространство, *n.*, subspace
подпрямо, *adv.*, subdirectly, subdirect
подпрямой, *adj.*, subdirect
подпучок, *m.*, sub-bundle
подравнивание, *n.*, leveling, trimming
подражать, *v.*, imitate
подразбиение, *n.*, sub-partition, subdivision
подразделение, *n.*, subdivision, refinement, division, decomposition
подразделяемый, *adj.*, partitionable; **подразделяемое пространство,** partitionable space
подразделять, *v.*, subdivide, partition
подразмах, *m.*, subrange
подразумеваемый, *adj.*, implicit, subtended
подразумевать, *v.*, imply, mean, subtend
подробно, *adv.*, in detail, at length, explicitly
подробность, *f.*, detail
подробный, *adj.*, detailed, explicit, extensive
подряд, *adv.*, in succession
подсектор, *m.*, subsector
подсемейство, *n.*, subfamily
подсеть, *f.*, subnet, subnetwork
подсистема, *f.*, subsystem
подсказываемый, *adj.*, suggested, prompting, prompted
подсказывать (подсказать), *v.*, suggest, prompt
подслучай, *m.*, subcase
подслушивание, *n.*, detection
подсобный, *adj.*, subsidiary, secondary, auxiliary
подсовокупность, *f.*, subset
подставление, *n.*, substitution
подставленный, *adj.*, substituted
подставляемый, *adj.*, substituted, being substituted; **подставляемое (выражение),** *n.*, substituend
подставлять (подставить), *v.*, substitute
подставляя, *adv. part.*, substituting, by substituting, if we substitute
подстановка, *f.*, substitution, permutation
подстановление, *n.*, substitution
подструктура, *f.*, sublattice, substructure
подступ, *m.*, approach
подсчет, *m.*, count, enumeration, calculation
подсчитывать (подсчитать), *v.*, count, calculate, compute
подсчитываться, *v.*, be calculated, be counted, be estimated
подтверждать (подтвердить), *v.*, confirm, corroborate, verify
подтверждаться, *v.*, be verified
подтверждение, *n.*, confirmation, corroboration, affirmation
подтвержденный, *adj.*, confirmed, verified
подтело, *n.*, subfield
подуровень, *f.*, sublevel
подушкообразный, *adj.*, pincushion type; **подушкообразная дисторсия,** pincushion type distortion

подформула, *f.*, corollary formula, corollary

подфункция, *f.*, minorant, minorant function

подхарактер, *m.*, subcharacter

подход, *m.*, approach

подходить (подойти), *v.*, approach, arrive at, come to

подходяще, *adv.*, suitably, properly, appropriately

подходящий, *adj.*, suitable, proper, appropriate; **подходящая дробь,** convergent of a continued fraction

подчас, *adv.*, sometimes

подчеркивать (подчеркнуть), *v.*, underline, emphasize, stress

подчинение, *n.*, subordination, subjection

подчиненность, *f.*, subordination

подчиненный, *adj.*, subordinate, subordination

подчинять (подчинить), *v.*, subordinate, subject to

подчиняться, *v.*, obey, be subjected to, be subordinate to

подчиняющийся, *adj.*, submitting to, subject (to), subordinate (to)

подцепь, *f.*, subchain

подшипник, *m.*, bearing, bushing

подъем, *m.*, rise, lift, ascent

подъемный, *adj.*, lifting, hoisting, elevating, lift; **подъемная сила,** body force, buoyant force, lift, buoyancy force; **коэффициент подъемной силы,** lift coefficient

подынтегральный, *m.*, integrand

подынтегральный, *adj.*, integrand; **подынтегральная функция,** *f.*, integrand

подынтервал, *m.*, subinterval

подыскивать (подыскать), *v.*, seek, try to find

подытоженный, *adj.*, summed up, summarized

подытоживать (подытожить), *v.*, sum up

подэра, *f.*, pedal (of a curve or surface)

пожалуй, *adv.*, perhaps, maybe

позаботиться (cf. **заботиться**), *v.*, take care of, be concerned about

позади, *prep.*, behind, in back of

позволение, *n.*, permission

позволительный, *adj.*, permissible

позволять (позволить), *v.*, permit, allow

позволяющий, *adj.*, permitting, allowing

поздний, *adj.*, late

поздно, *adv.*, late

позже, *adv.*, later, later on

позитивизм, *m.*, positivism

позитивность, *f.*, positivity, positiveness

позитивный, *adj.*, positive

позитрон, *m.*, positron

позиционный, *adj.*, positional

позиция, *f.*, position, stand, attitude

познавательный, *adj.*, perceptive, perceptual, cognitive

познакомиться (cf. **знакомить**), *v.*, be acquainted, become acquainted

познание, *n.*, knowledge, perception

поиск, *m.*, search; **поиски,** *pl.*, search; **случайный поиск,** random search; **в поисках,** in search (of)

поискать, *v.*, look for, search

поистине, *adv.*, indeed

пойдет (from **пойти**), he (it) will go

пойдут (from **пойти**), they will go

пойти (cf. **идти, ходить**), *v.*, go, begin to

пока, *conj.*, while, until, as long as; **пока не**, until

покажется (from **показываться**), seems, appears, will seem, will appear

показ, *m.*, demonstration, illustration

показание, *n.*, evidence, reading (from meter)

показанный, *adj.*, shown, demonstrated; **как показано,** as is shown

показатель, *m.*, index, exponent; **показатель степени,** exponent; **показатель адиабаты,** isentropic exponent

показательный, *adj.*, exponential, demonstration, demonstrative, significant, representative; **показательная**

выборка, representative sample; **показательная функция,** exponential function
показать (cf. **показывать**), *v.*, show, register, read
показаться (cf. **показываться**), *v.*, seem, appear
показывать (показать), *v.*, show, exhibit, register, read
показываться (показаться), *v.*, seem, appear
покидать (покинуть), *v.*, abandon, leave
покоиться, *v.*, rest, rest on, lie, be at rest
покой, *m.*, rest; **масса покоя,** rest-mass; **в покое,** at rest; **точка покоя,** stationary point
поколение, *n.*, generation
покомпонентно, *adv.*, component by component, component-wise
покомпонентный, *adj.*, component-wise
покоординатно, *adv.*, coordinate-wise, by coordinates
покоящийся, *adj.*, rest; **покоящаяся масса,** rest-mass
покрываемый, *adj.*, coverable, covered
покрывать (покрыть), *v.*, cover, cover by, cover with, overlap
покрывающий, *adj.*, covering, overlapping
покрытие, *n.*, covering, overlapping; **множество покрытия,** range set, range
покрытый, *adj.*, covered
покрышка, *f.*, covering, cover, lid
покуда (= **пока**), as long as
покупатель, *m.*, buyer, purchaser, customer
покупательный, *adj.*, purchasing; **покупательная способность,** purchasing power
покупать (купить), *v.*, buy, purchase
полагать, *v.*, suppose, assume, set, let
полагая, *adv. part.*, setting, letting, assuming, if we set, by setting
полдень, *m.*, noon
поле, *n.*, field; **поле отношений,** quotient field; **поле расширения,** extension field; **расширение поля,** field extension; **поле деления окружности,** cyclotomic field; **простое поле,** prime field
полевой, *adj.*, field
полезность, *f.*, usefulness, utility
полезный, *adj.*, useful, helpful, efficient; **полезное время работы,** good time; **коэффициент полезного действия,** efficiency
полемизировать, *v.*, argue against, enter into controversy
полемика, *f.*, dispute, controversy
полет, *m.*, flight
ползун, *m.*, slide block, slide
ползунок, *m.*, movable indicator
ползучесть, *f.*, creeping, creep
полиадический, *adj.*, polyadic
поливектор, *m.*, multivector, linear tensor, skew-symmetric tensor
полигармонический, *adj.*, polyharmonic, multiharmonic
полигенный, *adj.*, polygenic
полигон, *m.*, polygon, ground; **испытательный полигон,** proving ground
полигональный, *adj.*, polygonal
полиграфический, *adj.*, polygraphic
поликалорический, *adj.*, polycaloric
поликомпонентный, *adj.*, multicomponent
поликонический, *adj.*, polyconic
полилинейный, *adj.*, multilinear
полимерный, *adj.*, polymeric
полиморфный, *adj.*, polymorphic
полином, *m.*, polynomial
полиномиальнозначный, *adj.*, polynomial-valued
полиномиальный, *adj.*, polynomial, multinomial
полиотношение, *n.*, multirelation
полисинтетический, *adj.*, multisynthetic, polysynthetic
полиспаст, *m.*, pulley block
полисферический, *adj.*, polyspherical, hyperspherical
политехнический, *adj.*, polytechnic
политический, *adj.*, political

политоп, *m.*, polytope
политропа, *f.*, polytropy; **показатель политропы,** polytropic exponent
политропический, *adj.*, polytropic; **политропическое движение,** polytropic expansion
политропный, *adj.*, polytropic
полициклический, *adj.*, polycyclic
полицилиндр, *m.*, polycylinder
полиэдр, *m.*, polyhedron, polytope
полиэдральный, *adj.*, polyhedral
полиэдрический, *adj.*, polyhedral
полиэдроид, *m.*, polyhedroid, polyhedron
полновесность, *f.*, full weight, soundness
полнодоступный, *adj.*, fully accessible, accessible
полность, *f.*, completeness
полностью, *adv.*, completely, entirely; **полностью учтя то обстоятельство,** taking full account of the fact; **полностью рандомизированный план,** completely randomized design
полнота, *f.*, completeness; **условием полноты,** because of completeness; **аксиома полноты,** completeness axiom
полноценный, *adj.*, rigorous, of full value, valid, valuable
полный, *adj.*, full, complete, total, perfect; **полное произведение,** final product; **полный дифференциал,** total differential, **полное упорядочение,** complete ordering, well-ordering; **полная ошибка,** total error; **полный прообраз,** pre-image, complete prototype; **полная аддитивность,** complete additivity, countable additivity; **полная информация,** perfect information; **полный класс (стратегий),** complete class (of strategies); **полный коэффициент корреляции,** total coefficient of correlation; **полное сопротивление,** impedance
полным-полно, *adv.*, full
половина, *f.*, one-half
половинный, *adj.*, half
пологий, *adj.*, slanting, sloping
положение, *n.*, situation, position, condition, state, aspect, statement; **возвращение в исходное положение,** resetting; **возвращать в исходное положение,** *v.*, reset; **устанавливать в исходное положение,** *v.*, clear
положителен (short form of **положительный**), (is) positive
положительно, *adv.*, positive; **положительно определенный,** *adj.*, positive definite; **положительно,** *pred.*, (is) positive
положительность, *f.*, positiveness
положительный, *adj.*, positive, affirmative
положить (cf. **класть**) *v.*, put, place, lay, assume
поломать, *v.*, break
поломка, *f.*, breakage, fracture
полоса, *f.*, band, strip, zone, region, fringe; **интерференционная полоса,** fringe
полосатый, *adj.*, band, striped; **полосатый спектр,** band spectrum
полоска, *f.*, strip, band, zone, belt
полосовой, *adj.*, band, strip
полосообразный, *adj.*, strip; **полосообразная область,** strip region
полость, *f.*, cavity, concavity, sheet, nappe
полтора, *num.*, one and a half
полтораста, *num.*, one hundred and fifty
полу-, *prefix*, semi-, hemi-, half
полуавтоматический, *adj.*, semi-automatic
полуаддитивный, *adj.*, semiadditive
полуалгебраический, *adj.*, semi-algebraic
полубесконечный, *adj.*, semi-infinite
полубилинейный, *adj.*, semi-bilinear, sesquilinear
полувариация, *f.*, semi-variation
полуволна, *f.*, half wave
полувыпуклый, *adj.*, semiconvex
полугруппа, *f.*, semi-group
полугрупповый, *adj.*, semi-group

полугруппоид, *m.*, semi-groupoid
полудедекиндовость, *f.*, semimodularity
полудедекиндовый, *adj.*, semi-modular; **полудедекиндовая структура,** semi-modular lattice
полудистрибутивный, *adj.*, semi-distributive
полудополнение, *n.*, semisupplement, semicomplement
полудополнительный, *adj.*, semisupplementary, semicomplementary
полузамкнутый, *adj.*, half-closed
полуинвариант, *m.*, semi-invariant
полуинтегральный, *adj.*, semi-integral, semi-integrable
полуинтервал, *m.*, half-interval, half-open interval
полуитеративный, *adj.*, semi-iterative
полукасательная, *f.*, half-tangent, semi-tangent
полуквадрика, *f.*, regulus
полукватернион, *m.*, semi-quaternion
полукольцо, *n.*, semi-ring
полукруг, *m.*, half-disk, semi-circle
полукруглый, *adj.*, semicircular
полукубический, *adj.*, semicubical; **полукубическая парабола,** semi-cubical parabola
полулинейный, *adj.*, semi-linear
полулогарифмический, *adj.*, semi-logarithmic
полулокальный, *adj.*, semilocal
полумартингал, *m.*, semi-martingale
полуметрический, *adj.*, semi-metric
полумодулярность, *f.*, semimodularity
полумодулярный, *adj.*, semi-modular
полунаследственный, *adj.*, semi-hereditary
полунатуральный, *adj.*, semi-natural
полунепрерывно, *adv.*, semicontinuously
полунепрерывность, *f.*, semicontinuity; **полунепрерывность сверху (снизу),** upper (lower) semi-continuity
полунепрерывный, *adj.*, semi-continuous; **полунепрерывный сверху,** *adj.*, upper semi-continuous; **полунепрерывный снизу,** *adj.*, lower semi-continuous
полунорм, *m.* **(полунорма,** *f.*), semi-norm
полуограниченность, *f.*, semiboundedness, boundedness from one side
полуограниченный, *adj.*, semi-bounded, bounded from one side, semi-closed, half-closed
полуокрестность, *f.*, half-neighborhood
полуокружность, *f.*, semicircle
полуопределенный, *adj.*, semi-definite
полуординарный, *adj.*, semi-ordinary
полуортоцентрический, *adj.*, semi-orthocentric
полуось, *f.*, semi-axis
полуоткрытый, *adj.*, semi-open, half-open; **полуоткрытый интервал,** half-open interval
полупериодный, *adj.*, semiperiodic
полупластичность, *f.*, semi-plasticity
полуплоскость, *f.*, half-plane
полуплотный, *adj.*, semi-compact, semi-dense
полуповерхность, *f.*, semi-surface
полуповерхностный, *adj.*, semi-surface
полуправильный, *adj.*, semi-regular
полупревращение, *n.*, half reaction; **период полупревращения,** half-life
полуприведенный, *adj.*, half-reduced, semi-reduced
полуприводимый, *adj.*, semi-reducible
полупроводник, *m.*, semi-conductor, transistor
полупроводниковый, *adj.*, semi-conducting; **полупроводниковый прибор,** transistor; **полупроводниковый триод,** transistor; **схема с непосредственной связью на полупроводниковых триодах,** directly-coupled transistor circuit; **кремниевый полупроводниковый триод,** silicon transistor; **тянутый плоскостной полупроводниковый триод,** grown-junction transistor; **выполнять на полупроводниковых триодах,** *v.*, transistorize; **плоскостной полупроводниковый триод,** junction transistor;

полупроводниковый триод с пространственным зарядом, spacistor
полупроницаемый, *adj.*, semipermeable
полупростой, *adj.*, semi-simple
полупростота, *f.*, semi-simplicity
полупространство, *n.*, half-space
полупрямая, *f.*, ray, half-line
полупрямой, *adj.*, semidirect, subdirect
полупсевдоординарный, *adj.*, semi-pseudo-ordinary
полуравномерно, *adv.*, semi-uniformly, quasi-uniformly
полуравномерный, *adj.*, quasi-uniform, semi-uniform
полуразмах, *m.*, semi-range
полураспад, *m.*, half-decay; **период полураспада,** half-life
полурегулярность, *f.*, semi-regularity
полурегулярный, *adj.*, semiregular
полурефлексивный, *adj.*, semi-reflexive
полусегмент, *m.*, half-segment, half-open interval
полусимметрический, *adj.*, semi-symmetric
полусимметрия, *f.*, half-symmetry, semi-symmetry
полусимплициальный, *adj.*, semi-simplicial
полуслед, *m.*, semi-trace, half-trace
полуспециальный, *adj.*, semi-special
полуспинор, *m.*, semi-spinor
полуструктура, *f.*, semi-lattice
полусумма, *f.*, half-sum
полусумматор, *m.*, half-adder
полусфера, *f.*, hemisphere
полусферический, *adj.*, hemispherical
полусходящийся, *adj.*, semi-convergent, asymptotic
полутень, *f.*, penumbra
полутеоретический, *adj.*, semitheoretical
полуторный, *adj.*, sesquialteral, of one and a half; **в полуторном размере,** half as much again
полуточный, *adj.*, semi-exact; **полуточная пара,** semi-exact couple
полутраектория, *f.*, semi-trajectory
полуунитарный, *adj.*, semi-unitary
полуупорядочение, *n.*, semi-ordering, partial ordering
полуупорядоченный, *adj.*, partially ordered
полуфабрикат, *m.*, intermediate product, half-finished product
полуфеноменологический, *adj.*, semi-phenomenological
полуформальный, *adj.*, semi-formal
полуфункция, *f.*, semi-function
полуцелый, *adj.*, half-integer
полуцилиндр, *m.*, semi-cylinder, semi-tube
полуцилиндрический, *adj.*, semi-cylindrical, semi-tube
получать (получить), *v.*, get, obtain, receive
получаться, *v.*, result, come out, be obtained
получающийся, *adj.*, resulting, obtained
получение, *n.*, receipt, obtaining, receiving
полученный, *adj.*, obtained, received
получебышевский, *adj.*, semi-Chebyshevskian
получистый, *adj.*, semi-pure
полушарие, *n.*, hemisphere
полуширина, *f.*, half-width (of spectrum)
полуэллиптический, *adj.*, semi-elliptical
полуэмпирический, *adj.*, semi-empirical
полуячейка, *f.*, half-cell
полый, *adj.*, hollow; **полый шар,** spherical shell
польза, *f.*, use, advantage
пользование, *n.*, use, utilization
пользоваться, *v.*, make use of; **пользоваться случаем,** *v.*, take the opportunity
пользуясь, *adv. part.*, using, making use of, if we use, by using
полюс, *m.*, pole, terminal; **Северный полюс,** North pole
полюсник, *m.*, pole, contact pole, terminal network
полюсный, *adj.*, polar
поляр, *m.* (**поляра,** *f.*), polar, polar-line

поляризатор, *m.*, polarizer
поляризационный, *adj.*, polarizable, polarization
поляризация, *f.*, polarization
поляризуемость, *f.*, polarizability; **поляризуемость диэлектрика,** electric susceptibility
поляризируемый, *adj.*, polarizable
поляризованный, *adj.*, polarized
поляризовать, *v.*, polarize
поляризующий, *adj.*, polarizing
поляризующийся, *adj.*, polarizable
поляритет, *m.*, polarity, polar mapping
полярно-симметрический, *adj.*, polar-symmetric
полярность, *f.*, polarity
полярный, *adj.*, polar
поменять (cf. **менять**), *v.*, interchange
поместить (cf. **помещать**), *v.*, place, locate, imbed, invest
поместиться (cf. **помещаться**), *v.*, be, be located, have room
поместный, *adj.*, placed, located
пометка, *f.*, mark, note
помеха, *f.*, hindrance, obstacle, nuisance; **помехи,** *pl.*, noise; **случайные помехи,** random noise; **свободный от помех,** *adj.*, noiseless
помехоустойчивость, *f.*, noise stability
помеченный, *adj.*, marked
помещать (поместить), *v.*, put, place, locate, imbed, invest
помещаться, *v.*, be, be located, have room, belong
помещение, *n.*, room, location, investment
помещенный, *adj.*, included, placed, put, imbedded, invested
помимо, *prep.*, besides, except, aside from
помнить, *v.*, remember, keep in mind
помножать (помножить), *v.*, multiply
помогать (помочь), *v.*, help, aid
помощь, *f.*, help, aid, assistance; **с помощью,** with the help of; **при помощи,** with the help of, by means of
понадобиться, *v.*, be necessary, be needed
поневоле, *adv.*, necessarily, against one's will
пондеромоторный, *adj.*, ponderomotive; **пондеромоторная сила,** normal stress on a conductor, ponderomotive force
понижать (понизить), *v.*, reduce, lower, decrease
понижаться (понизиться), *v.*, fall, diminish, be reduced
понижающий, *adj.*, reducing, lowering, decreasing
понижение, *n.*, lowering, reduction, depression
пониженный, *adj.*, reduced, lowered, decreased
понизить (cf. **понижать**), *v.*, reduce, lower
понимание, *n.*, understanding, comprehension; **в обычном понимании,** in the usual sense; **в узком понимании,** in a narrow sense, in a restricted sense
понимать (понять), *v.*, understand, comprehend
пониматься, *v.*, be regarded, be understood
по-новому, *adv.*, in a new fashion, in the modern way
понтрягинский, *adj.*, pertaining to Pontrjagin; **понтрягинское произведение,** Pontrjagin product
понятие, *n.*, concept, notion, idea
понятийный, *adj.*, conceptual
понятный, *adj.*, clear, intelligible, natural
понять (cf. **понимать**), *v.*, understand
поочередно, *adv.*, in turn, by turns
поощрение, *n.*, encouragement, stimulation, reward
поощрять (поощрить), *v.*, stimulate, excite, encourage
попавший, *adj.*, having hit, having occurred, hitting, occurring
попадание, *n.*, hit; **прямое попадание,** direct hit
попадать (попасть), *v.*, hit, hit a target, get into, find oneself
попадаться, *v.*, occur, come across, get, be caught

попадающий, *adj.*, hitting, falling into
попарно, *adv.*, in pairs, pairwise, mutually; **попарно не пересекаться,** be mutually exclusive, be mutually disjoint
попеременно, *adv.*, alternately, by turns
поперечина, *f.*, cross-beam, cross-bar, cross-cut; **неприводимая поперечина,** irreducible cross-cut
поперечник, *m.*, diameter
поперечный, *adj.*, cross, transverse, transversal, diametrical, cross-cut; **поперечное колебание,** transverse vibration; **поперечное сечение,** cross-section; **поперечное увеличение,** lateral magnification; **поперечный разрез,** cross-section
пополам, *adv.*, in two, in halves; **делить пополам,** *v.*, divide in two, bisect; **деление пополам,** *n.*, bisection
пополнение, *n.*, supplement, replenishment, augmentation, addition, completion; **компактное пополнение,** compactification
пополненный, *adj.*, completed, complete, augmented
пополнять (пополнить), *v.*, supplement, enlarge, complete, augment
пополняющий, *adj.*, supplementing, enlarging, augmentation
поправимый, *adj.*, reparable, rectifiable
поправка, *f.*, correction; **вносить поправки,** *v.*, correct
поправочный, *adj.*, correction; **поправочный коэффициент,** correction factor; **поправочный член,** correction term
по-предыдущему, *adv.*, as before
по-прежнему, *adv.*, as before
попробовать (cf. **пробовать**), *v.*, try, attempt, experiment
попросту, *adv.*, merely, simply
популярный, *adj.*, popular
популяция, *f.*, population
попутно, *adv.*, in passing, incidentally, simultaneously
попытаться (cf. **пытаться**), *v.*, try, attempt, undertake
попытка, *f.*, try, attempt
попятный, *adj.*, retrograde
пора, *f.*, time, period, pore; **на первых порах,** at first; **до сих пор,** until now, up to this point; **с тех пор,** since, since then; **до тех пор,** until, as long as; **с тех самых пор,** ever since
поразительно, *adv.*, strikingly
поразительный, *adj.*, striking, startling
порвать (cf. **порывать**), tear, break
пористость, *f.*, porosity
пористый, *adj.*, porous
поровну, *adv.*, equally, in equal parts
порог, *m.*, threshold
пороговый, *adj.*, threshold; **пороговая функция,** threshold function
породить (породиться), cf. **порождать (порождаться)**
порождаемый, *adj.*, generated
порождать (породить), *v.*, generate, induce, provide
порождаться, *v.*, be generated, be induced, be achieved, be produced
порождающий, *adj.*, generating
порождение, *n.*, result, outcome
порожденный, *adj.*, generated, induced
порознь, *adv.*, separately, apart
порой (порою), *adv.*, occasionally, now and then
порочный, *adj.*, faulty, fallacious; **порочный круг,** vicious circle
порошок, *m.*, powder
портативный, *adj.*, portable
портить, *v.*, spoil, mar
поручительство, *n.*, guarantee
порция, *f.*, portion
порча, *f.*, damage, breakage
поршенек, *m.*, piston, plunger
поршень, *m.*, piston, plunger
поршневой, *adj.*, piston
порыв, *m.*, burst, gust, rush, gap, tear
порывать (порвать), *v.*, tear, break
порываться (порваться), *v.*, try (to), attempt (to)
порядковый, *adj.*, ordinal, order, serial; **порядковое число,** ordinal number;

порядковая статистика. order statistics; **порядковое числительное,** *n.*, ordinal; **порядковый тип,** *m.*, order-type

порядок, *m.*, order; **выравнивание порядков,** matching of exponents; **выравнивать порядки,** *v.*, match exponents; **порядок чисел,** exponent

посвящать (посвятить), *v.*, devote, dedicate

посвященный, *adj.*, dealing with, devoted to, dedicated to

посеребренный, *adj.*, silvered, silver-plated

посещать (посетить), *v.*, visit, attend, resort (to)

поскольку, *conj.*, as far as, as long as, since

посланный, *adj.*, transmitted

после, *prep.*, after; **после того как,** after; **после всех,** last; *adv.*, later

последействие, *n.*, aftereffect, persistence, contagion; **распределение последействия,** contagious distribution

последнее, *n.*, the latter, the last

последний, *adj.*, last, latter; **в последнее время,** recently; **последняя теорема Ферма,** Fermat's last theorem

последователь, *m.*, successor

последовательно, *adv.*, in turn, successively, consecutively

последовательность, *f.*, sequence, succession; **фундаментальная последовательность,** fundamental sequence, Cauchy sequence; **последовательность команд,** routine; **схема регулирования последовательности,** sequence circuit; **схема последовательности операции,** flow chart

последовательный, *adj.*, sequential, consecutive, successive; **план последовательных выборок,** sequential-sampling plan; **последовательная выборка,** sequential sampling; **игра с усеченной последовательной выборкой,** truncated-sequential game; **последовательные приближения,** successive approximations; **параллельно - последовательный метод выполнения операций,** parallel-serial mode; **последовательная выборка команд,** control sequence

последовать (cf. **следовать**), *v.*, follow

последствие, *n.*, consequence, corollary

последующий, *adj.*, consequent, following, next, subsequent, successive

пословный, *adj.*, word-for-word, word-by-word, literal; **пословный перевод,** word-for-word translation (*comp.*)

послойно, *adv.*, layerwise

послужить (cf. **служить**), *v.*, serve, be used for

посмертный, *adj.*, posthumous

посмотреть (cf. **смотреть**), *v.*, look at

посмотрим (from **смотреть**), we shall see, let us see

пособие, *n.*, manual, textbook

поспешный, *adj.*, hasty, hurried

посреди, *prep.*, in the middle of

посредине, *adv.*, in the middle, half-way

посредство, *n.*, means, agency, medium; **при посредстве,** by means of

посредством, *prep.*, by means of

поставить (cf. **ставить**), *v.*, put, place, set, set down; **поставить вопрос,** *v.*, raise the question (of)

поставленный, *adj.*, posed, set, formulated; **корректно поставленный,** *adj.*, correctly formulated, reasonably formulated

поставщик, *m.*, supplier, caterer; **задача о поставщике,** caterer problem

постановка, *f.*, statement, posing, formulation; **постановка вопроса,** *v.*, statement of a question

постепенно, *adv.*, gradually, step-by-step, progressively

постепенный, *adj.*, gradual, step-by-step, progressive

постолбцовый, *adj.*, along the column, column; **постолбцовый средний,** column mean, column average

посторонний, *adj.*, outside, strange, foreign, extraneous, irrelevant
постоянная, *f.*, constant
постоянный, *adj.*, constant, fixed; **метод вариации постоянных,** method of variation of parameters; **постоянная величина,** *f.*, constant; **постоянный сигнал,** steady signal; **постоянный ток,** direct current
постоянство *n.*, constancy, steadiness
построение, *n.*, structure, construction, tracing
построенный, *adj.*, constructed
построить (cf. **строить**), *v.*, construct
построчный, *adj.*, row, pertaining to row, along the row; **построчный средний,** row mean, row average
постскриптум, *m.*, postscript
постулат, *n.*, postulate, axiom, hypothesis; **постулат выбора,** axiom of choice; **метод постулатов,** postulational method
постулативный, *adj.*, postulational, postulative, postulate
постулационист, *m.*, postulationist
постулированный, *adj.*, postulated
постулировать, *v.*, postulate
постулироваться, *v.*, be postulated
поступательный, *adj.*, forward, advancing, progressive, translational, translation; **поступательное движение,** translation, translational movement
поступать (поступить), *v.*, behave, act, treat, deal with, enter
поступающий, *adj.*, at hand, entering, incoming, behaving
поступление, *n.*, inflow, entry, receipt
посылать (послать), *v.*, transmit, send; **посылать импульсы,** *v.*, pulse
посылка, *f.*, premise, sending; **большая посылка,** major premise; **меньшая посылка,** minor premise
посыпать, *v.*, pour, sprinkle, powder; **посыпать песком,** *v.*, sand
потемнение, *n.*, darkening, occultation
потенциал, *m.*, potential
потенциально, *adv.*, potentially, potential-
потенциальный, *adj.*, potential; **сигнал потенциального типа,** steady-state signal; **вычислительная машина потенциального типа,** direct-current computer; **потенциальная бесконечность,** potential infinity, constructive infinity
потенциометр, *m.*, potentiometer
потерпевший, *adj.*, undergone, suffered
потерпеть (cf. **терпеть**), *v.*, undergo, suffer
потеря, *f.*, loss, waste; **функция потерь,** loss function; **без потери общности,** without loss of generality
потерянный, *adj.*, lost, missed
потерять (cf. **терять**), *v.*, lose
поток, *m.*, stream, flow, current, flux; **магнитный поток,** flux; **массовая плотность потока,** mass flux density
потолок, *m.*, ceiling
потом, *adv.*, later, afterwards
потомок, *m.*, offspring, descendant
потомство, *n.*, descendants, race, posterity
потому, *adv.*, therefore; **потому что,** because
поточечный, *adj.*, pointwise; **поточечная сходимость,** pointwise convergence
поточный, *adj.*, continuous; **поточная линия,** production line, assembly line
потребитель, *m.*, customer, consumer
потребительский, *adj.*, consumer
потребление, *n.*, consumption, expenditure, input; **потребление-производство,** *n.*, input-output; **граница возможного потребления,** consumption-possibility frontier
потребляемый, *adj.*, consumable
потребляющий, *adj.*, consuming, consumer
потребность, *f.*, want, need, demand, requirement
потребный, *adj.*, necessary, required
потребовавшийся, *adj.*, required
потребовать (cf. **требовать**), *v.*, require; **потребуется,** it will be necessary

потрясающий, *adj.*, tremendous, startling
поучать, *v.*, teach, instruct, lecture
поучение, *n.*, lesson, lecture
поучительно, *adv.*, instructively
поучительность, *f.*, instructiveness
поучительный, *adj.*, instructive
похожий, *adj.*, similar, like, resembling
почва, *f.*, ground, land, soil; **на твердой почве,** on sure ground
почему, *adv.*, why
почему-то, *adv.*, for some reason
почерпать (почерпнуть), *v.*, get, obtain, draw
починить (cf. **чинить**), *v.*, repair, mend
почитаемый, *adj.*, respected, esteemed
почитаться, *v.*, be respected
почленно, *adv.*, termwise, term by term; **складывать почленно,** *v.*, add term by term
почленный, *adj.*, term-by-term, termwise
почта, *f.*, post, mail
почти, *adv.*, almost; **почти инвариантный,** *adj.*, almost invariant; **почти всюду,** almost everywhere; **почти во всех точках,** almost everywhere
почти-кольцо, *n.*, near-ring
почти-периодический, *adj.*, almost-periodic
поэлементно, *adv.*, element-wise, element by element
поэтому, *adv.*, therefore
появиться (cf. **появляться**), *v.*, appear
появление, *n.*, appearance
появляться (появиться), *v.*, appear, show up, emerge
пояс, *m.*, belt, zone
пояснение, *n.*, explanation, clarification
поясной, *adj.*, zone, belt; **поясное время,** zone time
пояснять (пояснить), *v.*, explain, clarify
поясняющий, *adj.*, explaining, clarifying
правда, *f.*, truth; it is true (that)
правдоподобие, *n.*, probability, likelihood, plausibility
правдоподобный, *adj.*, probable, likely, reliable, plausible
правее, *adv.*, to the right (of)
правило, *n.*, rule, principle, law
правильно (from **правильный**), *adv.*, tamely; **правильно вложенный,** *adj.*, tamely imbedded, tame
правильность, *f.*, regularity, correctness, validity, accuracy
правильный, *adj.*, right, true, proper, regular, rectilinear, faithful, tame; **правильное вложение,** tame imbedding; **правильное множество,** tame set
правка, *f.*, correcting; **правка корректуры,** proof-reading
правоальтернативный, *adj.*, right-alternative
правовинтовой, *adj.*, right-handed; **правовинтовая система,** right-handed system
право-инвариантный, *adj.*, right-invariant
правоспособность, *f.*, capacity, capability
правоспособный, *adj.*, capable, competent
правосторонний, *adj.*, right, right-hand, right-side
правоуничтожающий, *adj.*, right-annihilating
правоупорядоченный, *adj.*, right-ordered
правый, *adj.*, right, right-hand; **правый идеал,** right ideal; **на правой стороне,** on the right, on the right-hand side
практика, *f.*, practice; **на практике,** in practice
практиковать, *v.*, practice
практикум, *m.*, practical work
практикующий, *adj.*, practicing
практически, *adv.*, practically, in practice
практический, *adj.*, practical; **практический смысл,** common sense
практичность, *f.*, practicality, efficiency
практичный, *adj.*, practical, efficient
пребывание, *n.*, stay, period
превалентный, *adj.*, prevalent

превалирующий, *adj.*, prevalent, prevailing

превзойти (cf. **превосходить**), *v.*, exceed

превзошел (from **превзойти**), (he, it) exceeded

превзошли (from **превзойти**), (they) exceeded

превосходить (превзойти), *v.*, exceed, surpass

превосходный, *adj.*, excellent, exceeding, superior (to), greater (than)

превосходство, *n.*, superiority

превосходящий, *adj.*, greater (than), exceeding, superior (to)

превратить (cf. **превращать**), *v.*, convert, turn into

превратиться (cf. **превращаться**), *v.*, be converted, turn into, become

превратность, *f.*, falsity, changeability

превращать (превратить), *v.*, convert, turn into, change

превращаться, *v.*, be converted, turn into

превращающий, *adj.*, converting, changing

превращение, *n.*, transformation, conversion, transmutation, obversion

превышать (превысить), *v.*, exceed

превышающий, *adj.*, exceeding

превышение, *n.*, excess, exceeding

преграда, *f.*, barrier, obstacle

предварение, *n.*, prediction, precession; **предварение равноденствий,** precession of the equinoxes

предваренный, *adj.*, preliminary, preceding; **предваренная форма (формула),** prenex form (formula), (log.)

предварительно, *adv.*, beforehand, as a preliminary; **предварительно введенный параметр,** preset parameter

предварительный, *adj.*, preliminary; **счетчик с предварительной установкой,** predetermined counter

предвосхищать (предвосхитить), *v.*, anticipate

предвосхищение, *n.*, anticipation

предгармонический, *adj.*, preharmonic

предгильбертовый, *adj.*, pre-Hilbert; **предгильбертова норма,** pre-Hilbert norm

предгрупповой, *adj.*, proto-group, pregroup

предел, *m.*, limit, bound; **предел текучести,** yield point, yield stress

предельный, *adj.*, limit, limiting; **предельное множество,** cluster set, limit set; **предельная ограниченность,** ultimate boundedness; **предельный переход,** passage to the limit; **предельный случай,** limiting case; **предельное представление,** limit representation; **работа в предельном режиме,** marginal operation; **предельная точка,** limit point; **предельное условие,** boundary condition; **предельный цикл,** limiting cycle, boundary cycle

предикабельный, *adj.*, predicable

предикат, predicate; **исчисление предикатов,** predicate calculus

предикатный, *adj.*, predicate, predicative

прединтегральный, *adj.*, pre-integral

предисловие, *n.*, preface, foreword, introduction

предистория, *f.*, prehistory, previous history

предлагать (предложить), *v.*, offer, propose, suggest

предложение, *n.*, conjecture, proposal, sentence, proposition; **перевод по предложениям,** sentence-for-sentence translation (*comp.*); **предложение цены,** bidding; **предложение и спрос,** supply and demand

предложить (cf. **предлагать**), *v.*, offer propose, suggest

предмет, *m.*, subject, object, unit, topic, article

предметный, *adj.*, object, objective; **предметный указатель,** subject index

предназначать, *v.*, intend (for), mean (for), be destined (for)

предназначение, *n.*, destination
предназначенный, *adj.*, intended, meant, destined
преднамеренный, *adj.*, purposive, nonrandom; **преднамеренная выборка,** purposive sampling
предначертание, *n.*, outline, plan, design
предначертать, *v.*, outline in advance
предоставлять (предоставить), *v.*, let, submit, leave, allow
предоставляться, *v.*, be permitted, be allowed, be given
предостерегать (предостеречь), *v.*, warn, caution
предостережение, *n.*, warning, caution
предосторожность, *f.*, precaution
предотвращать (предотвратить), *v.*, prevent
предохранитель, *m.*, safety device, protector, safeguard
предписание, *n.*, prescription, prescribing
предписанный, *adj.*, prescribed
предписывать (предписать), *v.*, prescribe, order, direct
предполагаемый, *adj.*, supposed, conjectural, tentative
предполагать (предположить), *v.*, assume, presuppose
предположение, *n.*, supposition, assumption, premise
предположенный, *adj.*, postulated, presupposed, assumed
предположить (cf. **предполагать**), *v.*, presuppose
предпоследний, *adj.*, penultimate, next to the last
предпосылать (предпослать), *v.*, presuppose, premise, preface
предпосылка, *f.*, premise, prerequisite
предпочитать (предпочесть), *v.*, prefer
предпочтение, *n.*, preference; **отношение предпочтений,** preference relation, preference pattern
предпочтительный, *adj.*, preferred, preferable
предпреждающий, *adj.*, warning; **предпреждающая система,** warning system
предприниматель, *m.*, industrialist, employer
предпринимать (предпринять), *v.*, undertake, launch
предпринятый, *adj.*, undertaken
предприятие, *n.*, enterprise, undertaking, business; **анализ деятельности предприятия,** break-even analysis
предпусковой, *adj.*, restarting, reset; **предпусковой режим,** reset condition
предрешать, *v.*, determine, predetermine
предсказание, *n.*, prediction, forecast
предсказанный, *adj.*, predicted
предсказатель, *m.*, predictor
предсказывать (предсказать), *v.*, predict
представимость, *f.*, representability
представимый, *adj.*, representable
представитель, *m.*, representative, specimen
представительный, *adj.*, representative
представить (cf. **представлять**), *v.*, represent, present, offer, assume, produce
представление, *n.*, representation, presentation; idea; **двоичное представление,** binary notation; **представление числа в обычном виде,** true representation; **дискретное представление величины,** sampling; **графическое представление программы,** flow diagram; **представление числа с учетом порядков,** floating-point notation; **алгебра с ограниченными степенями представлений,** algebra of bounded representation type
представленный, *adj.*, represented
представлять (представить), *v.*, represent, present; **представлять собой,** *v.*, represent, is represented; **представлять себе,** *v.*, imagine, conceive, suppose; **доказательство представляем читателю,** we leave the proof to the reader
представляющий, *adj.*, representing, representative

представляя, *adv. part.*, representing, if we represent
предубеждение, *n.*, bias, prejudice, preconception
предубежденный, *adj.*, biased, prejudiced
предупреждать (предупредить), *v.*, notify, caution
предупредительный, *adj.*, warning, preventive; **предупредительная линия,** warning limit
предусматриваемый, *adj.*, specified, provided
предусматривать (предусмотреть), *v.*, provide, stipulate, specify
предусмотренный, *adj.*, provided, specified, stipulated
предшественник, *m.*, predecessor
предшествовать, *v.*, precede
предшествующий, *adj.*, preceding, former, previous, antecedent
предъявленный, *adj.*, produced
предъявляемый, *adj.*, producing, presenting, producible
предъявлять (предъявить), *v.*, produce, present, show
предыдущий, *adj.*, previous; **предыдущий член,** antecedent (log.)
предынтегральный, *adj.*, pre-integral
предыстория, *f.*, previous history
преемник, *m.*, successor
прежде, *adv.*, before, first, formerly **прежде всего,** first of all, first; **прежде чем,** *conj.*, before
преждевременный, *adj.*, premature, early
прежний, *adj.*, previous, former
преимущественно, *adv.*, mainly, chiefly, in preference
преимущественный, *adj.*, primary
преимущество, *n.*, advantage, preference
прекомпактный, *adj.*, precompact
прекрасный, *adj.*, excellent, fine
прекращать (прекратить), *v.*, stop, discontinue, cease, suspend
прекращаться (прекратиться), *v.*, come to an end, cease, stop
прекращение, *n.*, stopping, ceasing, curtailment
преломление, *n.*, refraction, breaking
преломленный, *adj.*, refracted
преломляемость, *f.*, refraction, refractability
преломляемый, *adj.*, refractable, refracted
преломлять (преломить), *v.*, refract, break
премия, *f.*, bonus, premium, prize
пренебрегаемый, *adj.*, negligible, neglected
пренебрегать (пренебречь), *v.*, neglect, disregard
пренебрежение, *n.*, neglect, disregard
пренебрежимый, *adj.*, negligible
пренебрежительный, *adj.*, neglectful, slighting
пренебречь (cf. **пренебрегать**), *v.*, neglect; **можно пренебречь,** can be neglected
преобладание, *n.*, preponderance, predominance, prevalence
преобладать, *v.*, predominate, dominate, majorize
преобладающий, *adj.*, dominant, predominant, prevalent
преобразование, *n.*, transformation, transform, mapping, conversion, processing; **обратное преобразование,** inverse transformation, reconversion; **преобразование Фурье,** Fourier transform; **линейное преобразование,** linear transformation; **преобразование отображения,** mapping transformation; **устройство для преобразования,** transcriber; **система преобразования информации,** information processing; **устройство для преобразования углового положения в цифровую форму,** digital angular position encoder; **подобное преобразование,** similarity transformation, **система преобразования данных (информации),** data reduction system, data conversion system

преобразованный, *adj.*, transformed, converted, processed

преобразователь, *m.*, transformer, transducer, converter, translator; **оптимальный преобразователь,** optimum transducer; **преобразователь данных,** data converter; **линейно-логарифмический преобразователь,** linear-to-log converter; **шаговый преобразователь,** step-switch converter; **обратный преобразователь,** inverter

преобразовательный, *adj.*, transforming, converting, converter, transformer

преобразовывать (преобразовать), *v.*, transform, change, convert; **преобразовывать в цифровую форму,** *v.*, digitize

преобразуемый, *adj.*, transformable

преобразующийся, *adj.*, transforming, converting, processing

преодолевать (преодолеть), *v.*, overcome, surmount

преодоление, *n.*, overcoming, surmounting

препарат, *m.*, preparation, compound

преподавание, *n.*, instruction

преподаватель, *m.*, instructor

препозитивный, *adj.*, pre-positive

препятствие, *n.*, obstacle, barrier, obstruction; **второе препятствие,** secondary obstruction

препятствовать, *v.*, hinder, obstruct, prevent

препятствующий, *adj.*, obstructing, obstruction; **препятствующий ∇-цикл,** obstruction cocycle

прерывание, *n.*, interruption, break

прерыватель, *m.*, cut-out, circuit breaker

прерывать (прервать), *v.*, interrupt, break

прерывистый, *adj.*, discontinuous, broken, interrupted, intermittent

прерывный, *adj.*, discontinuous

преследовать, *v.*, pursue

пресс, *m.*, press

претворение, *n.*, conversion, realization

претворять (претворить), *v.*, transform, change; **претворять в жизнь,** realize, put into practice

претендовать, *v.*, claim, pretend

претендующий, *adj.*, claiming

претензия, *f.*, claim, pretention

претерпевание, *n.*, undergoing, enduring

претерпевать (претерпеть), *v.*, undergo, endure

преткновение, *n.*, obstacle, impediment; **камень преткновения,** stumbling block

преупорядоченный, *adj.*, preordered

прецессионный, *adj.*, precession; **прецессионное колебание,** precession oscillation, wobbling

прецессия, *f.*, precession

прецизионный, *adj.*, precision

при, *prep.*, at, in, under, by; **при условии,** under the condition; **при этом,** in addition, in this connection

прибавить (cf. **прибавлять**), *v.*, add

прибавление, *n.*, addition, supplement, augmentation

прибавляемый, *adj.*, added, being added

прибавлять (прибавить), *v.*, adjoin, add, increase

прибегать (прибегнуть), *v.*, resort (to), have recourse (to)

приближать (приблизить), *v.*, approximate, bring nearer

приближаться, *v.*, approach, approximate

приближение, *n.*, approximation, approach, fitting; **степень приближения,** degree of approximation; **последовательные приближения,** successive approximations

приближенно, *adv.*, approximately; **приближенно равняться,** *v.*, approximate, be approximately equal (to)

приближенный, *adj.*, approximate, rough, designated; **приближенное изображение функций,** curve fitting

приблизительно, *adv.*, approximately, roughly

приблизительность, *f.*, approximateness
приблизительный, *adj.*, approximate, rough
приблизиться (cf. **приближаться**), *v.*, approach, approximate
прибор, *m.*, apparatus, device, instrument; **полупроводниковый прибор,** transistor; **решающий прибор,** resolver
прибывать (прибыть), *v.*, arrive, increase, grow
прибывающий, *adj.*, arriving, coming, incoming, increasing
прибыль, *f.*, gain, profit
прибытие, *n.*, arrival
приведение, *n.*, reduction, adduction
приведенность, *f.*, reducibility
приведенный, *adj.*, reduced, mentioned, adduced
привел (**привели,** etc.), past of **привести**
привес, *m.*, increase in weight, overweight
привести (cf. **приводить**), *v.*, bring, reduce, adduce, mention
привзнос, *m.*, contribution
привлекательный, *adj.*, attractive
привлекать (привлечь), *v.*, attract, draw
привлечение, *n.*, attraction
привнесенный, *adj.*, introduced
привносить (привнести), *v.*, introduce
привод, *m.*, drive
приводимость, *f.*, reducibility
приводимый, *adj.*, cited, brought out, reducible, separable
приводить (привести), *v.*, reduce, reduce to, bring, cite, deduce, adduce; **приводить к масштабу,** *v.*, scale
приводящий, *adj.*, reducing
привычка, *f.*, habit
привычный, *adj.*, customary, habitual, usual
приглашать (пригласить), *v.*, invite, ask
пригодиться, *v.*, be of use, prove useful
пригодность, *f.*, fitness, suitability, usefulness
пригодный, *adj.*, suitable
приготовление, *n.*, preparation
приготовлять (приготовить), *v.*, prepare
придавать (придать), *v.*, add, attach, give; **придавать значение,** attach importance (to), give meaning (to)
приданный, *adj.*, attached
придать (cf. **придавать**), *v.*, give, add, attach
придающий, *adj.*, adding, giving, attaching
придерживаться, *v.*, hold, keep, adhere, confine oneself
придется (from **приходиться**), it will be necessary
придумание, *n.*, invention
придумывать (придумать), *v.*, invent, devise
прием, *m.*, acceptance, receiving, reception, method, way, mode, device, step, stage; **в два приема,** in two steps, in two stages; **эмпирический прием,** empirical method, rule of thumb
приемка, *f.*, acceptance, accepting; **линия приемки,** acceptance line; **область приемки,** acceptance region
приемлемость, *f.*, acceptability, admissibility
приемлемый, *adj.*, plausible, acceptable, admissible
приемник, *m.*, receiver, collector, container
приемочный, *adj.*, reception, acceptance; **приемочное испытание,** acceptance test
прижимать (прижать), *v.*, press, compress
призма, *f.*, prism
призма-отражатель, *m.*, reflecting prism, prism
призматический, *adj.*, prismatic, prism
призматоид, *m.*, prismatoid
признавать (признать), *v.*, recognize, acknowledge
признак, *m.*, indication, sign, mark, test; **признак равномерной сходимости,** test for uniform convergence
признать (cf. **признавать**), *v.*, acknowledge, recognize, regard

призрак, *m.*, phantom, illusion
призывать (призвать), *v.*, call, summon
прийти (cf. **приходить**), *v.*, arrive
прийтись (cf. **приходиться**), *v.*, fit, suit, be necessary
прикасаться (прикоснуться), *v.*, touch, be tangent
прикладка, *f.*, adding; **прикладки,** *pl.*, calculation, computation
прикладной, *adj.*, applied; **прикладная математика,** applied mathematics
прикладываемый, *adj.*, applied, applicable
приклеивание, *n.*, attaching, pasting; **приклеивание ярлыков,** tagging
приклеивать (приклеить), *v.*, paste, attach, stick
приконтактный, *adj.*, contact
прикосновение, *n.*, tangency, contact; **точка прикосновения,** adherent point, point of tangency
прикосновенный, *adj.*, adherent, implicated, involved
прикоснуться (cf. **прикасаться**), *v.*, touch, be tangent (to)
прикреплять (прикрепить), *v.*, append, attach
прилагать (приложить), *v.*, add, apply
прилегать, *v.*, adjoin, be adjacent (to)
прилегающий, *adj.*, adjacent, adjoining, contiguous
прилежащий, *adj.*, adjacent, adjoining
прилив, *m.*, flow, influx, tide
приливный, *adj.*, tidal
прилипание, *n.*, adhesion, sticking
прилипать, *v.*, adhere, adhere to
приложен (short form of **приложенный**), applied, (is) applied
приложение, *n.*, application, supplement
приложенный, *adj.*, applied
приложимость, *f.*, applicability
приложить (cf. **прилагать**), *v.*, apply, add
прим, *m.*, prime, accent
прим. перев., *abbrev.* **(примечание переводчика),** translator's remark
464 прималь, *n.*, primal
примальный, *adj.*, primal
примарность, *f.*, primality
примарный, *adj.*, primary, prime; **примарный идеал,** prime ideal
примем (from **принимать**), we shall accept, let us assume
применение, *n.*, application
применив, *adv. part.*, having applied, by applying
применимость, *f.*, applicability, adaptability, validity
применимый, *adj.*, applicable, suitable
применительно (к), *prep.*, in connection with, in conformity (to)
применительный, *adj.*, suitable, applicable
применявшийся, *adj.*, employed, applied
применяемый, *adj.*, applied, used
применять (применить), *v.*, adapt, apply, employ
применяя, *adv. part.*, applying, if we apply
пример, *m.*, example, instance
примерно, *adv.*, roughly, approximately, by way of example
примерный, *adj.*, exemplifying, exemplary, approximate
примесный, *adj.*, extrinsic
примесь, *f.*, ingredient, admixture
примечание, *n.*, remark, note
примирять (примирить), *v.*, reconcile
примитивно-рекурсивный, *adj.*, primitive recursive
примитивность, *f.*, primitiveness, primitivity
примитивный, *adj.*, primitive, primary, initial; **собственно примитивный,** properly primitive
примордиальный, *adj.*, primordial, original
примыкание, *n.*, contiguity, joining
примыкать (примкнуть), *v.*, adjoin, abut, border on
примыкающий, *adj.*, abutting, adjoining, adherent; **близко примыкающий,** closely approximating; **примыкающий ряд,** adherent series

принадлежать, *v.*, belong, belong to, pertain (to)
принадлежащий, *adj.*, belonging (to), pertaining (to), contoured (by)
принадлежность, *f.*, membership, belonging, affiliation
принести (cf. **приносить**), *v.*, bring
принимать (принять), *v.*, take, receive, accept, admit, assume; **принимать во внимание,** take into account
приниматься (приняться), *v.*, begin (with), start (with)
приноравливать (приноровить), *v.*, fit, adapt, adjust
приноравливаться, *v.*, accommodate, adapt
приносить (принести), *v.*, bring, yield
принудительный, *adj.*, forced, compulsory, positive
принуждать (принудить), *v.*, compel, force, constrain
принуждение, *n.*, compulsion, constraint
принужденно, *adv.*, constrainedly, by force
принужденность, *f.*, constraint, tension
принужденный, *adj.*, constrained, forced
принцип, *m.*, principle; **в принципе,** theoretically, in principle; **принцип дирихле,** Dirichlet principle; **принцип двойственности,** duality principle; **принцип минимакса,** minimax principle
принципиальный, *adj.*, principal, fundamental, of principle; **принципиальная схема,** schematic diagram, principal circuit; **с принципиальной точки зрения,** fundamentally
принятие, *n.*, assumption, taking, admission, acceptance
принять (cf. **принимать**), *v.*, take, accept; **принять во внимание,** take into consideration
принятый, *adj.*, accepted, adopted, used
приобретать (приобрести), *v.*, gain, obtain, acquire
приобретение, *n.*, acquisition, gain
приобщать (приобщить), *v.*, unite, join
приобщение, *n.*, union, junction
приоритет, *m.*, priority
припаивание, *n.*, soldering
приписать (cf. **приписывать**), *v.*, ascribe (to)
приписываемый, *adj.*, ascribed, attributed
приписывать (приписать), *v.*, assign, attach, attribute, register, add
приписываться, *v.*, be ascribed (to), be attributed (to)
приписывающий, *adj.*, assigning, ascribing
припой, *m.*, solder
приравнивание, *n.*, equating, setting equal to, equalization
приравнивать (приравнять), *v.*, equate (to)
прирастать (прирасти), *v.*, increase, grow, adhere (to)
приращение, *n.*, increment, increase; **приращение теплоты,** heat differential; **отношение приращения,** difference quotient
приращенный, *adj.*, pertaining to increment, increment
природа, *f.*, nature, character
природный, *adj.*, natural; **природные богатства,** natural resources
прирост, *m.*, increase, growth, increment, gain
присваивать (присвоить), *v.*, appropriate, confer, give
присвоение, *n.*, appropriation, awarding
присвоить (cf. **присваивать**), *v.*, appropriate, give, award
присоединение, *n.*, association, connection, joining, addition, adjunction
присоединенно-полупростой, *adj.*, adjoint semi-simple
присоединенно-простой, *adj.*, adjoint-simple
присоединенный, *adj.*, joined, adjoined, associated, adjugate, adjoint; **присоединенная масса,** apparent additional mass; **присоединенная матрица,** adjoint matrix, augmented matrix

присоединять (присоединить), *v.*, join, adjoin, connect, associate

приспосабливать (= приспособлять), *v.*, adapt

приспособление, *n.*, adaptation, adjustment, accommodation, apparatus

приспособленный, *adj.*, adjusted, suited, adapted

приспособляемый, *adj.*, adjustable, adaptable, applicable

приспособлять (приспособить), *v.*, adjust, adapt, fit, accommodate

приставка, *f.*, prefix

приставлять (приставить), *v.*, put (against), set (against), adjoin

пристрастность, *f.*, bias

пристрастный, *adj.*, biased; **пристрастный выбор,** biased sampling

пристройка, *f.*, addition, annex, extension

приступать (приступить), *v.*, enter upon, begin, proceed

присуждать (присудить), *v.*, adjudge, award

присуждение, *n.*, judgment, awarding

присутствие, *n.*, presence

присутствовать, *v.*, be present

присутствующий, *adj.*, present

присущий, *adj.*, inherent (in), intrinsic

приток, *m.*, influx, tributary

притом, *conj.*, besides, moreover

притягивать (притянуть), *v.*, attract

притягивающий, *adj.*, attracting

притяжение, *n.*, attraction

притяжимость, *f.*, attraction

притязание, *n.*, claim, pretense

притязательный, *adj.*, exacting

притязать, *v.*, pretend, lay claim (to)

притянуть (cf. **притягивать**), *v.*, attract

приурочивать (приурочить), *v.*, coordinate, time, adapt

приходится (from **приходиться**), *v.*, it is necessary

приходить (прийти), *v.*, arrive, come

приходиться (прийтись), *v.*, fit, suit, have to

приходящийся, *adj.*, being necessary, necessary, fitting; taken over; **приходящаяся на единицу объема сила,** force per unit volume; **интеграл, приходящийся на** D, the integral taken over D

прицел, *m.*, aim, sight

прицеливание, *n.*, aiming

прицельный, *adj.*, sighting, aiming

причем, *conj.*, where, moreover, and also

причина, *f.*, cause, reason, motive; **причина и следствие,** cause and effect

причинность, *f.*, causality

причинный, *adj.*, causal, causative

причинять (причинить), *v.*, cause

причиняющий, *adj.*, causing

пришел (пришли, etc.), past of **приходить**

про, *prep.*, about, for

проанализировать, *v.*, analyze

проба, *f.*, test, trial, sample

пробабилизация, *f.*, probabilization

пробабилизм, *m.*, probabilism

пробег, *m.*, run, course (of value)

пробегаемый, *adj.*, running (through)

пробегать (пробежать), *v.*, pass, pass by, run, pass through; **пробегать значение от . . . до . . .,** run from . . . to . . .

пробегающий, *adj.*, passing, running; **пробегающий индекс,** running index

пробел, *m.*, gap, omission, lacuna, blank

пробивка, *f.*, puncture, piercing, punching

пробит, *m.*, probit, probe, try

проблема, *f.*, problem; **проблема переноса,** transport problem; **проблема сравнения двух средних,** two-means problem

проблематика, *f.*, problems

проблематический, *adj.*, problematical

пробный, *adj.*, test, experimental, trial, tentative, sample, sampling; **пробная точка,** sampling point; **пробная серия,** test run

пробовать (попробовать), *v.*, try, attempt, test

пробоотборник, *m.*, sampler
проведение, *n.*, carrying out, execution, conducting
проведенный, *adj.*, conducted, led, drawn, traced
проведывать (проведать), *v.*, find out, learn, trace, pass
проверенный, *adj.*, revised, inspected, examined
проверить (cf. **проверять**), *v.*, check, verify
проверка, *f.*, testing, test, check, verification, control; **проверка гипотез,** test of hypothesis; **проверка предположения, что,** test of whether, test of the assumption that, ascertaining whether; **проверка методом в две руки,** twin check; **проверка с помощью контрольных разрядов,** redundant check; **проверка на дефектность,** marginal checking; **предварительная проверка,** pre-check; **программа проверки,** check program, check routine; **профилактическая проверка,** checking procedure, marginal checking; **решение проверкой,** solution by inspection
проверочный, *adj.*, control, checking, verifying; **проверочная схема,** checking circuit
проверяемый, *adj.*, verifiable
проверять (проверить), *v.*, check, verify
проверяться, *v.*, be verified
провести, cf. **проводить**
провод, *m.*, conductor, wire, lead
проводимость, *f.*, conductivity, conductance
проводить (провести), *v.*, lead, conduct, draw, develop, carry out
проводник, *m.*, conductor, lead
проволока, *f.*, wire
прогиб, *m.*, deflection, sagging
прогибаться, *v.*, sag, cave in, deflect
прогноз, *m.*, prediction, forecast
прогнозирование, *n.*, prediction
прогностический, *adj.*, prognostic
прогнуться (cf. **прогибаться**), *v.*, deflect, sag, cave in
программа, *f.*, code, program, schedule, course; **программа восстановления информации,** rerun routine; **ведущая программа,** master program; **наборная программа,** plugged program; **блок-схема программы,** flow diagram; **графическое представление программы,** flow diagram
программирование, *n.*, programming; **автоматическое программирование,** self-programming, computer-aided programming
программируемый, *adj.*, programmed
программист, *m.*, programmer
прогресс, *n.*, progress
прогрессия, *f.*, progression; **геометрическая прогрессия,** geometric progression
продавать (продать), *v.*, sell
продажа, *f.*, sale, selling
продажный, *adj.*, sale, selling; **продажная цена,** selling-price; **отношение продажных цен,** barter-price ratio
продвигавшийся, *adj.*, progressing, advancing
продвигать (продвинуть), *v.*, advance, progress
продвижение, *n.*, progress, advance
проделанный, *adj.*, done
проделывать (проделать), *v.*, do, make, perform
продеформированный, *adj.*, deformed
продеформировать, *v.*, deform
продиктованный, *adj.*, imposed, dictated
продиктовать (cf. **диктовать**), *v.*, dictate, impose
продифференцировав, *adv. part.*, having differentiated, after differentiating
продифференцированный, *adj.*, differentiated, derived
продифференцировать, *v.*, differentiate
продлевать (продлить), *v.*, prolong, extend
продление, *n.*, extension, prolongation
продолговатый, *adj.*, oblong, extended, elongated, prolate

продолжаемость, *f.*, continuability, extendability

продолжаемый, *adj.*, extendable, continuable

продолжать (продолжить), *v.*, continue, prolong, produce

продолжающийся, *adj.*, continued, extended

продолжая, *adv. part.*, continuing, extending, if we continue

продолжение, *n.*, continuation, extension

продолженный, *adj.*, extended, prolonged, continued

продолжимость, *f.*, continuability, extendability

продолжимый, *adj.*, extendable, continuable

продолжительность, *f.*, duration, period; **продолжительность колебания,** period of oscillation

продольный, *adj.*, longitudinal, lengthwise; **продольная масса,** longitudinal mass; **продольный изгиб стержня,** buckling

продукт, *m.*, product, good; **продукты,** *pl.*, goods

продуктивный, *adj.*, productive, product; **продуктивное множество,** productive set

продукция, *f.*, output, production

продуманность, *f.*, reasoning

проезд, *m.*, passage

проект, *m.*, project, plan

проективитет, *m.*, projectivity

проективно, *adv.*, projectively

проективно-геометрический, *adj.*, projective-geometric

проективно-дифференциальный, *adj.*, projective-differential

проективность, *f.*, projectivity

проективно-тождественный, *adj.*, projectively identical

проективный, *adj.*, projective; **проективная плоскость,** projective plane

проектирование, *n.*, projection, design; **проектирование логики,** logical design

проектировать, *v.*, project, plan

проектировочный, *adj.*, projecting, designing

проектируемый, *adj.*, projected, projectible

проектирующий, *adj.*,. projecting

проектируя, *adv. part.*, projecting, by projecting, if we project

проектор, *n.*, projector

проекционный, *adj.*, projective, projection

проекция, *f.*, projection, view; **горизонтальная проекция,** side view

проем, *m.*, aperture, opening

прозрачность, *f.*, transparency, transmittance

прозрачный, *adj.*, transparent

проигрывать, *v.*, lose, play over

проигрыш, *m.*, loss, failure

произведение, *n.*, product, composition, bundle; **полное произведение,** final product; **произведение матриц,** matrix product; **внутреннее произведение,** inner product, scalar product; **координатное произведение,** coordinate bundle; **косое произведение,** fiber bundle; **произведение уитни,** Whitney product, cap-product; **произведение Колмогорова-Александера,** Kolmogorov-Alexander product, cup-product; **произведение классов когомологий,** cup-product; **произведение пространств,** product space

произвести (cf. **производить**), *v.*, produce, perform, construct

производимый, *adj.*, producible

производитель, *m.*, producer, generator

производительность, *f.*, efficiency, productivity, capacity, output

производительный, *adj.*, efficient, productive

производить (произвести), *v.*, produce, construct, make, create, derive, carry out

производная, *f.*, derivative; **производная по,** derivative with respect to;

косая производная, directional derivative; **частная производная,** partial derivative

производный, *adj.*, derivative, derived

производственный, *adj.*, industrial, manufacturing; **производственная мощность,** productive capacity; **производственный способ,** activity; **анализ производственной деятельности,** activity analysis

производство, *n.*, production, manufacture, output; **коэффициент производства,** capital output ratio; **уровень производства,** output level

производя, *adv. part.*, performing, carrying out

производящий, *adj.*, productive, generating, reproducing; **производящая функция,** generating function, course-of-value function (log.); **производящее ядро,** reproducing kernel

произвол, *m.*, arbitrariness, arbitrary rule

произвольно, *adv.*, arbitrarily; **произвольно взятая функция,** arbitrary function

произвольность, *f.*, arbitrariness

произвольный, *adj.*, arbitrary, unrestricted

произойти (cf. **происходить),** *v.*, arise, happen, occur

произошел (произошла, произошло), past of **произойти**

проиллюстрировать, *v.*, illustrate

проинтегрировать, *v.*, integrate; **проинтегрировать по,** integrate over

проистекать (проистечь), *v.*, result, ensue, originate

проистекающий, *adj.*, resulting, resultant

происходить (произойти), *v.*, happen, take place, originate, be the result (of)

происходящий, *adj.*, arising (from), originating (from), taking place

происхождение, *n.*, origin, descent, extraction

происшедший, *adj.*, happening

пройденный, *adj.*, traversed, passed

пройти (cf. **проходить**), *v.*, pass

прокалываемый, *adj.*, pierced; punctured

прокалывать (проколоть), *v.*, pierce, perforate, puncture

проканонизировать (cf. **канонизировать**), *v.*, reduce to canonical form

прокатка, *f.*, rolling

проквантовать, *v.*, quantize

проколотый, *adj.*, punctured, deleted; **проколотая окрестность,** deleted neighborhood

пролет, *m.*, span, arch, spacing

проливать (пролить), *v.*, spill, shed; **проливать свет,** shed light (on), illuminate

прологарифмировав, *adv. part.*, having taken the logarithm, after taking the logarithm

прологарифмировать, *v.*, take the logarithm

промах, *m.*, gross error, error, blunder

промежуток, *m.*, interval, space, span; gap; **на промежутке**, in the interval; **промежуток времени**, time interval

промежуточнозначный, *adj.*, intermediate-value

промежуточность, *f.*, betweenness

промежуточный, *adj.*, intermediate, interstitial, intervening

промер, *m.*, measurement, error in measurement

промерзания, *f.*, freezing

промышленность, *f.*, industry

промышленный, *adj.*, industrial, business

пронесение, *n.*, transfer

пронизывать (пронизать), *v.*, pierce, penetrate, permeate

пронизывающий, *adj.*, piercing, penetrating

проникать (проникнуть), *v.*, penetrate

проникающий, *adj.*, penetrating, permeating

проникновение, *n.*, penetration, permeation

проницаемость, *f.*, permeability, penetrability

проницаемый, *adj.*, permeable, penetrable

проницание, *n.*, permeation, penetration

проницательность, *f.*, insight, penetration

проницательный, *adj.*, penetrating

пронормировать, *v.*, normalize

проносимый, *adj.*, conveyed

пронумерованный, *adj.*, enumerated, indexed

пронумеровываться, *v.*, be indexed, be enumerated

прообраз, *m.*, prototype, original, preimage, inverse image

проортогонализировать, *v.*, orthogonalize

пропаганда, *f.*, propaganda, propagation

пропагандировать, *v.*, advocate, propagandize, popularize

пропадать (пропасть), *v.*, vanish, disappear, be missing

пропеллер, *m.*, propeller

прописной, *adj.*, capital, copy-book; **прописная буква,** capital letter

пропозициональный, *adj.*, propositional, proposition; **пропозициональная связка,** propositional connective

пропорционально, *adv.*, proportionally, in proportion (to); **обратно (прямо) пропроционально,** *pred.*, inversely (directly) proportional to

пропорциональность, *f.*, proportionality, proportion

пропорциональный, *adj.*, proportional; **прямо пропорциональный,** directly proportional; **обратно пропорциональный,** inversely proportional

пропорция, *f.*, proportion, ratio

пропуск, *m.*, skip, gap, omission; **теорема (Адамара) о пропусках,** (Hadamard) gap theorem

пропускание, *n.*, passage, admission; transmission; **пропускание импульса,** pulse advancing

пропускать, *v.*, pass, pass through, omit, miss, transmit

пропускной, *adj.*, absorbent, permeable, conducting; **пропускная способность канала,** channel capacity

пропустить (cf. **пропускать**), *v.*, pass over, omit, skip

пропущенный, *adj.*, omitted, skipped

прореагировавший, *adj.*, reacted

прореагировать (cf. **реагировать**), *v.*, react

прорез, *m.*, retresection

прорезанный, *adj.*, cut, slit

прорыв, *m.*, break, gap

просачиваться, *v.*, leak, exude, filter

просверленный, *adj.*, drilled, perforated

прослеживание, *n.*, tracing

прослеживать (проследить), *v.*, trace, track, observe

просматривать (просмотреть), *v.*, look over, overlook, miss

просочиться (cf. **просачиваться**), *v.*, leak, exude, filter

простаивать, *v.*, stand, stand idle, stay

простейший, *adj.*, simplest, elementary; **простейшая дробь,** partial fraction

простирание, *n.*, extension, reach

простираться, *v.*, extend, reach, range

простирающийся, *adj.*, extending, reaching, stretching

просто, *adv.*, simply, simple

просто-бесконечный, *adj.*, simply infinite

простогармонический, *adj.*, simply harmonic, simple harmonic

простой, *adj.*, simple, prime, primary, easy, tame; **простой идеал,** prime ideal; **простое число,** prime number; **простой двоичный,** *adj.*, pure binary; **простая кривая,** tame curve, simple curve; **простой случайный выбор,** simple sampling; **взаимно простой,** relatively prime; mutually distinct, mutually disjoint; **простой конец,** prime end; **простой базис,** proper base

просто-периодический, *adj.*, simply periodic

простор, *m.*, spaciousness, scope

просторный, *adj.*, spacious, wide, ample
простота, *f.*, simplicity, primality
простотранзитивный, *adj.*, simply-transitive
пространный, *adj.*, extensive, diffuse
пространственно, *adv.*, spatially
пространственноподобный, *adj.*, spatially similar
пространственный, *adj.*, space, spatial; **пространственная кривая,** space curve, twisted curve
пространство, *n.*, space; **пространство выборок,** sample space; **пространство равномерной сходимости,** uniconvergence space; **пространство траекторий,** trajectory space, orbit space; **пространство близости,** proximity space; **пространство (косого) произведения,** bundle space
пространство-время, *n.*, space-time
просуммировать, *v.*, sum
просчет, *m.*, error, miscalculation, checking
протабулированный, *adj.*, tabulated
протаскивание, *n.*, drawing through, pulling through
протаскивать (протащить), *v.*, drag through, pull through
протеин, *m.*, protein
протекание, *n.*, course, passing, flowing
протекать (протечь), *v.*, flow past, elapse, run its course
против, *prep.*, against, opposite, facing; **против часовой стрелки,** counterclockwise
противник, *m.*, opponent, adversary
противное, *n.*, the contrary, the opposite
противный, *adj.*, opposite, contrary; **(доказательство) от противного,** (proof) by contradiction; **в противном случае,** otherwise; **если не оговорено противное,** unless otherwise stated
противовес, *m.*, counterbalance, counterpoise, counterweight, balance weight
противодавление, *n.*, counterpressure
противодействие, *n.*, opposition, counteraction, reaction
противодействовать, *v.*, counteract, react, oppose
противолежащий, *adj.*, opposite, lying opposite; **противолежащий угол,** alternate angle
противоположение, *n.*, antithesis, contradistinction, contraposition
противоположно, *adv.*, contrariwise, contrarily, in an opposite way
противоположность, *f.*, contrast, opposition, contradiction
противоположный, *adj.*, opposite, inverse, negative, contrary, antipodal; **диаметрально противоположный,** *adj.*, diametrically opposite, antipodal
противопомеховый, *adj.*, noise-cutting, anti-noise; **противопомехоый фильтр,** noise filter
противопоставлять, *v.*, oppose, contrast, set off
противоречащий, *adj.*, contradicting, contradictory; **противоречащий пример,** *m.*, counterexample
противоречиво, *adv.*, in contradiction, contradictorily, inconsistently
противоречивость, *f.*, inconsistency, variance, contradictoriness; **внешняя противоречивость,** external inconsistency
противоречивый, *adj.*, contradictory, inconsistent, conflicting
противоречие, *n.*, contradiction
противоречить, *v.*, contradict
противосовпадающий, *adj.*, anti-coincident
противоставление, *n.*, contraposition
противостояние, *n.*, opposition
протокол, *m.*, report, record, protocol
протон, *m.*, proton
протонный, *adj.*, proton
протон-протонный, *adj.*, proton-proton; **протон-протонная реакция,** proton-proton reaction
прототетика, *f.*, protothetics

прототип, *m.*, prototype, pre-image, inverse image

протягивать (протянуть), *v.*, extend, prolong

протяжение, *n.*, extent, duration, stretch; **на протяжении работы,** in the course of the work; *K*-**протяжение,** *n.*, *K*-spread

протяженность, *f.*, expansion, extension, content, extent, magnitude, spread; **протяженность поля,** length of field (optics)

протяженный, *adj.*, stretched, extensive, lengthy

профакторизовать, *v.*, factor out

профилактика, *f.*, preventive inspection, prophylaxis

профилактический, *adj.*, prophylactic, preventive; **профилактический контроль,** checking, checking procedure

профиль, *m.*, profile, section, side-view

профильный, *adj.*, profile; **профильное сопротивление,** profile drag

профильтрованный, *adj.*, filtered

профильтровать, *v.*, filter

профсоюз, *abbrev.* **(профессиональный союз),** *m.*, trade union

проходимость, *f.*, permeability, practicability

проходимый, *adj.*, passable, practicable, permeable

проходить (пройти), *v.*, pass, go, go through, take on, assume; **проходить через значение,** pass through a value, assume the value

проходящий, *adj.*, transient, passing, progressing, advancing; **проходящая волна,** transient wave, transient; **проходящий через,** passing through

прохождение, *n.*, passage; **прохождение импульса,** pulse advancing

процедура, *f.*, procedure, process, method

процент, *m.*, percent, percentage, rate; **проценты,** *pl.*, interest; **сложные проценты,** compound interest; **формула простых процентов,** simple interest formula

процентиль, *m.*, centile, percentile, percentile rank

процентный, *adj.*, percentage

процесс, *m.*, process

процессия, *f.*, procession

прочесть (cf. **читать**), *v.*, read

прочий, *adj.*, other; **и прочее,** et cetera; **помимо всего прочего,** in addition

прочитанный, *adj.*, read, delivered

прочитать, *v.*, read

прочность, *f.*, strength, durability, solidity, stability; **прочность на разрыв,** tensile strength

прочный, *adj.*, stable, durable, resistant; **прочный фундамент,** stable foundation

прочувствовать, *v.*, experience, feel

прошедший, *adj.*, past, previous

прошел (прошла, прошло), past of **проходить**

прошествие, *n.*, lapse, end; **по прошествии,** after a lapse of, at the end of

прошлое, *n.*, the past

прошлый, *adj.*, past, last

проще (*comp. of* **простой**), *adj.*, easier, simpler; (*comp. of* **просто**), *adv.*, more easily, more simply

проявлять (проявить), *v.*, show, exhibit

проявляться, *v.*, develop, become apparent, appear

пружина, *f.*, spring, coil

прут, *m.*, rod, bar, switch

прыжок, *n.*, jump

прядение, *n.*, spinning

пряжа, *f.*, thread

прямая, *f.*, straight line

прямо, *adv.*, outright, straight, directly

прямой, *adj.*, straight, direct, right, straightforward, erect; **прямая линия,** straight line; **прямое произведение,** direct product, product bundle; **прямое разложение,** direct sum; **прямая сумма,** direct sum; **прямой угол,** right angle; **прямой код,** true representation

прямолинейность, *f.*, linearity, rectilinearity; **мера прямолинейности,** degree of linearity
прямолинейный, *adj.*, rectilinear, linear
прямопропорциональный, *adj.*, directly proportional
прямоугольник, *m.*, rectangle
прямоугольный, *adj.*, rectangular, right angled; **прямоугольная система координат,** Cartesian coordinate system; **формирователь прямоугольных импульсов,** squaring circuit; **генератор прямоугольных импульсов,** square wave-form oscillator; **прямоугольный треугольник,** right triangle
прячущийся, *adj.*, hiding
псевдо, *prefix*, pseudo-, quasi-, semi-
псевдоабелевый, *adj.*, pseudo-Abelian
псевдоалгебра, *f.*, pseudo-algebra
псевдоаналитический, *adj.*, pseudo-analytic, quasi-conformal
псевдобазис, *m.*, sub-basis, pseudo-basis
псевдовекторный, *adj.*, pseudo-vector, axial vector
псевдовыпуклый, *adj.*, pseudo-convex, wegsam (*German*)
псевдогармонический, *adj.*, pseudoharmonic
псевдоглавный, *adj.*, pseudo-principal; **псевдоглавное решение,** pseudo-principal solution
псевдогруппа, *f.*, pseudogroup
псевдодлина, *f.*, pseudo-length
псевдодополнение, *n.*, pseudo-complement
псевдодуга, *f.*, pseudo-arc
псевдоевклидовый, *adj.*, pseudo-euclidean
псевдокомпактность, *f.*, pseudo-compactness
псевдокомпактный, *adj.*, pseudo-compact, semi-compact
псевдокомплексный, *adj.*, pseudo-complex
псевдокомпозиционный, *adj.*, pseudo-composite, pseudo-composition
псевдоконгруэнция, *f.*, pseudo-congruence, semi-congruence
псевдоконформно, *adv.*, pseudo-conformally, quasi-conformally
псевдоконформный, *adj.*, pseudo-conformal, quasi-conformal
псевдокососимметрический, *adj.*, pseudo-skewsymmetric
псевдокреативный, *adj.*, pseudo-creative
псевдокривая, *f.*, pseudocurve
псевдоломанный, *adj.*, pseudo-broken, pseudo-polygonal
псевдомера, *f.*, pseudomeasure
псевдометрика, *f.*, pseudometric, semimetric, pseudo-valuation
псевдометрический, *adj.*, pseudometric, semimetric
псевдомногочлен, *m.*, pseudo-polynomial
псевдонорма, *f.*, pseudonorm
псевдонормированный, *adj.*, pseudo-normalized
псевдоортогональный, *adj.*, pseudo-orthogonal
псевдопараллельный, *adj.*, pseudo-parallel
псевдополный, *adj.*, pseudo-complete, semi-complete
псевдопредел, *m.*, pseudolimit
псевдопроизведение, *n.*, pseudoproduct
псевдопростой, *adj.*, pseudo-simple
псевдоравностепенно, *adv.*; **псевдоравностепенно непрерывный,** *adj.*, semi-equicontinuous, pseudo-equicontinuous
псевдорасстояние, *n.*, pseudo-distance
псевдорациональный, *adj.*, pseudo-rational
псевдорекуррентность, *f.*, pseudo-recurrence
псевдорекуррентный, *adj.*, pseudo-recurrent
псевдоримановый, *adj.*, pseudo-Riemannian
псевдоскалярный, *adj.*, pseudoscalar; **псевдоскалярная ковариантная величина,** *f.*, pseudoscalar covariant

псевдослучайный, *adj.*, pseudo-random; **псевдослучайные числа,** pseudo-random numbers
псевдосопряженный, *adj.*, pseudoconjugate
псевдосторона, *f.*, pseudo-side
псевдоструктура, *f.*, pseudo-lattice, pseudo-structure, semi-lattice
псевдосферический, *adj.*, pseudo-spherical
псевдосходимость, *f.*, semiconvergence, pseudo-convergence
псевдосходящийся, *adj.*, semi-convergent, pseudo-convergent
псевдотранспонирование, *n.*, pseudo-transposition, pseudo-conjugation
псевдотреугольник, *m.*, pseudo-triangle
псевдоунитарный, *adj.*, pseudo-unitary
псевдоцикл, *m.*, pseudo-cycle
псевдоэллиптический, *adj.*, pseudo-elliptic, quasi-elliptic
псевдоэрмитовый, *adj.*, pseudo-Hermitian
психологически, *adv.*, psychologically
психологический, *adj.*, psychological
психология, *f.*, psychology
пуассоновский, *adj.*, Poisson, pertaining to Poisson
пуассоновый, *adj.*, Poisson, pertaining Poisson
публиковаться, *v.*, be published
пульверизация, *f.*, pulverization
пульс, *m.*, pulse
пульсированный, *adj.*, pulsed, pulsate
пульсирующий, *adj.*, pulsing, pulsating, beating
пульт, *m.*, desk, panel, console; **пульт управления,** control panel, **оператор у пульта управления,** console operator
пуля, *f.*, bullet, projectile, shot
пункт, *m.*, point, item, article; **начальный пункт,** initial point; **исходный пункт,** starting point; **конечный пункт,** terminal point
пунктир, *m.*, dotted line
пунктирный, *adj.*, dotted; **пунктирная линия,** dotted line; **пунктирная кривая,** broken curve
пунктировать, *v.*, dot, punctuate
пускание, *n.*, starting, allowing; **пускание в ход машины,** starting a machine
пусковой, *adj.*, starting, start; **пусковая кнопка,** start button
пустой, *adj.*, empty, vacuous
пустота, *f.*, emptiness, void, vacuum; **скорость истечения в пустоте,** escape velocity
пусть, *part.*, let
путаница, *f.*, confusion
путаный, *adj.*, confused, confusing
путать, *v.*, confuse, confuse with, implicate
путем, *prep.*, by means of; **таким путем,** in this way
путь, *m.*, curve, path, way, course
пучок, *m.*, bundle, pencil, cluster, beam, sheaf; **тензорный пучок,** tensor bundle; **пучок света,** beam of light; **пучок сфер,** sphere bundle; **касательный пучок,** tangent bundle; **пучок электронов,** electron beam
пушка, *f.*, gun; **электронная пушка** electron gun
пфаффов, *adj.*, Pfaffian; **пфаффова форма,** Pfaffian form, Pfaffian
пылевой, *adj.*, dust
пылинка, *f.*, dust particle, grain
пыль, *f.* dust, powder
пытать (попытать), *v.*, attempt
пытаться (попытаться), *v.*, attempt, try
пьезо, *prefix*, piezo, piezoelectric
пьезопроводность, *f.*, piezoconductivity
пьезоэлектрический, *adj.*, piezoelectric
пьезоэлектричество, *n.*, piezoelectricity
пятеричный, *adj.*, quinary; **пятеричный разряд,** quinary digit
пятерка, *f.*, five, set of five
пяти, *prefix*, penta-, five-
пятигранник, *m.*, pentahedron

пятигранный, *adj.*, pentahedral, five-sided
пятиугольник, *m.*, pentagon
пятиугольный, *adj.*, pentagonal, five-cornered
пятиэлементный, *adj.*, five-element
пятнадцать, *num.*, fifteen
пятно, *n.*, spot, blemish, patch; **солнечное пятно,** sun spot
пятый, *adj.*, fifth
пять, *num.*, five
пятьдесят, *num.*, fifty
пятьсот, *num.*, five hundred

Р

работа, *f.*, work, paper, performance
работать, *v.*, work
работник, *m.*, worker
работодатель, *m.*, employer
работоспособность, *f.*, efficiency, capacity for work
рабочий, *adj.*, working, worker; **рабочее запоминающее устройство,** working storage, store; **рабочие характеристики,** working characteristics, performance
равен (short form of **равный**), equal, is equal (to)
равенство, *n.*, equality, equation; **знак равенства,** equality sign
равнина, *f.*, flatness, plain
равнинный, *adj.*, flat, plain
равно (short form of **равный**), equal, is equal (to)
равно, *adv.*, in like manner, similarly
равно-, *prefix*, equi-, uniformly
равнобедренный, *adj.*, isosceles
равнобочный, *adj.*, equilateral
равновеликий, *adj.*, isometric, equivalent, equal, of equal magnitude
равновероятный, *adj.*, equiprobable
равновесие, *n.*, equilibrium, balance; **устойчивое равновесие,** stable equilibrium
равновесность, *f.*, equilibrium, balance
равновесный, *adj.*, in equilibrium, equilibrium, balanced
равновзвешенный, *adj.*, equally weighted
равновозможный, *adj.*, equally possible, equally likely
равновычетный, *adj.*, equiresidual
равнодействующий, *adj.*, equal in effect, resultant; **равнодействующая (сила),** *f.*, resultant (force)
равноденствие, *n.*, equinox; **весеннее равноденствие,** vernal equinox; **осеннее равноденствие,** autumnal equinox; **точка весеннего (осеннего) равноденствия,** vernal (autumnal) equinox
равнозначащий, *adj.*, equivalent
равнозначный, *adj.*, equivalent
равнокоррелированный, *adj.*, uniformly correlated
равномерно, *adv.*, uniformly, evenly; **равномерно ограниченный,** *adj.*, uniformly bounded
равномерно-распределенный, *adj.*, uniformly distributed, equidistributed
равномерность, *f.*, uniformity
равномерный, *adj.*, uniform, proportional; **равномерная структура,** uniformity
равномощный, *adj.*, equivalent, of equal strength
равноостаточный, *adj.*, congruent
равноотстоящий, *adj.*, equidistant, equally spaced
равноправный, *adj.*, equivalent, having the same rights
равнораспределение, *n.*, equidistribution, uniform distribution
равнораспределенность, *f.*, uniform distribution, equidistribution

равнораспределенный, *adj.*, uniformly distributed
равнородный, *adj.*, of equal genus
равносилие, *n.*, equivalence, equipotency
равносильность, *f.*, equivalence
равносильный, *adj.*, equivalent, equipotent
равносоставленность, *f.*, homogeneity
равносоставленный, *adj.*, homogeneous
равностепенно, *adv.*, equipotentionally; **равностепенно непрерывный,** *adj.*, equicontinuous
равностепенно-непрерывный, *adj.*, equicontinuous
равностепенный, *adj.*, equipotential, uniform, of the same degree; **равностепенная непрерывность,** *f.*, equicontinuity
равносторонний, *adj.*, equilateral
равносуммируемый, *adj.*, equisummable
равносходимость, *f.*, equiconvergence
равноточный, *adj.*, of equal accuracy, uniformly precise
равноугольный, *adj.*, equiangular, isogonal
равноудаленный, *adj.*, equidistant
равноускоренный, *adj.*, uniformly accelerated
равнохарактеристический, *adj.*, equicharacteristic
равноценность, *f.*, equivalence
равноценный, *adj.*, of equal value, equivalent
равноэкцессный, *adj.*, homokurtic
равный, *adj.*, equal; **кривая равных вероятностей,** equiprobability curve; **почти равный,** nearly equal
равнять (сравнять), *v.*, equate, equalize, even
равняться, *v.*, be equal to, amount to, be equivalent to; **приближенно равняться,** *v.*, approximate, be approximately equal (to)
рад., *abbrev.* **(радиан,** *m.***),** radian
радар, *m.*, radar
радарный, *adj.*, radar, radar-location
ради, *prep.*, for the sake of
радиально, *adv.*, radially
радиальный, *adj.*, radial
радиан, *m.*, radian
радианный, *adj.*, radian
радиационный, *adj.*, radiation, radiative
радиация, *f.*, radiation
радикал, *m.*, radical; **знак радикала,** radical sign
радикальный, *adj.*, radical
радио, *n.*, radio, radio set
радиоактивность, *f.*, radioactivity
радиоактивный, *adj.*, radioactive
радиоастрономия, *f.*, radio astronomy
радиоволна, *f.*, radiowave
радиоизотоп, *m.*, radioisotope
радиология, *f.*, radiology
радиолокационный, *adj.*, radar, radiolocating
радиолокация, *f.*, radar, radar-location
радионавигационный, *adj.*, radio navigational, radar
радиоприемный, *adj.*, receiving, radio
радиосвязь, *f.*, radio communication
радиотехника, *f.*, radio engineering
радиотехнический, *adj.*, radio, radio engineering
радиохимия, *f.*, radiochemistry
радиочастота, *f.*, radio-frequency
радиус, *m.*, radius
радиус-вектор, *m.*, radius vector
раз, *m.*, time; *adv.*, once; *conj.*, since; **на этот раз,** this time; **еще раз,** once again; **как раз,** just, even, exactly; **два раз,** twice; **много раз,** many times; **не раз,** not once, repeatedly
разбавление, *n.*, dilution
разбавленный, *adj.*, dilute, diluted
разбивать (разбить), *v.*, divide, partition, lay out, break (up), decompose, split
разбивая, *adv. part.*, dividing, partitioning, if we divide
разбиение, *n.*, partitioning, subdivision, separation, fragmentation, decomposition; **клеточное разбиение,** complex, triangulation

разбирать (разобрать), *v.*, analyze, take apart, examine
разбираться, *v.*, examine, investigate
разбитый, *adj.*, broken up, decomposed
разбить (cf. **разбивать**), *v.*, decompose, split, break up
разбор, *m.*, analysis, critique
разбраковка, *f.*, gauging, measuring
разбраковываться, *v.*, be gauged, be measured
разброс, *m.*, scattering, dispersion, range, scatter; **коэффициент разброса,** scatter coefficient
разбросанный, *adj.*, scattered, dispersed
разве, *part.*, perhaps, if, unless; **разве только,** unless
разведанный, *adj.*, explored, surveyed
развернутый, *adj.*, expanded, developed, explicit; **развернутая форма,** expanded form, explicit form; **развернутый угол,** straight angle
развернуть (cf. **развертывать**), *v.*, unroll, develop, expand
развертка, *f.*, evolute, development, evolvent; **блок развертки,** sweep circuit; **схема развертки,** scanning circuit
развертывание, *n.*, development; **развертывание функции,** development of the function, expansion of a function
развертывать (развернуть), *v.*, unroll, develop, expand, scan
развертывающийся, *adj.*, developable, scanning; **развертывающаяся поверхность,** developable surface
разветвление, *n.*, branching, ramification; **точка разветвления,** branch point
разветвленный, *adj.*, ramified, branching
разветвляться, *v.*, branch, ramify
разветвляющийся, *adj.*, ramifying, branching, branch
развивать (развить), *v.*, develop, evolve, unwind
развитие, *n.*, development
развитой, *adj.*, developed
разграниченный, *adj.*, delineated, bounded
разграфленный, *adj.*, drawn, ruled
раздвигать (раздвинуть), *v.*, move apart
раздвижной, *adj.*, extensible, expansible
раздвоенный, *adj.*, forked, dichotomous
раздел, *m.*, division, section, class, partition; **поверхность раздела,** interface (between two media)
разделение, *n.*, separation, partition, division; **разделение переменных,** separation of variables; **цепь (схема) разделения,** buffer circuit; **разделение капитала,** capital decumulation
разделенный, *adj.*, divided, separated
разделимость, *f.*, divisibility, separability
разделимый, *adj.*, separable, divisible
разделитель, *m.*, divisor, separator
разделительный, *adj.*, dividing, separating, dichotomous, disjunctive; **разделительная дизъюнкция,** exclusive disjunction
разделить (cf. **разделять**), *v.*, divide, separate
раздельно, *adv.*, separately
разделять (разделить), *v.*, divide, separate
разделяющийся, *adj.*, separating, separable
разделяя, *adv. part.*, separating, dividing
раздетый, *adj.*, stripped
раздражение, *n.*, irritation
раздражитель, *m.*, irritant, stimulus
раздроблять (раздробить), *v.*, shatter, break in pieces
разжатие, *n.*, release, giving way
разлагать (разложить), *v.*, decompose, expand, resolve, factor, rearrange
разлагаться, *v.*, expand, decompose, decay, split up
разлагая, *adv. part.*, expanding, rearranging
разладка, *f.*, discord, disharmony, dissonance
разлиновывать, *v.*, rule, make lines
различать (различить), *v.*, distinguish
различаться, *v.*, differ

различающий, *adj.*, distinguishing, differentiating, discriminating; **различающая ∇-цепь,** difference cochain

различение, *n.*, discrimination, distinguishing

различие, *n.*, distinction, difference

различимость, *f.*, distinguishability

различимый, *adj.*, distinguishable

различительный, *adj.*, distinctive

различный, *adj.*, different, distinct, various

разложение, *n.*, expansion, decomposition, factorization; **разложение на множители,** factorization; **разложение в ряд Фурье,** Fourier-series expansion; **поле разложения,** splitting field

разложенный, *adj.*, decomposed, expanded, factored, developed

разложимость, *f.*, decomposability, separability

разложимый, *adj.*, decomposable, separable, factorable

разложить (cf. **разлагать**), *v.*, decompose, develop, expand, factor

размах, *m.*, range, slope, amplitude, span; **размах колебания,** amplitude of oscillation; **коэффициент изменчивости размаха,** coefficient of variation of range

размельчение, *n.*, making small, pulverization

размер, *m.*, amount, dimension, size, measure

размерение, *n.*, measuring, measurement

размеривание, *n.*, measurement, measuring

размеривать, *v.*, measure

размерно-дополненный, *adj.*, dimensionally complemented

размерностный, *adj.*, dimensional

размерность, *f.*, dimension, dimensionality, degree

размечать (разметить), *v.*, label, mark, graduate

размеченный, *adj.*, marked, graduated

размещение, *n.*, distribution, arrangement, allocation, investment, permutation

размножаемость, *f.*, reproducibility, potential of population to increase

размножать, *v.*, multiply, reproduce

размножение, *n.*, reproduction, multiplication, propagation, breeding, birth; **простой процесс размножения и гибели,** simple birth and death process

размыкание, *n.*, breaking, disconnecting disconnection

размыкать (разомкнуть), *v.*, break, disconnect; **размыкать контакт,** *v.*, break contact; **размыкать ток,** *v.*, break the current

размыкающий, *adj.*, breaking, disconnecting

размытие, *n.*, diffusion

размытый, *adj.*, diffusion

размышление, *n.*, reflection, speculation

разниться, *v.*, differ, be unlike

разница, *f.*, difference, distinction

разновидность, *f.*, variety, kind, species

разное, *n.*, miscellany

разнообразие, *n.*, variety, diversity; **необходимое разнообразие,** requisite variety

разнообразный, *adj.*, diverse, various

разнораспределенный, *adj.*, differently distributed, variously distributed

разнородный, *adj.*, heterogeneous, miscellaneous

разностный, *adj.*, difference; **разностный аналог,** difference analogue; **разностная аппроксимация,** difference approximation; **разностно-дифференциальное уравнение,** difference-differential equation; **разностное исчисление,** calculus of finite differences; **разностное уравнение,** difference equation

разносторонний, *adj.*, scalene

разность, *f.*, difference, remainder (after subtraction)

разноцветный, *adj.*, many-colored, variegated
разноценный, *adj.*, indifferent, not preferred
разноэкцессный, *adj.*, heterokurtic
разный, *adj.*, different, various
разобранный, *adj.*, analyzed, examined, taken apart
разобрать (cf. **разбирать**), *v.*, take apart, analyze, examine
разобраться, *v.*, clear up
разобщать (разобщить), *v.*, disconnect, separate, disunite
разобьем (from **разбить**), we shall separate, we shall divide; **доказательство разобьем на два шага,** we shall divide the proof into two steps
разогрев, *m.*, initial heating, warming up
разомкнутый, *adj.*, open, clear, open cycle; **разомкнутая цель,** open circuit, open loop
разорвать (cf. **разрывать**), *v.*, tear, tear apart
разорение, *n.*, ruin, destruction
разорять (разорить), *v.*, destroy, ruin
разрабатывать (разработать), *v.*, work out, develop
разработанный, *adj.*, worked out, developed; **хорошо разработанный,** detailed
разработать (cf. **разрабатывать**)
разработка, *f.*, development, elaboration
разреженный, *adj.*, rarefied, thinned out
разрез, *m.*, cut, cross-cut, slit, section; **поперечный разрез,** cross-section
разрезаемый, *adj.*, cut; **разрезаемый континуум,** cut continuum
разрезание, *n.*, cut, section
разрезанный, *adj.*, cut, slit
разрезать, *v.*, cut, section
разрезающий, *adj.*, cutting, cut; **разрезающая точка,** cut point
разрешать (разрешить), *v.*, solve, resolve, permit
разрешающий, *adj.*, solving, resolving, solution, decision; **разрешающий процесс,** decision process; **статистическое разрешающее правило,** statistical decision procedure; **разрешающее ядро,** solving kernel, resolvent
разрешение, *n.*, solution, permission, reduction
разрешенный, *adj.*, solved, allowed
разрешимость, *f.*, solvability, decidability; **проблема разрешимости,** decision problem, decidability problem
разрешимый, *adj.*, solvable, decidable, resolvable; **аффино-разрешимый,** *adj.*, affine-resolvable
разрешитель, *m.*, resolvent
разрешительный, *adj.*, resolving
разрозненно, *adv.*, separately
разрозненный, *adj.*, disconnected, separated, separate
разрушать (разрушить), *v.*, destroy
разрушаться, *v.*, fail, collapse
разрушающий, *adj.*, destroying, critical
разрушение, *n.*, destruction, collapse
разрушительный, *adj.*, destructive, destroying
разрыв, *m.*, break, gap, discontinuity
разрывать (разорвать), *v.*, tear, tear apart
разрывной, *adj.*, explosive; **разрывной снаряд,** explosive shell
разрывность, *f.*, discontinuity
разрывный, *adj.*, discontinuous, disconnected; **вполне разрывный,** *adj.*, totally disconnected; **всюду разрывный,** *adj.*, totally disconnected
разряд, *m.*, order, class, rank, category, digit, discharge; **значащий разряд,** significant digit; **старший разряд,** high order, top digit; **самый старший разряд,** highest order, most significant digit; **самый младший разряд,** least significant digit; **разряд переполнения,** extra order; **десятичный разряд,** decimal digit, decimal, decimal location; **счетчик на один разряд,** digit counter; **контрольный разряд,** check bit;

двоичный разряд, binary digit bit; **проверка с помощью контрольных разрядов,** redundant check; **цифра второго разряда,** second order digit; **разряд десятков,** tens digit; **разряд единиц,** ones digit; **сумматор высшего (левого) разряда,** left-hand adder; **сумматор низшего (правого) разряда,** right-hand adder; **апериодический разряд,** overdamping

разрядка, *f.*, discharging, unloading

разрядный, *adj.*, discharging, discharge

разряжать (разрядить), *v.*, discharge, unload

разряжение, *n.*, discharge

разум, *m.*, reason

разумение, *n.*, understanding

разуметь, *v.*, understand

разуметься, *v.*, be understood; **разумеется,** it is clear; **это само собой разумеется,** that is self-understood

разумность, *f.*, reasonableness

разумный, *adj.*, reasonable; **разумным образом,** in a reasonable way

разъедаемость, *f.*, corrosiveness

разъедаемый, *adj.*, corroded, corrosive

разъедание, *n.*, corrosion

разъедать, *v.*, corrode, erode

разъедающий, *adj.*, corroding, corrosive, caustic

разъединение, *n.*, separation, disconnection, dissociation

разъединенный, *adj.*, disconnected, disengaged, discrete

разъединимость, *f.*, disconnectedness

разъединительный, *adj.*, separating, disconnecting, disengaging

разъединять (разъединить), *v.*, separate, disengage, disconnect

разъединяющий, *adj.*, separating, disconnecting, disengaging

разъяснение, *n.*, explanation, interpretation

разъяснять (разъяснить), *v.*, make clear, explain

разъясняться, *v.*, be cleared up

разыскание, *n.*, research, investigation

разыскивать (разыскать), *v.*, search, find

разыскиваться, *v.*, be found

ракета, *f.*, rocket

ракетный, *adj.*, rocket, rocket-powered

рама, *f.*, frame, chassis

рамка, *f.*, frame; **рамки,** *pl.*, scope, limits

ранг, *m.*, class, rank, trace, spur, range

рангированный, *adj.*, ranked, ranged; **рангированное пространство,** ranked space, ranged space

ранговый, *adj.*, rank, order

рандомизационный, *adj.*, randomization

рандомизация, *f.*, randomization

рандомизированный, *adj.*, randomized

ранее, *adv.*, previously, earlier

ранжированный, *adj.*, ranked, ranged; **ранжированное пространство,** ranged space

ранжироваться, *v.*, be ranked

ранжировка, *f.*, ranking, classification

ранний, *adj.*, early

рано, *adv.*, early

раньше, *adv.*, previously, earlier, before

раскаленный, *adj.*, incandescent, glowing

раскачиваться, *v.*, oscillate, swing

раскладывать, *v.*, lay out, decompose, distribute

раскодирование, *n.*, decipherability, decoding

раскодируемость, *f.*, decipherability

раскраска, *f.*, coloring

раскрашиваемый, *adj.* colorable

раскрашивание, *n.*, coloring

раскрашивать (раскрасить), *v.*, color

раскручивающийся, *adj.*, spiraling, twisting

раскрываемый, *adj.*, opened, uncovered, revealed

раскрывать (раскрыть), *v.*, uncover, open, reveal, develop; **раскрывать скобки,** remove the parentheses, multiply out

раскрытие, *n.*, uncovering, opening, exposure, expansion

раскрытый, *adj.*, open, disclosed, exposed

раскрыть (cf. **раскрывать**), *v.*, uncover, reveal

распавшийся, *adj.*, reducible, breakable

распад, *m.*, disintegration, decay, decomposition, collapse

распадаться (распасться), *v.*, fall (into), decompose, disintegrate, split

распадающийся, *adj.*, reducing, disintegrating, decomposing, splitting

распадение, *n.*, disintegration, decay, decomposition, dissociation

расписание, *n.*, schedule; **теория расписаний,** scheduling theory

расплывчато, *adv.*, vaguely

расплывчатость, *f.*, diffusion, diffusiveness

распознавать (распознать), *v.*, recognize, discern

распознавающий, *adj.*, discerning, recognizing

распознание, *n.*, discernment, recognition

располагать (расположить), *v.*, have available, arrange, place, dispose

расположение, *n.*, disposition, situation, arrangement, distribution, location, ordering

расположенный, *adj.*, situated, ordered, disposed; **расположенное поле,** ordered field

расположить (cf. **располагать**), *v.*, arrange, dispose

расположиться, *v.*, be arranged

распоряжаться, *v.*, order, deal with, dispose

распоряжение, *n.*, instruction, direction, disposal, arrangement; **имеющийся в распоряжении,** *adj.*, available

распределение, *n.*, distribution, population, partitioning, assignment, scheduling; **асимптотически-нормальное распределение,** asymptotically normal distribution; **бимодальное распределение,** bimodal distribution; **распределение вероятностей,** probability distribution; **распределение выборки,** distribution of a sample; **выборочное распределение,** sampling distribution; **биномиальное распределение,** binomial distribution; **логарифмически-нормальное распределение,** logarithmically normal distribution; **мультимодальное распределение,** multimodal distribution; **несобственное распределение,** singular distribution; **мультиномиальное распределение,** multinomial distribution; **нормальное распределение,** normal distribution; **совместное распределение,** joint distribution, simultaneous distribution; **собственное распределение,** non-singular distribution; **унимодальное распределение,** unimodal distribution; **условное распределение,** conditional distribution; **усеченное распределение,** truncated distribution; **частное распределение,** marginal distribution; **отрицательно-биномиальное распределение,** negative-binomial distribution; **прямоугольное распределение,** rectangular distribution; **треугольное распределение,** triangular distribution; **распределение Стьюдента,** Student's distribution; **функция распределения,** distribution function, partition function; **распределение экспоненциального типа,** distribution of exponential type; **распределение рабочих,** employment scheduling

распределитель, *m.*, distributor

распределительный, *adj.*, distributive

распределять (распределить), *v.*, distribute

распростирать (распростереть), *v.*, extend, widen

распространение, *n.*, spreading, propagation, extension, diffusion, prevalence

распространенность, *f.*, prevalence

распространенный, *adj.*, extended, expanded, propagated

распространимость, *f.*, extendability, expansion, extension, spreading
распространять (распространить), *v.*, spread, extend, diffuse
распространяться, *v.*, extend, enlarge, spread
распрямлять (распрямить), *v.*, straighten, unbend, rectify
рассеиваемый, *adj.*, scattered, dispersed
рассеивание, *n.*, dispersion, scattering
рассеивать, *v.*, disperse, scatter, diffract
рассеивающий, *adj.*, dispersing, scattering, diffracting
рассекание, *n.*, dissection, cut
рассекать (рассечь), *v.*, cut, dissect
рассекающий, *adj.*, dissecting, cutting
рассечение, *n.*, section, cleavage, retresection
рассеченный, *adj.*, dissected, cut
рассечь (cf. **рассекать**), *v.*, cut, dissect
рассеяние, *n.*, scattering, dispersion, dissipation; **эллипс рассеяния,** ellipse of concentration; **эллипсоид рассеяния,** ellipsoid of concentration
рассеянный, *adj.*, scattered, dispersed, diffused
расслаиваемый, *adj.*, stratifiable
расслаивать, *v.*, stratify
расслаивающий, *adj.*, fibering, fibre; **расслаивающее отображение,** fibre map
расследование, *n.*, investigation
расслоение, *n.*, fibering, stratification, fibre; **расслоение по степени близости,** proximity stratification
расслоенный, *adj.*, stratified, laminated, fiber; **расслоенный пучок,** fiber bundle; **расслоенное пространство,** fiber space; **расслоенная выборка,** stratified sample
расслоить (cf. **расслаивать**), *v.*, stratify
расслояемый, *adj.*, stratifiable, fiber; **расслояемое пространство,** fiber space
рассматриваемый, *adj.*, under consideration, considered; **рассматриваемый в целом,** *adj.*, global
рассматривать, *v.*, examine, consider
рассматриваться, *v.*, be regarded, be considered
рассмотрение, *n.*, examination, consideration
рассмотренный, *adj.*, examined, analyzed
рассмотреть (cf. **рассматривать**), *v.*, examine, consider
расстановка, *f.*, arrangement, order
расстояние, *n.*, distance, space, separation (of a lens), spread; **расстояние от вершины до объекта,** object distance; **управление на расстоянии,** remote control
расстройство, *n.*, disorder, disruption
рассуждать, *v.*, reason, argue
рассуждение, *n.*, reasoning, argument
рассчитанный, *adj.*, calculated, computed
рассчитывать (рассчитать, расчесть), *v.*, calculate, reckon, count, count on, expect, depend (on)
рассылать, *v.*, deliver, distribute, circulate
раствор, *m.*, opening; **с углом раствора** 45°, of angle 45°
растворитель, *m.*, solvent
растение, *n.*, plant
расти, *v.*, grow, increase
расторгать (расторгнуть), *v.*, break, rupture, cancel, dissolve
растущий, *v.*, increasing, growing
растягивать (растянуть), *v.*, stretch, expand
растягивающий, *adj.*, expanding, stretching
растяжение, *n.*, tension, expansion, dilatation; **растяжение времени,** time dilatation
растяжимость, *f.*, extensibility, expandability, tensile strength
растяжимый, *adj.*, extendable, expansible, tensile
растяжка, *f.*, extension, stretching
расход, *m.*, expenditure, expense, outlay, consumption; **приход и расход,** income and expenditure; **карта**

расхода (материалов), flow chart (of materials); **списать в расход,** *v.*, write off
расходимость, *f.*, divergence
расходиться, *v.*, diverge, differ
расходование, *n.*, expenditure
расходоваться, *v.*, spend, be consumed, be spent
расходящийся, *adj.*, nonconvergent, divergent; **расходящийся класс,** divergence class; **расходящиеся прямые,** *pl.*, hyperparallels
расхождение, *n.*, divergence, deviation; **мера расхождения,** measure of deviation; **коэффициент расхождения,** coefficient of divergence
расцвечивание, *n.*, coloring
расценивать, *v.*, estimate, value, appraise
расчет, *m.*, calculation, computation, estimate
расчетливо, *adv.*, economically, sparingly
расчетливость, *f.*, economy
расчетливый, *adj.*, economical, calculating
расчетный, *adj.*, rated, calculated, designed
расчленение, *n.*, partition, dissection
расчлененный, *adj.*, partitioned, multipartite
расчленять, *v.*, partition, dismember, analyze
расчленяющий, *adj.*, partitioning
расшатанность, *f.*, instability
расшатывать (расшатать), *v.*, loosen, shatter
расширение, *n.*, extension, prolongation, expansion, dilatation, completion; **поле расширения**, field extension, extension field; **алгебраическое расширение поля**, algebraic extension over a field; **аналитическое расширение**, analytic completion
расширенный, *adj.*, extended, widened, augmented; **расширенная матрица**, augmented matrix; **расширенная плоскость**, extended plane
расширимость, *f.*, extendability, expandability
расширяемость, *f.*, extendability, expandability
расширять (расширить), *v.*, widen, extend, expand
расширяющийся, *adj.*, expanding, extending
расшифровка, *f.*, deciphering, determination, evaluation
расшифровывать (расшифровать), *v.*, decipher, decode, determine, find the value of
расщепление, *n.*, decomposition, fission, splitting
расщепленный, *adj.*, split, decomposed
расщепляемый, *adj.*, decomposable, splittable, fissionable, disjunction; **расщепляемая структура,** disjunction lattice
расщепляться, *v.*, decompose, split
расщепляющий, *adj.*, splitting, decomposing
рацион, *m.*, ration
рационализатор, *m.*, rationalizer
рационально, *adv.*, rationally
рациональность, *f.*, rationality
рациональный, *adj.*, rational, ration; **рациональная стоимость,** ration price; **бюджет рациональных цен,** ration-point budget
реагент, *m.*, reactant, reagent
реагировать, *v.*, react
реагирующий, *adj.*, reacting
реактив, *m.*, reagent
реактивность, *f.*, reactance
реактивный, *adj.*, reactive, reacting, jet
реактор, *m.*, reactor
реакция, *f.*, reaction
реализация, *f.*, realization, model
реализм, *m.*, realism
реализовать, *v.*, realize
реализуемость, *f.*, realizability
реализуемый, *adj.*, realizable
реализующий, *adj.*, realizing
реалист, *m.*, realist
реалистичный, *adj.*, realistic
реально, *adv.*, substantively; **реально ничем не,** not substantively

реальный, *adj.*, real, actual, workable; **реальный газ,** imperfect gas
ребристый, *adj.*, ridge, edge; **ребристая точка,** ridge point
ребро, *n.*, edge, rib; **ребро возврата,** cuspidal edge
реверберация, *f.*, reverberation
реверс, *m.*, reversion, reverse
реверсивность, *f.*, reversibility
реверсивный, *adj.*, reverse, reversing, reversible
реверсированный, *adj.*, reversed
реверсировать, *v.*, reverse
реверсируемость, *f.*, reversibility
реверсируемый, *adj.*, reversible, reversed
регенерация, *f.*, regeneration; **число обращений между регенерациями,** read-around ratio
регистр, *m.*, register; **регистр множителя-частного,** multiplier-quotient register; **динамический регистр,** revolver; **емкость регистра,** register length; **регистр команды,** operation-address register; **статический регистр,** staticizer
регистрация, *f.*, registration, recording, logging
регистрированный, *adj.*, registered, recorded
регистрироваться, *v.*, be registered, be recorded
регистрирующий, *adj.*, registering, recording
регламентация, *f.*, regulation
регрессивный, *adj.*, regression, regressive
регрессировать, *v.*, regress, retrogress
регрессия, *f.*, regression; **линейная регрессия,** linear regression; **ортогональная регрессия,** orthogonal regression; **параболическая регрессия,** parabolic regression; **эллипсоид регрессии,** ellipsoid of regression; **плоскость регрессии,** regression plane; **поверхность регрессии,** regression surface; **кривая регрессии,** regression curve; **коэффициент регрессии,** coefficient of regression
регулирование, *n.*, regulation, control, adjustment
регулированный, *adj.*, regulated
регулировать, *v.*, govern, regulate, adjust
регулировка, *f.*, regulation, control
регулируемый, *adj.*, regulative, adjustable, controlled; **регулируемое сопротивление,** varistor
регулирующий, *adj.*, regulating, control
регуляризация, *f.*, regularization, regularity
регуляризирующий, *adj.*, regulating, regularizing
регулярность, *f.*, regularity
регулярный, *adj.*, regular
редактировать, *v.*, edit
редактор, *m.*, editor
редакция, *f.*, editorship, editorial staff
редкий, *adj.*, scarce, sparse, infrequent
редкоземельный, *adj.*, rare-earth
редукция, *f.*, reduction
редуцированный, *adj.*, reduced; **редуцированный нормальный закон,** reduced normal law; **редуцированный выборочный контроль,** reduced sampling
редуцировать, *v.*, reduce
редуцироваться, *v.*, be reduced
редуцирующий, *adj.*, reducing
режим, *m.*, condition, conditions, policy, duty, rate, behavior; **тяжелый режим,** heavy duty; **режим фиксации решения,** hold condition; **предпусковой режим,** reset condition; **режим работы,** operating conditions; **работа в предельном режиме,** marginal operation
резание, *n.*, cutting
резать, *v.*, cut
резекция, *f.*, resection
резерв, *m.*, reserve, standby
резервный, *adj.*, reserve, standby
резидуальный, *adj.*, residual
резкий, *adj.*, harsh, sharp
резко, *adv.*, sharply, abruptly
резольвент, *m.* (**резольвента,** *f.*), resolvent, resolution

резольвентный, *adj.*, resolvent, resolution

резолюция, *f.*, resolution

резонанс, *m.*, resonance

резонансный, *adj.*, resonance

резонатор, *m.*, resonator

резонирующий, *adj.*, resonance inducing, resonant

результант, *m.*, resultant

результат, *m.*, result; **в результате,** as a result; **иметь результатом,** *v.*, result in

результативный, *adj.*, resultant

результирующий, *adj.*, resulting

резьба, *f.*, thread; **винт с правой резьбой,** right-threaded screw, right-hand screw

резюме, *n.*, summary, résumé, abstract

резюмировать, *v.*, summarize, sum up, abstract

рейс, *m.*, trip, run

реклама, *f.*, advertisement, advertising; **задача о рекламе,** advertising problem

рекламировать, *v.*, advertise

рекомбинационный, *adj.*, recombinational

рекомбинация, *f.*, recombination

рекомбинировать, *v.*, recombine

рекомендация, *f.*, recommendation

рекомендовать, *v.*, recommend

рекомендуется (from **рекомендовать**), it is recommended

рекорд, *m.*, record

рекуррентно, *adv.*, recursively, recurrently

рекуррентный, *adj.*, recursion, recurrence, recurrent; **рекуррентная формула,** recursion (recurrence) relation

рекурсивно, *adv.*, recursively

рекурсивно-перечислимый, *adj.*, recursively enumerable

рекурсивно-проективный, *adj.*, recursively projective

рекурсивность, *f.*, recursiveness

рекурсивный, *adj.*, recursive, recursion; **рекурсивное определение,** definition by recursion; **частично рекурсивный,** *adj.*, partial recursive

рекурсия, *f.*, recursion

релаксационный, *adj.*, relaxational, relaxation, relaxion

релаксация, *f.*, relaxation; **множитель релаксации,** relaxation factor

реле, *n.*, relay; **реле времени,** timer

релейно-контактный, *adj.*, contact-relay, relay switching

релейный, *adj.*, relay

рельеф, *m.*, relief, contour; **потенциальный рельеф,** charge pattern; **рельеф функции,** modular surface

рельсовый, *adj.*, rail; **рельсовый путь,** rail track

релятивизация, *f.*, relativization

релятивизированный, *adj.*, relativized

релятивизм, *m.*, relativism, relativity

релятивистский, *adj.*, relativistic; **релятивистская поправка,** relativistic correction constant

реляционный, *adj.*, relational, relation

ремонт, *m.*, repairs, maintenance

ремонтировать, *v.*, repair, refit

ремонтируемый, *adj.*, reparable

ренормировка, *f.*, renormalization

рента, *f.*, rent; annuity; **ежегодная рента,** annuity; **государственная рента,** government securities, government annuity

рентабельность, *f.*, profitability, earning capacity

рентген-диффракционный, *adj.*, X-ray diffraction

рентген-диффракция, *f.*, X-ray diffraction

рентгеновский, *adj.*, X-ray, Roentgen

рентгенографический, *adj.*, X-ray

репер, *m.*, frame, frame of reference, reference point, mark; ***K*-репер,** *K*-frame, *K*-hedron, *K*-tuple; **сопровождающий репер (кривой),** moving *n*-hedron (of a curve)

репертуар, *m.*, repertory

репрезентативный, *adj.*, representative; **репрезентативная выборка,** representative sampling
репродуктор, *m.*, reproducer, loudspeaker
репродукция, *f.*, reproduction
ресурс, *m.*, resource
ретрагирование, *n.*, retraction
ретрагировать, *v.*, retract
ретрагирующий, *adj.*, retracting, retraction; **ретрагирующее отображение,** retract, retraction
ретракт, *m.*, retract; **окрестностный ретракт,** neighborhood retract
ретракция, *f.*, retraction
реферат, *m.*, abstract, review
реферативный, *adj.*, review, reviewing
референт, *m.*, reviewer
референция, *f.*, reference
реферируемый, *adj.*, (being) reviewed
рефлекс, *m.*, reflex
рефлексивно, *adv.*, reflexively
рефлексивность, *f.*, reflexivity
рефлексивный, *adj.*, reflexive
рефлективный, *adj.*, reflective
рефракция, *f.*, refraction
рецензент, *m.*, reviewer
рецензия, *f.*, review, critique
рецепт, *m.*, prescription, formula
рецептор, *m.*, receptor
рецептурный, *adj.*, prescribed
рециркуляция, *f.*, recirculation
речь, *f.*, word, term, speech, question, discourse; **идет речь о,** the question is; **мир речи,** universe of discourse
решать (решить), *v.*, solve, decide, determine
решающий, *adj.*, resolving, deciding, decision, decisive; **решающая функция,** decision function; **решающее устройство,** resolver; **решающий прибор,** resolver
решая, *adv. part.*, solving, by solving, if we solve
решение, *n.*, solution, decision, determination; **функция решения,** decision function
решенный, *adj.*, determined, solved
решетка, *f.*, lattice, grating, heads; **герб и решетка,** "heads" and "tails"
решето, *n.*, sieve; **решето Эратосфена,** sieve of Eratosthenes
решетчатый, *adj.*, lattice, latticed
решимость, *f.*, solvability
решимый, *adj.*, solvable
решительный, *adj.*, decisive
решить, cf. **решать**
римановой, *adj.*, Riemann, Riemannian; **риманова поверхность,** Riemann surface; **римановое многообразие,** Riemannian manifold, Riemannian variety
римский, *adj.*, Roman; **римская цифра,** Roman numeral
риск, *m.*, risk; **функция риска,** risk function
рисовать, *v.*, design, draw, picture
риссовский, *adj.*, Riesz, pertaining to Riesz
рисунок, *m.*, design, drawing, figure
ритм, *m.*, rhythm
ритмический, *adj.*, rhythmic
ритмично, *adv.*, rhythmically
ритмичный, *adj.*, rhythmic
робот, *m.*, robot
ровно, *adv.*, equally, exactly, regularly, precisely
ровный, *adj.*, even, smooth, flat, level; **ровная поверхность,** plane surface
рог, *m.*, horn
род, *m.*, family, genus, sort, kind; **конечного рода,** of finite genus; **своего рода,** in its own way; **в своем роде,** in its own way; **в некотором роде,** in some way, to some extent
родительский, *adj.*, parental, parent
родственный, *adj.*, related, contiguous; **родственная функция,** contiguous function
рождаемость, *f.*, birth-rate
рождение, *f.*, birth; **статистика рождений,** birth statistics

розничный, *adj.*, retail, purchasing; **розничная цена,** retail price, purchasing cost
розыгрыш, *m.*, drawing (lottery), draw (game)
рой, *m.*, cluster, swarm
роль, *f.*, role, part, function
ромб, *m.*, rhombus
ромбический, *adj.*, rhombic, rhombus; **"ромбическая диаграмма",** " lozenge diagram "
ромбовидный, *adj.*, diamond-shaped
ромбоид, *m.*, rhomboid
ромбоидальный, *adj.*, rhomboidal
рост, *m.*, growth, increase, height; **темп роста модели,** factor of a model
россыпь, *f.*, deposit, scattering, distribution
росток, *m.*, sprout, shoot, germ
ротатор, *n.*, rotator
ротация, *f.*, rotation
ротор, *m.*, rotor, rotation, curl, vorticity
ртутный, *adj.*, mercury; **ртутная линия задержки,** mercury tank
рубеж, *m.*, boundary, border; **рубеж эффективности,** efficiency frontier
рубрика, *f.*, heading, column
руда, *f.*, ore
рудимент, *m.*, rudiment
рудиментарный, *adj.*, rudimentary
рудник, *m.*, mine, pit
рудничный, *adj.*, mine, mining
рука, *f.*, hand, arm
руководство, *n.*, guidance, direction, guide book
руководствовать, *v.*, direct, guide
руководствоваться, *v.*, follow, be guided
рукопись, *f.*, manuscript
рулевой, *adj.*, steering
румб, *m.*, bearing, rhumb
рупор, *m.*, horn
ручаться, *v.*, guarantee
ручка, *f.*, handle
ручной, *adj.*, hand
рынок, *m.*, market
рыночный, *adj.*, market; **по рыночной цене,** at market price; **модель рыночной купли,** market model; **анализ рыночных цен во времени,** market trend
рыскание, *n.*, search, yaw; **угол рыскания,** angle of yaw
рыскать, *v.*, search, roam, yaw
рыскающий, *adj.*, yawing
рычаг, *m.*, lever; **плечо рычага,** lever arm
рычажный, *adj.*, lever
ряд, *m.*, series, row, line, sequence; **ряд данных,** sequence (series) of data; **ряд фурье,** Fourier series; **ряд одного переменного,** univariable series; **ряды клавиш,** key sets
рядом, *adv.*, in a row, side by side, alongside

С

с (со), *prep.*, with, from, by, of, out of
С., *abbrev.* **(север,** *m.*), North
сабина, *f.*, sabine (unit of total acoustic absorption)
сагитта, *f.*, sagitta; **сагитта дуги,** sagitta of an arc
сагиттальный, *adj.*, sagittal
сам (сама, само), *pron.*, self (myself, itself, etc.); **само по себе,** by itself; **само собой разумеется,** it stands to reason, of course, it is understood
самовозбуждаемый, *adj.*, self-exciting; **самовозбуждаемый контур,** self-exciting circuit
самовосстанавливающийся, *adj.*, self-renewing, self-regenerating
самодвойственный, *adj.*, self-dual
самодуальный, *adj.*, self-dual

самоинверсный, *adj.*, self-inversive, self-inverse
самоиндукция, *f.*, self-induction
самокасание, *n.*, self-contact; **точка самокасания,** double cusp
самокасаться, *v.*, be tangent to itself
самолет, *m.*, aeroplane
самом, cf. **самый** and **сам**
самонаведение, *n.*, homing guidance
самонадводящийся, *adj.*, homing
самонастраивающийся, *adj.*, self-adjusting, self-orienting, self-aiming
самонепересекаться, *v.*, not to intersect itself, be free of self-intersections
самонепересекающийся, *adj.*, non-self-intersecting
самоочевидный, *adj.*, self-evident, axiomatic
самопересекающийся, *adj.*, self-crossing, self-intersecting
самопересечение, *n.*, self-intersection, self-crossing
самописец, *m.*, automatic recorder
самоподача, *f.*, self-feeding
самоприкосновение, *n.*, self-contact, self-tangency; **точка самоприкосновения,** point of osculation
самоприсоединенный, *adj.*, self-adjoined
самопрограммирующий, *adj.*, self-programming
самопроизвольность, *f.*, spontaneity
самопроизвольный, *adj.*, spontaneous
самораспространяющийся, *adj.*, self-spreading, self-propagating
самосогласованный, *adj.*, (self-) consistent, self-coordinated, self-congruent
самосоприкосновение, *n.*, self-tangency
самосопряженность, *f.*, self-conjugacy, self-adjointness
самосопряженный, *adj.*, self-adjoint, self-conjugate, self-adjoined
самостоятельный, *adj.*, independent
самоуравновешенный, *adj.*, self-balanced
самоцентрирование, *n.*, self-centering, self-alignment
самый, *pron.*, same, very; **переводить в самое себя,** *v.*, transform into itself; **тот же самый,** the same; **в самом деле,** indeed; *indication of superlative* (cf. *Grammar*, § 3.3)
сантиметр, *m.*, centimeter, tape measure
сантиметровый, *adj.*, centimeter
сателлит, *m.*, satellite
сбалансированность, *f.*, balance
сбалансированный, *adj.*, balanced
сбегать, *v.*, run down, diminish
сбегающий, *adj.*, running down, diminishing
сбивать (сбить), *v.*, knock down, put out
сбивчивый, *adj.*, inconsistent, confused
сближаться, *v.*, approach, come close, come together, approximate
сближение, *n.*, coming together, approach, approximation
сбор, *m.*, gathering, collection; **сбор данных,** data gathering
сборка, *f.*, assembling, assembly; **график (план) сборки,** assembly schedule
сборник, *m.*, transactions, collection (of works), compendium
сборный, *adj.*, combined, assembly, miscellaneous
сбрасывать (сбросить), *v.*, drop, throw off, shed
сбыт, *m.*, sale, marketing
сведение, *n.*, information, intelligence, reduction, contraction; **принять к сведению,** take into consideration; **сведение к абсурду,** reductio ad absurdum
сведенный, *adj.*, brought, reduced
свезти, cf. **свозить**
свелось (cf. **сводить**), reduced, has reduced itself
сверить, cf. **сверять**
свернутый, *adj.*, convolution, contracted
свернуть, cf. **свертывать**
свертка, *f.*, convolution, fold, folding; **интеграл свертки,** convolution
свертывание, *n.*, convolution, rolling up, curtailment, turning, folding, contraction (of tensors)

свертывать, *v.*, contract, fold, roll up, curtail
сверх, *prep.*, over, above, beyond, super-, hyper-, ultra-; **сверх того,** in addition, moreover
сверхгигант, *m.*, supergiant
сверхзвуковой, *adj.*, supersonic, ultrasonic
сверхкомпактный, *adj.*, supercompact, hypercompact
сверхкритический, *adj.*, supercritical
сверхмодулярный, *adj.*, super-modular, hypermodular
сверхопределенный, *adj.*, overdetermined, overdefined
сверхполный, *adj.*, saturated, superabundant
сверхпроводимость, *f.*, superconductivity
сверхпроводник, *m.*, superconductor, superconducting matter
сверхпроводящий, *adj.*, superconducting
сверхразрешимый, *adj.*, supersoluble, hypersolvable
сверхрелаксация, *f.*, overrelaxation, super-relaxation
сверхсоприкасающийся, *adj.*, hyperosculating
сверхстационарный, *adj.*, superstationary
сверхсходимость, *f.*, overconvergence
сверхсходящийся, *adj.*, overconvergent
сверхтонкий, *adj.*, hyperfine
сверху, *adv.*, *prep.*, above, from above, on top; **полунепрерывный сверху,** *adj.*, upper semicontinuous
сверхурочный, *adj.*, overtime
сверхустойчивость, *f.*, overstability
свершать (свершить), cf. **совершать**
сверять, *v.*, compare (with), check
сверяться, *v.*, be compared, be checked
свести (cf. **сводить**), *v.*, reduce
свет, *m.*, light, world; **в свете,** in view (of)
светимость, *f.*, luminosity, brightness
светлый, *adj.*, light, clear
световой, *adj.*, light, pertaining to light, luminous, photonic
светочувствительность, *f.*, photosensitivity, speed
светочуствительный, *adj.*, photosensitive, light-sensitive, sensitive
светоэлектрический, *adj.*, photoelectric
светящийся, *adj.*, luminous, phosphorescent; **светящаяся точка,** focus
свечение, *n.*, luminescence, brightness, fluorescence
свидетельство, *n.*, testimony, evidence, indication
свидетельствовать, *v.*, testify (to), attest (to), indicate
свидетельствующий, *adj.*, indicative, indicating
свинец, *m.*, lead
свинцовый, *adj.*, lead, leaden
свобода, *f.*, freedom, liberty
свободно, *adv.*, freely
свободнодеформируемый, *adj.*, deformation-free
свободоструйный, *adj.*, free-flow
свободный, *adj.*, free
свод, *m.*, arch, vault, code
сводимость, *f.*, reducibility
сводимый, *adj.*, reducible
сводить (свести), *v.*, reduce
сводиться, *v.*, be reduced, reduce (itself), come; **сводится к нулю,** reduces to zero
сводка, *f.*, résumé, summary
сводный, *adj.*, summary, compound, combined, multiple; **сводный коэффициент корреляции,** multiple coefficient of correlation
сводящийся, *adj.*, reducing (to), leading to
своевременно, *adv.*, in time, opportunely
своевременный, *adj.*, timely, opportune
своеобразие, *n.*, singularity, peculiarity
своеобразность, *f.*, singularity, peculiarity
своеобразный, *adj.*, distinctive, singular, peculiar
свозить (свезти), *v.*, bring (together), take
свой, *pron.*, his (her, its, their, one's) own

свойственность, *f.*, peculiarity, singularity, property
свойственный, *adj.*, peculiar (to), characterized (by), incident (to)
свойство, *n.*, property, character; **свойства,** *pl.*, characteristics
сворачивать, *v.*, displace, remove, turn, swing
свыше, *adv.*, from above; *prep.*, over, beyond
связанный, *adj.*, connected, linked, dependent, coupled, combined, implied, bound, associated, **связанный вектор,** bound vector, localized vector
связать (cf. **связывать**), *v.*, tie, bind, connect
связка, *f.*, sheaf, bundle, bunch, connective; **пропозициональная связка,** propositional connective
связность, *f.*, connectedness, connectivity, coherence; **связность с помощью дуг,** arcwise connectedness; **пространство аффинной связности,** affinely connected space; **линейная связность,** arcwise connectedness; **нелинейная связность,** non-linear connection
связный, *adj.*, connected, coherent; **линейно связный,** *adj.*, arcwise connected
связующий, *adj.*, connecting
связывание, *n.*, binding, linking, coupling
связывать (связать), *v.*, connect, bind
связываться, *v.*, communicate (with), be bound (to), be combined
связывающий, *adj.*, connecting
связь, *f.*, relation, connection, tie, bond, association, communication, constraint, binding; **сила связи,** constraint force; **обратная связь,** feedback; **в тесной связи,** closely connected (to); **в связи,** in connection (with); **взаимная связь,** coupling; **ширина связи,** band width
сгиб, *m.*, bend
сгибание, *n.*, inflection, bending
сглаженность, *f.*, flattening, flatness; **сглаженность кривой плотности,** flatness of a frequency curve
сглаженный, *adj.*, smoothed, leveled, modified
сглаживание, *n.*, smoothing, fitting
сглаживать (сгладить), *v.*, smooth out, level, smooth over
сглаживающий, *adj.*, smoothing; **сглаживающий оператор,** smoothing operator
сгруппировать, *v.*, group (together), arrange into groups, classify
сгустившийся, *adj.*, condensed, thickened
сгусток, *m.*, group, clot
сгущаемость, *f.*, condensability, compressibility
сгущаемый, *adj.*, condensable, compressible
сгущаться, *v.*, be condensed, be concentrated
сгущение, *n.*, condensation, concentration
сдавать (сдать), *v.*, return, give, deal; **сдавать карты,** *v.*, deal (cards)
сдача, *f.*, surrender, change, lease, turn; **сдача карт,** dealing cards
сдваивать (сдвоить), *v.*, double
сдвиг, *m.*, displacement, translation, shift, shear; **напряжение сдвига,** shear; **средний модуль сдвига,** mean shear modulus; **сдвиг влево,** left-shift
сдвигать (сдвинуть), *v.*, shift, displace, move
сдвинутый, *adj.*, shifted
сдвоенный, *adj.*, doubled, double, paired; **сдвоенная линия,** double line; **сдвоенная прямая,** doubly straight line
сделанный, *adj.*, made, done, manufactured, suitable, certain
сделать (cf. **делать**), *v.*, make, do
сделка, *f.*, agreement, bargain, deal, transaction; **задача о сделке,** bargaining problem

сдельный, *adj.*, job, piece; **сдельная оплата труда,** piece-rate system; **сдельная плата,** contract price
себестоимость, *f.*, price, cost price, cost-in-process, production cost, net cost, manufacturing cost
себя, *pron.*, himself, itself, oneself
север, *m.*, North
северный, *adj.*, north, northern; **северный полюс,** North Pole
сегмент, *m.*, segment, section, line segment
седло, *n.*, saddle, seat, saddle point
седловой, *adj.*, saddle; **седловая точка,** saddle point
седлообразный, *adj.*, saddle; **седлообразная точка,** saddle point
седло-фокус, *m.*, saddle-focus
седьмой, *adj.*, seventh
сезонный, *adj.*, seasonal
сей, *pron.*, this
сейсмический, *adj.*, seismic
сейсмограмма, *f.*, seismogram
сейсмограф, *m.*, seismograph
сейсмологический, *adj.*, seismological
сейсмология, *f.*, seismology
сейчас, *adv.*, now, at once
сек., *abbrev.* (**секунда,** *f.*), second
секанс, *m.*, secant
секвенциально, *adv.*, sequentially; **секвенциально компактный,** sequentially compact
секвенциальный, *adj.*, sequential; **вальдовское секвенциальное испытание,** sequential probability ratio test, Wald sequential test
секвенция, *f.*, sequence, sequent; **сходные секвенции,** cognate sequents; **средняя секвенция,** midsequent
секондарный, *adj.*, secondary; **секондарный идеал,** secondary ideal
секстиль, *m.*, sextile
сектор, *m.*, sector
секториальный, *adj.*, sector, sectorial; **секториальная сферическая функция,** sectorial surface harmonic; **секториальная скорость,** areal velocity
секторный, *adj.*, sector
секунда, *f.*, second
секущая, *f.*, secant, transversal
секущий, *adj.*, intersecting, cutting; **секущая линия,** *f.*, secant; **секущая поверхность,** *f.*, cross-section, intersecting surface
секционирование, *n.*, partitioning
секционный, *adj.*, sectional, sectioned, partitioned
селективно, *adv.*, selectively
селектор, *m.*, selector
селекторный, *adj.*, selective, selector
селеновый, *adj.*, selenium
сельскохозяйственный, *adj.*, agricultural
семантика, *f.*, semantics
семантический, *adj.*, semantic
семантичный, *adj.*, semantic
семейство, *n.*, set, family, class, collection, aggregate
семиинвариант, *m.*, semi-invariant, cumulant
семи-инвариант, *m.*, semi-invariant, cumulant
семи-интерквартильный, *adj.*, semi-interquartile; **семи-интерквартильная широта,** semi-interquartile range
семиметрический, *adj.*, semimetric
семинар, *m.*, seminar
семинорма, *f.*, semi-norm
семитензор, *m.*, semi-tensor
семиугольник, *m.*, heptagon
семь, *num.*, seven
семьдесят, *num.*, seventy
сенсорный, *adj.*, sensory
сепарабелитет, *m.*, separability
сепарабельность, *f.*, separability
сепарабельный, *adj.*, separable
сепаранта, *f.*, separant
сепаративный, *adj.*, separative
сепаратриса, *f.*, separatrix, decimal point
сепарация, *f.*, separation
сервантный, *adj.*, serving; **сервантная подгруппа,** serving subgroup

серводвигатель, *m.*, servomotor, servomechanism
сервомеханизм, *m.*, servomechanism
сервомотор, *m.*, servomotor
сервопривод, *m.*, servo, servodrive
сервосистема, *f.*, servo-system
сервоусилитель, *m.*, servo-amplifier
сердечник, *m.*, core, center
сердцевина, *f.*, core, heart
серебро, *n.*, silver
середина, *f.*, middle, mean
сериальный, *adj.*, series, serial
серийно, *adv.*, serially
серийный, *adj.*, serial; **серийная продукция,** batch production, production bundle
серия, *f.*, series, run; **серия изображений,** set of patterns
серьезность, *f.*, seriousness, gravity
серьезный, *adj.*, serious, grave
сетка, *f.*, net, mesh, network, grid, frame
сеточный, *adj.*, net, grid, network; **сеточный оператор,** difference operator, network operator
сетчатый, *adj.*, network; **сетчатая номограмма,** alignment nomogram
сеть, *f.*, net, network
сечение, *n.*, cross-section, cut, section; **коническое сечение,** conic section
сжатие, *n.*, pressure, compression, pressing, contraction, compressibility
сжато, *adv.*, tersely, concisely
сжатость, *f.*, conciseness, compactness
сжатый, *adj.*, condensed, compressed, compact, contracted, oblate; **сжатый сфероид,** oblate spheroid
сжигать (сжечь), *v.*, burn, cremate
сжижать, *v.*, liquefy
сжижение, *n.*, liquefaction
сжимаемость, *f.*, compressibility, condensability, contractibility
сжимаемый, *adj.*, compressible, contractible
сжимать (сжать), *v.*, contract, shrink
сжиматься, *v.*, contract, shrink
сжимающий, *adj.*, contractive, contracting, shrinking
сзади, *prep.*, behind, from behind, from the end; **вид сзади,** rear view
сигнал, *m.*, signal; **сигнал записи,** write signal; **входной сигнал,** input; **сигнал потенциального типа,** steady-state signal
сигнальный, *adj.*, signal, signalling; **сигнальный код,** signalling alphabet
сигнатура, *f.*, signature, label
сигнифика, *f.*, denotation, meaning
сигнум-функция, *f.*, sign function, signum function
сидерический, *adj.*, sidereal
сизигия, *f.*, syzygy; **цепь сизигий,** chain syzygies
сила, *f.*, force, strength, power; **сохранить силу,** *v.*, remain valid; **в силе,** in force; **в силу** by virtue of, on the strength of; **момент силы,** torque, moment of force; **оптическая сила линзы,** optical power of a lens
силлогизм, *m.*, syllogism
силлогистика, *f.*, syllogistics
силлогический, *adj.*, syllogistic
силовой, *adj.*, power, force; **силовое поле,** field of force, force field; **силовая цепь,** power circuit
Силовский, *adj.*, Sylow; **Силовская группа,** Sylow group
сильнее (from **сильный**), *adj.*, stronger
сильнейший, *adj.*, strongest
сильно, *adv.*, strongly; **сильно демпфированный,** *adj.*, overdamped
сильнопаракомпактный, *adj.*, strongly paracompact
сильный, *adj.*, strong; **сильное демпфирование,** *n.*, overdamping
символ, *m.*, symbol; **символ частного,** quotient-symbol
символизация, *f.*, symbolization
символизировать, *v.*, symbolize
символизм, *m.*, symbolism
символика, *f.*, symbolics, symbolism, notation
символический, *adj.*, symbolic; **символический код,** pseudo-code
симметризационный, *adj.*, symmetrization

симметризация, *f.*, symmetrization
симметрирование, *n.*, symmetrization
симметризировать, *v.*, symmetrize
симметризуемый, *adj.*, symmetrizable
симметрический, *adj.*, symmetric
симметричность, *f.*, symmetry
симметричный, *adj.*, symmetric
симметрия, *f.*, symmetry, reflection
симплекс, *m.*, simplex
симплексный, *adj.*, simplex, simplicial
симплектический, *adj.*, simplicial, simplex, symplectic
симплициально, *adv.*, simplicially
симплициальность, *f.*, simpliciality
симплициальный, *adj.*, simplicial
симпозиум, *m.*, symposium
симптом, *m.*, symptom
синапс, *m.*, synapse
синглетный, *adj.*, singlet; **синглетное состояние,** singlet state
сингулярность, *f.*, singularity
сингулярный, *adj.*, singular
синоним, *m.*, synonym
синонимический, *adj.*, synonymous
синонимичный, *adj.*, synonymous
синоптический, *adj.*, synoptic
синтакс, *m.*, syntax
синтаксис, *m.*, syntax
синтаксический, *adj.*, syntactical
синтез, *m.*, synthesis, design
синтетический, *adj.*, synthetic, deductive
синус, *m.*, sine
синусный, *adj.*, sine
синусоида, *f.*, sinusoid, sine curve, harmonic curve
синусоидальный, *adj.*, sinusoidal, sine-shaped
синхронизация, *f.*, synchronization, synchronizing
синхронизирование, *n.*, synchronization
синхронизировать, *v.*, synchronize, bring into step
синхронизм, *m.*, synchronism
синхронно, *adv.* (from **синхронный**); *prefix*, synchro-
синхронно-следящий, *adj.*, synchronous tracking, synchro-tracking
синхронный, *adj.*, synchronous, coincident
синхротрон, *m.*, synchrotron
синхроциклотрон, *m.*, synchrocyclotron
система, *f.*, class, system; **система контроля с обратной связью,** feedback control system
систематизация, *f.*, systematization, classification
систематизированный, *adj.*, systematized, classified, systematic, methodical
систематизировать, *v.*, systematize
систематический, *adj.*, systematic, methodical
систематичность, *f.*, systematic character, systematic viewpoint
ситуация, *f.*, situation
сих (cf. **сей**), of these, to these; **до сих пор,** till now
скажем (cf. **сказать**), we shall say, let us say
сказанный (from **сказать**), *adj.*, said, asserted; **в соответствии со сказанным,** according to what has been said
сказать (*perf.* of **говорить**), say, tell, assert
сказуемое, *n.*, predicate
сказываться, *v.*, manifest itself, tell
скакать, *v.*, race
скаляр, *m.*, scalar
скалярный, *adj.*, scalar; **скалярная величина,** *f.*, scalar
сканирующий, *adj.*, scanning
скапливаться, *v.*, accumulate, pile up, gather
скат, *m.*, slope, incline, pitch; **метод наибольшего ската,** saddle-point method
скачок, *m.*, jump, saltus, shock, step; **скачок уплотнения,** shock wave
скачкообразно, *adv.*, spasmodically, very rapidly, step-wise
скачкообразный, *adj.*, spasmodic, uneven, transition; **скачкообразная функция,** jump function
скважина, *f.*, slit, chink, pore, hole

скважистость, *f.*, porosity, porousness
скважность, *f.*, porosity, porousness
сквозной, *adj.*, open, continuous, transparent, composition, through; **сквозное отображение,** composition (mapping); **сквозная характеристика,** through characteristics; **сквозная схема,** through circuit; **сквозная передача,** rippling through (*comp.*); **сквозной перенос,** ripple-through carry (*comp.*); **блок цепочки сквозного переноса,** ripple-through carry unit (*comp.*)
сквозь, *prep.*, through
скелет, *m.*, skeleton, frame, shell
скептический, *adj.*, skeptical
скидка, *f.*, discount, deduction, reduction; **норма скидки,** discount rate; **со скидкой в,** at a discount of
скин-эффект, *m.*, skin-effect
склад, *m.* warehouse; **помещать в склад,** *v.*, warehouse
складирование, *n.*, stacking, storing, warehousing; **задача складирования,** warehousing problem
складка, *f.*, fold, folding
складывание, *n.*, addition, putting together, stacking
складывать, *v.*, add, sum, combine, fold, put up
складываться, *v.*, be added
склеенный, *adj.*, glued, pasted, sewn, identified; **склеенная область,** sewn region, fused region
склеивание, *n.*, pasting together, assembling, identification, contraction, coalescence; **теорема склеивания,** sewing theorem
склеивать (склеить), *v.*, paste together, identify, fuse, contract, coalesce, sew
склерономный, *adj.*, scleronomous (independent of time in space-time coordinates)
склон, *m.*, slope
склонение, *n.*, declination, inclination, declension; **круг склонения,** hour circle
склонный, *adj.*, inclined
скобка, *f.*, parenthesis, bracket; **квадратные скобки,** square brackets; **прямые скобки,** square brackets; **круглые скобки,** parentheses; **фигурные скобки,** braces
сколь (from **сколько**), *adv.*, how much; **сколь угодно,** arbitrarily, as much as desired; **сколь бы мало ни было,** no matter how small
скольжение, *n.*, sliding, gliding, covering transformation, translation
скользить, *v.*, slide, glide
скользящий, *adj.*, sliding, slipping, skidding, moving; **скользящая пружина,** cantilever spring; **скользящая средняя,** moving average
сколько, *adv.*, how much, how many; **столько (же) сколько,** as much as, as many as
сколько-нибудь, *num.*, several, a few, some, any (amount)
скомбинировать (cf. **комбинировать**), *v.*, arrange, combine
скомканный, *adj.*, crumpled
скомкать (cf. **комкать**), *v.*, crumple, bunch up
сконструировать, *v.*, construct, design
сконцентрироваться (cf. **концентрироваться**), *v.*, crowd, concentrate
скопление, *n.*, accumulation, gathering
скопляться, *v.*, cluster, accumulate, store up
скорее (*comp.* of **скорый**), faster, rather; **скорее всего,** most likely, probably
скорейший, *adj.*, quickest, fastest; **метод скорейшего спуска,** method of steepest descent
скоростной, *adj.*, velocity, high speed, rapid; **скоростной напор,** velocity head, pressure head
скорость, *f.*, speed, velocity, rate; **секториальная скорость,** areal velocity; **скорость истечения в пустоте,** escape velocity; **средняя взвешенная по массам скорость,** mean mass velocity; **скорость**

изменения, rate of change; **скорость выборки (данных),** access speed (*comp.*)
скорый, *adj.*, fast, quick
скошенность, *f.*, bias, skewness
скошенный, *adj.*, oblique, skew
скрадывать, *v.*, conceal, hide
скрепление, *n.*, fastening (together), clamping
скреплять (скрепить), *v.*, fasten together, tie, clamp, strengthen, authenticate
скрещенный, *adj.*, crossed, cross; **скрещенное произведение,** cross product, crossed product
скрещивание, *adj.*, crossing
скрещиваться, *v.*, cross
скрещивающийся, *adj.*, crossing, cross; **скрещивающийся член,** cross-term; **скрещивающиеся прямые,** skew lines
скринабельность, *f.*, screenability
скринабельный, *adj.*, screenable
скруглять (скруглить), *v.*, round off, smooth out
скрученный, *adj.*, twisted, contorted
скручиваемый, *adj.*, twisted
скручивание, *n.*, twisting, tying up
скручивать, *v.*, twist, tie up, roll
скрывать (скрыть), *v.*, hide, conceal, cover
скрытый, *adj.*, hidden, latent; **скрытое состояние,** latency, latent state
скудный, *adj.*, scanty, poor, meager
скученность, *f.*, density, congestion
скученный, *adj.*, dense, congested
слабее, *adj.*, weaker
слабейший, *adj.*, the weakest, weaker
слабо, *adv.*, weakly
слабодополнительный, *adj.*, weakly complementary, weakly supplementary
слабонепрерывный, *adj.*, weakly continuous
слабый, *adj.*, weak, feeble, slack
слагаемое, *n.*, term, item, sum, summand, addend; **прямое слагаемое,** direct sum, direct summand
слагаемый, *adj.*, composed of, made up of, additive
слагать, *v.*, lay away, put together, add
слагаться, *v.*, be made up of
слагающий, *adj.*, component, constituent
слева, *adv.*, from the left
слегка, *adv.*, easily, slightly, somewhat
след, *m.*, trace, track, sign; **след игры,** imputation of the game
следить, *v.*, watch, leave traces
следовало (from **следовать**), ought to have, should have, followed
следование, *n.*, sequence, succession, movement; **частота следования импульсов,** pulse repetition rate; **функция следования (за),** successor function (of)
следовательно, *conj.*, consequently, hence, therefore
следовать (последовать), *v.*, follow, succeed; **как следует,** properly, well; **не следует думать,** it should not be supposed (that)
следствие, *n.*, corollary, consequence, implication; **причина и следствие,** cause and effect
следуемый, *adj.*, due to
следует (from **следовать**), it should be; one must; it follows that; **следует указать,** it should be pointed out; **не следует думать,** it should not be supposed (that)
следующий, *adj.*, following, next; **следующее,** *n.*, the following; **следующим образом,** in the following way
следящий, *adj.*, tracking; **следящая система,** servomechanism
слепой, *adj.*, blind; **слепая посадка,** instrument landing, radar landing
сливаться (слиться), *v.*, merge, combine
слившийся, *adj.*, combined, merged
слипшийся, *adj.*, bound together
слитно, *adv.*, together
слитность, *f.*, combination, unification
слитный, *adj.*, combined, unified, united
сличать, *v.*, compare, check

сличение, *n.*, comparison, checking
слишком, *adv.*, too, too much; **слишком мало,** too little
слияние, *n.*, confluence, junction, fusion
словарный, *adj.*, dictionary, lexicographic
словарь, *m.*, dictionary
словесный, *adj.*, verbal, oral
словно, *adv.*, as if
слово, *n.*, word; **другими словами,** in other words; **иными словами,** in other words; **время выборки одного слова,** word time; **группа слов,** message
слог, *m.*, syllable (*comp.*)
слоевой, *adj.*, layer, laminary
сложение, *n.*, addition, composition; **сложение сил,** composition of forces; **гомотопическая теорема сложения,** homotopy addition theorem
сложить (cf. **складывать**), *v.*, add, sum, add together, put together
сложно, *adv.*, in a complicated way
сложность, *f.*, complexity, complication
сложный, *adj.*, complicated, complex, compound, composite; **сложное число,** complex number; **сложное отношение,** cross-ratio, anharmonic ratio; **сложные проценты,** compound interest; **сложная функция,** composite function; **сложный коммутатор,** extended commutator
слой, *m.*, layer, band, shell, fibre; **пограничный слой,** boundary layer
слойно-конечный, *adj.*, finitely layered, layer-finite
слойный, cf. **слоевой**
сломанный, *adj.*, broken down
сломаться (cf. **ломаться**), *v.*, break down, get out of order
служащий, *adj.*, used for, serving
служба, *f.*, service; **служба тылов,** logistics
служить (послужить), *v.*, serve, be used (for)
случай, *m.*, case, event; **во всяком случае,** at all events; **в таком случае,** in that case; **в этом случае,** in this case; **на всякий случай,** just in case; **несчастный случай,** accident; **частный случай,** special case; **в тех случаях, когда,** where
случайность, *f.*, chance, randomness, contingency
случайный, *adj.*, random, accidental, stochastic; **случайная величина,** random variable; **случайная ошибка,** random error
случаться (случиться), *v.*, happen, come about, occur
слушатель, *m.*, listener, student; *pl.*, audience
слышимость, *f.*, hearing, audibility
слышимый, *adj.*, audible
см., *abbrev.* **(сантиметр,** *m.*), centimeter; *abbrev.* **(смотри)**, see, cf.
смежность, *f.*, contiguity, adjacency; **класс смежности,** co-set
смежный, *adj.*, adjacent, adjoining, contiguous; **смежный угол,** adjacent angle; **смежный класс,** co-set, residue class
смелость, *f.*, boldness, courage
смелый, *adj.*, bold, courageous
смена, *f.*, change, interchange, replacement
сменяемость, *f.*, removability
сменяемый, *adj.*, removable
сменять (сменить), *v.*, change, replace, relieve
смертность, *f.*, mortality, death rate
смеситель, *m.*, mixer
смесительный, *adj.*, mixing
сместить (cf. **смещать**), *v.*, displace, remove
смесь, *f.*, mixture; **анализ смеси,** composite analysis, compound analysis
смешанный, *adj.*, mixed, compound, composite; **смешанная задача,** mixed (boundary value) problem; **смешанная система счисления,** mixed-base notation; **смешанный момент,** product moment, mixed moment; **смешанное произведение,**

mixed product, triple scalar product; **смешанный момент второго порядка,** covariance; **смешанная стратегия,** mixed strategy

смешение, *n.*, mixture, blending, confusion

смешивать (смешать), *v.*, mix, mix up, confuse

смещать, *v.*, displace, remove, bias

смещение, *n.*, displacement, removal, parallax, bias, shift; **подавать смещение,** *v.*, bias; **красное смещение спектральных линий,** red shift of spectral lines; **критерий смещения,** test of location

смещенность, *f.*, bias, displacement, dislocation

смещенный, *adj.*, displaced, dislocated, out of line, biased

смог (from **мочь**), (he, it) could

смогли (from **мочь**), (they) could

смола, *f.*, resin, tar, pitch

смотреть (посмотреть), *v.*, look, look at, see, examine; **смотреть как (на),** *v.*, regard (as)

смотри (*imperative* of **смотреть**), see, look (at)

смотря, *adv. part.*, looking, looking at, seeing; **смотря по,** according to

смочь (cf. **мочь**), *v.*, be able to, prove able

смыкание, *n.*, joining, closing, coupling

смыкать, *v.*, close, join, link, couple

смыкаться, *v.*, close, interlock

смысл, *m.*, sense, meaning; **иметь смысл,** *v.*, have meaning, make sense

смычка, *f.*, union, linking

смычок, *m.*, bow

смягчение, *n.*, softening, relaxation

смятие, *n.*, contortion, crumpling

снабжать (снабдить), *v.*, furnish, provide

снабжение, *n.*, supply, provision

снабженный, *adj.*, equipped (with), provided (with)

снаружи, *adv.*, outside, on the outside, from the outside

снаряд, *m.*, projectile, missile, shell

снаряжение, *n.*, equipment, allowance

снасть, *f.*, instruments, tools, tackle

сначала, *adv.*, all over again, from the beginning, at first, first

снести (cf. **сносить**), *v.*, take, carry, carry down

снижать (снизить), *v.*, reduce, lower, lessen

снижение, *n.*, lowering, decrease, drop, reduction, depreciation

снизить (cf. **синжать**), *v.*, reduce, lower

снизу, *adv.*, below, from below; **полунепрерывный снизу,** *adj.*, lower semicontinuous

снимание, *n.*, cut (at cards), removal, taking off; **снимание карт,** cutting (the cards)

снимать (снять), *v.*, take, take off, make, cut, remove; **снимать карты,** *v.*, cut (the cards); **снимать нагрузку,** *v.*, unload; **снимать напряжение,** *v.*, dump

снова, *adv.*, again, anew

снос, *m.*, drift, deflection, pulling down; **снос ветром,** wind drift

сносить (снести), *v.*, blow off, drift, carry (away), take

сноска, *f.*, footnote

снятие, *n.*, removal, taking down

снять, cf. **снимать,**

со (=**с**), *prep.* with, from

собирание, *n.*, collection, gathering, aggregation

собирать (собрать), *v.*, gather, collect

собираться, *v.*, intend, assemble

соблюдать (соблюсти), *v.*, observe, keep to

соблюдаться, *v.*, be observed, be fulfilled

соблюдение, *n.*, validity, observance

соблюсти (cf. **соблюдать**), *v.*, observe

собой (*instr.* of **свой**), itself, themselves; **нести с собой,** *v.*, imply; **между собой,** among themselves; **представляет собой,** represents, is represented

собрание, *n.*, meeting, collection

собрать (cf. **собирать**), *v.*, gather, collect
собственно, *adv.*, properly, really; *part.*, proper; **собственно примитивный,** *adj.*, properly primitive; **собственно говоря,** strictly speaking; **собственно математика,** mathematics proper
собственный, *adj.*, characteristic, eigen, proper, own, non-singular; **собственное значение,** eigen-value, characteristic value; **собственное число,** eigen-value; **собственная функция,** eigen-function; **собственная частота,** fundamental frequency; **собственное нормальное распределение,** non-singular normal distribution
событие, *n.*, event
совершаемый, *adj.*, done, accomplished
совершать (совершить), *v.*, accomplish, perform
совершающий, *adj.*, accomplishing, performing
совершение, *n.*, accomplishment, fulfilment
совершенно, *adv.*, absolutely, quite, completely
совершенный, *adj.*, perfect, absolute, complete, principal; **совершенное число,** perfect number
совершенствование, *n.*, perfecting, perfection
совершить, cf. **совершать**
совещание, *n.*, conference, meeting
совместимость, *f.*, compatibility, consistency
совместимый, *adj.* compatible, consistent
совместить (cf. **совмещать**), *v.*, combine, combine with
совместно, *adv.*, simultaneously, jointly, combined
совместность, *f.*, compatibility
совместный, *adj.*, joint, combined, simultaneous, compatible; **совместная работа,** on-line operation, joint operation; **совместное распределение,** joint distribution, simultaneous distribution
совмещать (совместить), *v.*, combine, superpose, match
совмещаться, *v.*, coincide
совокуплять, *v.*, join, unite
совокупно, *adv.*, jointly, in common
совокупность, *f.*, totality, union, aggregate, population, universe; **генеральная совокупность,** population, parent population, universe
совокупный, *adj.*, joint, combined, cumulative, total
совпадать (совпасть), *v.*, coincide, concur; **не совпадать,** disagree (with), be inconsistent (with)
совпадающий, *adj.*, coinciding, coincident, congruent
совпадение, *n.*, coincidence, congruence, fit, fitness
совпасть (cf. **совпадать**), *v.*, coincide
современный, *adj.*, contemporary, modern
совсем, *adv.*, absolutely, entirely, completely
согласие, *n.*, conformity, accord; **критерий согласия,** goodness-of-fit test; **наилучшее согласие,** best fit
согласиться (cf. **соглашаться**), *v.*, agree
согласно, *adv.*, in accord
согласно, *prep.* according to, by
согласный, *adj.*, agreeing, agreeing with, consistent, concordant
согласование, *n.*, agreement, concordance, reconciliation
согласованность, *f.*, coordination, consistency, agreement
согласованный, *adj.*, coordinated, consistent, concordant, compatible
согласовывать (согласовать), *v.*, coordinate, adjust, make consistent
согласующийся, *adj.*, consistent, compatible, congruent
соглашаться (согласиться), *v.*, agree, concur
соглашение, *n.*, stipulation, agreement, contract, convention
согнутый, *adj.*, bent, curved

содействие, *n.*, assistance, cooperation
содействовать, *v.*, assist, further, contribute, promote
содействующий, *adj.*, contributing, contributory
содержание, *n.*, contents, intension (logic), matter, substance
содержательный, *adj.*, containing, supporting, intensional, contensive, meaningful, interesting
содержать, *v.*, contain, maintain, support; **содержать в себе,** *v.*, contain
содержаться, *v.*, be contained, contain
содержащий, *adj.*, containing
содержащийся, *adj.*, contained, contained in
соединение, *n.*, union, combination, junction, join, conjunction, juxtaposition
соединенный, *adj.*, united, joint, conjoint
соединительный, *adj.*, connective
соединять (соединить), *v.*, combine, join, connect, unite, juxtapose
соединяющий, *adj.*, connecting, combining, joining, uniting
сожаление, *n.*, regret; **к сожалению,** unfortunately
создаваемый, *adj.*, originating, being made
создавать (создать), *v.*, create, originate
создание, *n.*, creation, work
созерцание, *n.*, contemplation
созерцательный, *adj.*, contemplative
сознание, *n.*, consciousness
сознательно, *adv.*, knowingly, consciously, deliberately
соизмеримость, *f.*, commensurability
соизмеримый, *adj.*, commensurable
сократимость, *f.*, reducibility, contractibility
сократимый, *adj.*, reducible, contractible
сокращать (сократить), *v.*, shorten, reduce, cancel, contract
сокращающийся, *adj.*, being cancelled, cancelled, reduced
сокращение, *n.*, reduction, cancellation, shortening, abbreviation, contraction; **сокращение данных,** reduction of data
сокращенный, *adj.*, reduced, abbreviated, contracted, abridged
соленоид, *m.*, solenoid
соленоидальный, *adj.*, solenoidal
соленость, *f.*, salinity
солнечный, *adj.*, solar, sun
солнце, *n.*, sun
солнцестояние, *n.*, solstice; **точка летнего солнцестояния,** summer solstice; **точка зимнего солнцестояния,** winter solstice
сольется (cf. **сливаться**), will merge
сомневаться, *v.*, doubt
сомнение, *n.*, doubt
сомнительный, *adj.*, doubtful, questionable
сомножитель, *m.*, factor, co-factor
соображать, *v.*, consider, figure out, comprehend
соображение, *n.*, concept, consideration, reason, argument
сообразительный, *adj.*, alert, attentive
сообразить (cf. **соображать**), *v.*, figure out, comprehend
сообразно (с), *prep.*, according to, in conformity with
сообразность, *f.*, conformity
сообразный, *adj.*, conformable (to), consistent
сообщать (сообщить), *v.*, inform, communicate
сообщение, *n.*, information, report, communication, message
сооружение, *n.*, structure
соосный, *adj.*, coaxial
соотв., *abbrev.* **(соответственно),** respectively
соответственно, *adv.*, respectively, correspondingly
соответственность, *f.*, conformity, accordance, correspondence
соответственный, *adj.*, corresponding

соответствие, *n.*, correspondence, congruence, agreement, accordance; **в соответствии,** accordingly, according to; **в соответствии со сказанным,** according to what has been said

соответствовать, *v.*, correspond, correspond to, conform to

соответствующий, *adj.*, corresponding, appropriate, congruent

соотнесенный, *adj.*, associated, correlated, assigned, related

соотносительный, *adj.*, correlative

соотношение, *n.*, correlation, ratio, relation

сопло, *n.*, nozzle, jet; **сопло переменного сечения,** variable cross-section nozzle

сопловой, *adj.*, nozzle, jet; **сопловое регулирование,** jet regulation, jet control

сопоставление, *n.*, comparison, contrast, juxtaposition

сопоставлять (сопоставить), *v.*, compare, associate

соприкасание, *n.*, contact, juxtaposition

соприкасаться, *v.*, touch, be in contact, adjoin, osculate

соприкасающийся, *adj.*, touching, osculating, adjoining, contiguous

соприкосновение, *n.*, contact, contiguity, osculation

соприкосновенный, *adj.*, contiguous (to)

сопроводительный, *adj.*, accompanying

сопровождаемый, *adj.*, accompanied

сопровождать, *v.*, accompany

сопровождаться, *v.*, be accompanied

сопровождающий, *adj.*, accompanying, moving; **сопровождающий репер,** moving *n*-hedron (of a curve)

сопровождение, *n.*, accompaniment

сопротивление, *n.*, resistance, specific resistance, drag; **регулируемое сопротивление,** varistor; **емкостное сопротивление,** capacitance; **усилитель на сопротивлениях,** resistance coupled amplifier; **согласованное сопротивление,** matched impedance; **волновое сопротивление,** matched impedance, wave impedance; **индуктивное сопротивление,** induced drag; **профильное сопротивление,** profile drag; **полное сопротивление,** impedance; **счетчик с высокоомным сопротивлением,** high-resistance counter

сопротивляемость, *f.*, resistivity

сопрягать, *v*,. join, unite, refer

сопряжение, *n.*, union, junction, conjunction, conjugation, conjugating

сопряженность, *f.*, contingency, union, conjunction, conjugacy, electrically charged state; **коэффициент сопряженности,** coefficient of contingency; **таблица сопряженности признаков,** contingency table

сопряженный, *adj.*, conjugate, associated, charged, adjoint, apolar; **сопряженная матрица,** conjugate matrix; **комплексно сопряженный,** *adj.*, complex conjugate; **сопряженные измерения,** conditioned measurements

сопутствовать, *v.*, accompany

сопутствуемый, *adj.*, accompanied

сопутствующий, *adj.*, accompanying, concomitant

соразмерно, *adv.*, in proportion (to)

соразмерность, *f.*, proportionality

соразмерный, *adj.*, proportional, commensurate, balanced

сорок, *num.*, forty

сорт, *m.*, kind, quality

сортировка, *f.*, sorting, grading

сосед, *m.*, neighbor

соседний, *adj.*, neighboring, adjacent

соседство, *n.*, neighborhood, vicinity; **по соседству,** in the neighborhood (of)

соскальзывать (соскользнуть), *v.*, slide, slip

сослаться (cf. **ссылаться**), *v.*, refer to, quote; **сошлемся,** we refer to

сосредоточение, *n.*, concentration

сосредоточенный, *adj.*, concentrated; **сосредоточенная сила,** point force

сосредоточивать (сосредоточить), *v.*, concentrate, focus
состав, *m.*, composition, structure; **входить в состав,** *v.*, be part of
составление, *n.*, composition, compilation; **составление логической схемы,** logical design; **задача о составлении пар,** matching problem; **составление счетов,** billing (*comp.*)
составленный, *adj.*, composed, superposed, constituted
составлять (составить), *v.*, put together, compose, constitute, make up
составляющий, *adj.*, component, constituent
составной, *adj.*, component, composite, compound, constituent, combined; **составное число,** composite number; **составная величина,** combined variable; **составной индекс,** aggregate (aggregative) index; **составное отображение,** composition (mapping)
состояние, *n.*, state, condition; **мы в состоянии,** we are able to; **с одним устойчивым состоянием,** monostable; **скрытое состояние,** latency; **устойчивое состояние,** steady-state
состоятельность, *f.*, competence, justifiability, consistency
состоятельный, *adj.*, well-grounded, justifiable, consistent; **состоятельная оценка,** consistent estimate
состоять, *v.*, be, consist (of)
состояться, *v.*, take place
состоящий, *adj.*, consisting (of)
состязание, *n.*, competition, controversy
сосуд, *m.*, vessel, container
сосчитывать (сосчитать), *v.*, compute, calculate, sum up, count
сотая, *f.*, one hundredth
сотен, *num.* (*gen. pl.* of **сто**), hundred
сотканный, *adj.*, web, webbed, woven
сотрудник, *m.*, collaborator, contributor
сотрудничество, *n.*, collaboration, cooperation
соты, *pl.*, honeycomb; **звездные двумерные соты,** star-tessellation
сотый, *adj.*, hundredth
соударение, *n.*, collision, impact
софокусный, *adj.*, confocal
сохранение, *n.*, preservation, conservation, invariance; **сохранение энергии,** conservation of energy
сохранно, *adv.*, safely, securely, intact
сохранность, *f.*, safety, invariance, preservation, conservation
сохранный, *adj.*, safe, secure, intact, invariant, conservation
сохранять (сохранить), *v.*, preserve, retain, remain; **сохранить силу,** *v.*, remain valid
сохраняться, *v.*, keep, last, remain, survive
сохраняющий, *adj.*, preserving, retaining; **сохраняющий углы,** *adj.*, angle-preserving; **сохраняющий норму,** *adj.*, norm-preserving; **сохраняющий метрику,** *adj.*, metric-preserving, isometric; **сохраняющий порядок,** *adj.*, order-preserving; **сохраняющий слои,** *adj.*, fibre-preserving
социальный, *adj.*, social; **социальные науки,** social sciences
социометрический, *adj.*, sociometric
сочетание, *n.*, combination, set
сочетательность, *f.*, associativity
сочетательный, *adj.*, associative, combinative
сочетать, *v.*, combine, unite, associate
сочетаться, *v.*, combine, associate
сочинение, *n.*, composition, work
сочленение, *n.*, joint, articulation, concatenation
сошлемся (from **сослаться**), we refer to
союзный, *adj.*, adjoint, connected with, associated (with)
спаренный, *adj.*, paired, coupled, twin, dual; **спаренные векторные пространства,** dual vector spaces
спаривание, *n.*, pairing, coupling
спаривать (спарить), *v.*, pair, couple

спасовать (cf. **пасовать),** *v.*, pass
спектр, *m.*, spectrum
спектрально (from **спектральный),** *adv.*; **спектрально представимый,** *adj.*, representable by spectral decomposition
спектральность, *f.*, spectral property, spectrum
спектральный, *adj.*, spectral; **спектральная функция,** spectral function
спектрограф, *m.*, spectrograph
спектрографический, *adj.*, spectrographic
спектрометр, *m.*, spectrometer
спектроскопический, *adj.*, spectroscopic
спекулятивный, *adj.*, speculative
сперва, *adv.*, at first
спереди, *prep.*, in front of, before; *adv.*, at the front, from the front
специализация, *f.*, specialization
специализированный, *adj.*, specialized
специализироваться, *v.*, specialize (in), specialize (to)
специальный, *adj.*, special, specific
специфика, *f.*, specific character, characteristics
специфический, *adj.*, specific, characteristic
специфичность, *f.*, specificity, quality of being specific
спецкурс, *abbrev.* **(специальный курс),** *m.*, special course
спин, *m.*, spin
спина, *f.*, back
спинка, *f.*, back, back edge
спин-коллинеация, *f.*, spin-collineation
спиновой, *adj.*, spin, pertaining to spin
спинор, *m.*, spinor
спинорный, *adj.*, spinor; **спинорная алгебра,** spinor algebra
спиралевидный, *adj.*, spiral, helical
спираль, *f.*, spiral, helix; **спираль Архимеда,** spiral of Archimedes
спиральный, *adj.*, spiral, helical
список, *m.*, list, copy
сплав, *m.*, alloy, fusion, float
сплавлять, *v.*, melt, fuse, alloy
сплавляться, *v.*, interpenetrate, coalesce
сплетать (сплести), *v.*, interlace, weave
сплетение, *n.*, interlacing
сплетенный, *adj.*, mixed, interlaced
сплошной, *adj.*, continuous, entire, solid, total, compact; **сплошная проверка,** total inspection
сплошность, *f.*, entirety, continuity, uniformity
сплошь, *adv.*, without gaps, uninterruptedly, completely, entirely
сплюснутость, *f.*, flattening, flatness
сплюснутый, *adj.*, flattened, oblate
сплющенный, *adj.*, flattened out, oblate
сплющивание, *n.*, flattening, oblateness
сплющивать, *v.*, flatten
сплющиваться, *v.*, be flattened, be flat, be oblate
спокойный, *adj.*, at rest, latent, quiet
спор, *m.*, controversy, argument
спорадический, *adj.*, sporadic
спорить (поспорить), *v.*, argue
спорный, *adj.*, controversial, disputed
способ, *m.*, way, method; **таким способом,** in this way; **другим способом,** in a different way; **обычным способом,** in the usual way
способность, *f.*, capacity, power, ability, aptitude; **разрешающая способность,** resolution, resolving power; **отражательная способность,** reflectance
способный, *adj.*, able, capable
способствовать, *v.*, promote, further
способствующий, *adj.*, instrumental, contributing
справа, *adv.*, from the right, to the right
справедливо, *adv.*, correctly; *adj.*, short form of **справедливый**; **это неравенство справедливо,** this inequality is correct
справедливость, *f.*, correctness, validity
справедливый, *adj.*, valid, correct, true, just, equitable
справка, *f.*, reference, information, certificate

справочник, *m.*, handbook, reference book
справочный, *adj.*, reference
спрашивать (спросить), *v.*, ask, inquire, demand
спрашиваться, *v.*, ask; **спрашивается,** the question is
спроектированный, *adj.*, designed, planned, projected
спроектировать (cf. **проектировать**), *v.*, plan, design, project
спроектироваться (cf. **проектироваться**), *v.*, be projected
спрос, *m.*, demand, market; **кривая спроса,** demand curve; **переменная спроса,** demand variable; **производная спроса,** derived demand; **нулевой спрос,** zero demand, excluded activity
спросить, cf. **спрашивать**
спряжение, *n.*, conjugation
спрямление, *n.*, rectification
спрямляемость, *f.*, rectifiability
спрямляемый, *adj.*, rectifiable
спрямлять, *v.*, rectify
спрямляющий, *adj.*, rectifying; **спрямляющая плоскость,** rectifying plane
спуск, *m.*, slope, incline, descent, launching; **линия наиболее крутого спуска,** steepest descent; **метод скорейшего спуска,** method of steepest descent; **индукция спуска,** descending induction
спутник, *m.*, satellite, sputnik
срабатывание, *n.*, operation, functioning; **ложное срабатывание,** malfunctioning
срабатывать (сработать), *v.*, operate, function
сравнен, short form of **сравненный**
сравнение, *n.*, comparison, congruence, matching; **сравнение монет,** matching coins
сравненный, *adj.*, compared, equal, made equal to
сравниваемый, *adj.*, compared
сравнивать (сравнить), *v.*, compare, equal, equate
сравниваться, *v.*, equal, be equal, be compared, be congruent
сравнимость, *f.*, comparability, congruence
сравнимый, *adj.*, comparable, congruent; **сравнимые числа,** congruent numbers; **сравнимый по модулю** *A*, *adj.*, congruent modulo *A*
сравнительно, *adv.*, comparatively
сравнительный, *adj.*, comparative
сравнить (cf. **сравнивать**), *v.*, compare
сравнять (cf. **равнять**), *v.*, equate, equalize
сразу, *adv.*, at once
срастание, *n.*, combining, coalescence, accretion
срастаться (срастись), *v.*, grow together, coalesce
срастить (cf. **сращивать**), *v.*, join, unite
сращение, *n.*, union
сращивание, *n.*, union, joining, combination, coalescence
сращивать (срастить), *v.*, join, unite, splice
среда, *f.*, medium, surroundings
среди, *prep.*, among; **среди них,** among them
средина, *f.*, middle, mean
срединный, *adj.*, middle, mean, average; **срединное отклонение,** mean deviation
средне, *prefix*, mean, average
среднеарифметический, *adj.*, arithmetic mean, averaging, average
средневековый, *adj.*, medieval
средневзвешенный, *adj.*, weighted-mean
среднеквадратический, *adj.*, mean square, least square
среднеметрический, *adj.*, mean-metric
среднесуточный, *adj.*, daily average
среднее, *n.*, mean, average; **среднее (значение),** *n.*, mean, mean value; **арифметическое среднее,** arithmetic mean; **взвешенное среднее,** weighted mean, weighted average; **предельное среднее,** limiting mean;

предельное среднее размаха, limiting mean of range; **в среднем,** on the average; **сходимость в среднем,** mean convergence; **сходиться в среднем,** *v.*, converge in mean

средний, *adj.*, middle, average, mean; **средняя секвенция,** midsequent; **средняя точка,** centroid, midpoint; **в среднем,** on the average; **среднее арифметическое,** *n.*, arithmetic mean; **среднее значение,** mean value, average value; **средний член,** mean (of a ratio); **среднее пропорциональное,** *n.*, mean proportional; **средний пропорциональный,** *adj.*, mean proportional; **средняя линия,** *f.*, median; **средняя квадратичная ошибка,** mean square error, mean square deviation, standard deviation; **среднее квадратическое отклонение,** mean square deviation, standard deviation; **условное среднее значение,** conditional mean value; **среднее отклонение,** mean deviation; **средняя квадратическая регрессия,** mean square regression; **средняя квадратическая связанность,** mean square contingency; **выборочное среднее значение,** sample mean, sampling mean; **среднее линейное отклонение,** mean deviation; **средняя абсолютная ошибка,** mean absolute error; **сходиться в среднем,** *v.*, converge in mean; **сходимость в среднем,** mean convergence; **средняя орбита,** mean orbit; **средняя аномалия,** mean anomaly; **средняя кривизна профиля,** mean camber; **средняя взвешенная по массам скорость,** mean mass velocity; **средний импульс,** mean momentum; **средний модуль сдвига,** mean shear modulus

средство, *n.*, means, tool

срез, *m.*, cut, section, shearing

срезанный, *adj.*, cut, cut off, truncated

срезывающий, *adj.*, cutoff, shear; **срезывающее усилие,** shearing stress

срок, *m.*, time, period, fixed time, date; **срок службы,** life; **испытание на срок службы,** life test

срываться, *v.*, fail, break loose, fall

ссуда, *f.*, loan

ссылаться (сослаться), *v.*, refer to, quote

ссылаясь, *adv. part.*, referring, alluding, if we refer; **ссылаясь на,** referring to, with reference to

ссылка, *f.*, reference

стабилизатор, *m.*, stabilizer

стабилизация, *f.*, stabilization, constancy

стабилизирование, *n.*, stabilization, stabilizing

стабилизировать, *v.*, stabilize

стабильность, *f.*, stability

стабильный, *adj.*, stable, standard

ставить (поставить), *v.*, put, place, set, pose

ставка, *f.*, stake, bet, rate

стадия, *f.*, stage, phase; **по стадиям,** by stages

сталкивать (столкнуть), *v.*, push, shove, impel, bring (together)

сталкиваться, *v.*, collide (with), run into, encounter

стало (cf. **стать**), became; **стало быть,** *adv.*, so, therefore

стандарт, *m.*, norm, standard

стандартизация, *f.*, standardization

стандартизованный, *adj.*, standardized; **стандартизованная величина,** standardized variable, standardized quantity

стандартный, *adj.*, standard; **стандартное отклонение,** standard deviation; **стандартная ошибка,** standard error; **стандартный блок,** package

становиться (стать), *v.*, become, get

становление, *n.*, formation, composition

станок, *m.*, machine, machine-tool, mount

станция, *f.*, station, plant, exchange (tel.)

старание, *n.*, effort

стараться, *v.*, try, seek

старший, *adj.*, higher, highest, leading, older, senior; **старшая производная,** higher derivative; **самый старший разряд,** most significant digit; **старший коэффициент,** leading coefficient
старый, *adj.*, old
стаскивать (стащить), *v.*, pull off, drag down
стасовать (cf. **тасовать**), *v.*, shuffle
статика, *f.*, statics
статистик, *m.*, statistician
статистика, *f.*, statistics
статистический, *adj.*, statistical
статически, *adv.*, statically
статический, *adj.*, static
статконтроль, *m.*, statistical control
статус-функция, *f.*, status function
стать (cf. **становиться**), *v.*, become, begin (to)
статья, *f.*, article, item
стационарность, *f.*, stationary state
стационарный, *adj.*, stationary; **стационарное уравнение,** steady-state equation; **стационарный временный ряд,** stationary time series
стекло, *n.*, glass
стекловидный, *adj.*, glassy, vitreous
стеклянный, *adj.*, glass
стенка, *f.*, wall, partition
стенограмма, *f.*, shorthand record, verbatim account
степенной, *adj.*, power, degree; **степенной ряд,** power series
степень, *f.*, power, degree, extent; **степень свободы,** degree of freedom
стерадиан, *m.*, steradian, stereo-radian (unit of solid angle)
стереографически, *adv.*, stereographically
стереографический, *adj.*, stereographic
стереометрический, *adj.*, pertaining to solid geometry, stereometrical
стереометрия, *f.*, solid geometry, stereometry
стереоскоп, *m.*, stereoscope
стереоскопический, *adj.*, stereoscopic
стереть, cf. **стирать**
стержень, *m.*, rod, bar, pivot
стержнеобразный, *adj.*, rod-like
стертый, *adj.*, erased, obliterated; **стертая лента,** erased tape (*comp.*)
стеснение, *n.*, constraint, restraint
стесненный, *adj.*, constrained, restrained
стеснительно, *adv.*, inconveniently, restrictively
стеснительный, *adj.*, restrictive, inconvenient
стеснять (стеснить), *v.*, constrain, restrain, hinder, hamper
стигматичный, *adj.*, stigmatic
стиль, *m.*, style, fashion
стильный, *adj.*, fashionable
стимул, *m.*, stimulus, stimulant
стимулировать, *v.*, stimulate
стинродовский, *adj.*, Steenrod, pertaining to Steenrod
стирание, *n.*, erasure, cancellation
стирать (стереть), *v.*, erase, rub out, cancel
сто, *num.*, hundred
стоимость, *f.*, cost, value; **функция стоимости,** cost function
стоит (cf. **стоить, стоять**), costs, is worth (while); stands, stops, remains, is, there is; **стоит только доказать,** it remains only to prove
стоить, *v.*, cost, be worth, be worthwhile, be a matter of
стойка, *f.*, stand, support, post, pole
сток, *m.*, flow, drain, channel, sink
стократный, *adj.*, hundred-fold
стол, *m.*, board (*comp.*); **расчетный стол,** computer board
столб, *m.*, post, pole, column
столбец, *m.*, column
столбик, *m.*, column
столбцевой, *adj.*, column; **столбцевая матрица,** column matrix
столбчатый, *adj.*, bar; **столбчатая диаграмма,** bar graph
столетие, *n.*, century
столетний, *adj.*, centennial
столкновение, *n.*, collision, encounter

столкнуть (cf. **сталкивать**), *v.*, collide
столкнуться, *v.*, collide
столь, *adv.*, so, such
столько, *adv.*, as much, as many, so much, so many
стопа, *f.*, pile, ream
сторона, *f.*, side, aspect; **с другой стороны,** on the other hand; **непрерывный в обе стороны,** *adj.*, bi-continuous; **равномерный в обе стороны,** *adj.*, bi-uniform
стоуновский, *adj.*, Stone, pertaining to Stone
стохастика, *f.*, stochastics
стохастически, *adv.*, stochastically
стохастический, *adj.*, stochastic; **стохастический процесс,** stochastic process
стоять, *v.*, stand, stop, be, be situated, remain, last, be idle
стоячий, *adj.*, standing, stagnant, standard
стоящий, *adj.*, being, capable (of), standing, worth doing, lasting, idle
страдать, *v.*, suffer; **страдает недостатком,** has the defect (that)
страница, *f.*, page
странность, *f.*, strangeness, peculiarity, singularity
странный, *adj.*, odd, strange, singular
стратегия, *f.*, strategy
стратифицированный, *adj.*, stratified
страхование, *n.*, insurance; **статистика страхования,** actuarial statis tics
страхователь, *m.*, insurant
страховать, *v.*, insure
страховой, *adj.*, insurance, actuarial
страховщик, *m.*, insurer
стрела, *f.*, arrow
стрелка, *f.*, pointer, indicator, arrow; **по часовой стрелке,** clockwise; **против часовой стрелки,** counter-clockwise
стрельба, *f.*, shooting, firing
стрельчатый, *adj.*, arrow-shaped, pointed
стремиться, *v.*, approach, tend to
стремление, *n.*, convergence, tending, tendency
стремящийся, *adj.*, tending, approaching
стробирование, *n.*, gating (*comp.*)
стробировать, *v.*, gate (*comp.*)
стробирующий, *adj.*, gating; **стробирующий сигнал,** gating signal
стробоскопический, *adj.*, stroboscopic
строгий, *adj.*, rigorous, strict; **строгое вложение,** strict imbedding; **строгое неравенство,** strict inequality
строго, *adv.*, strictly, rigorously; **строго обратимый,** strongly reversible
строение, *n.*, structure, construction
строитель, *m.*, designer, builder
строительство, *n.*, construction, project
строить (построить), *v.*, construct, build, form
стройность, *f.*, orderliness, just proportion
стройный, *adj.*, orderly, well-proportioned
строка, *f.*, line, row, series; *n*-**строка,** *n*-tuple
строфоида, *f.*, strophoid
строчка, *f.*, line, row, series, stitch
строчной, *adj.*, lower-case; **строчная буква,** small letter
строя, *adv. part.*, forming, constructing, by forming, if we form
строящийся, *adj.*, projected; **строящееся произведение,** projected bundle
структура, *f.*, lattice, structure; **структура с заменой,** exchange lattice; *M*-**структура,** matroid lattice
структуризуемый, *adj.*, (being) made into a lattice
структурно (from **структурный**), *adv.*; **структурно упорядоченный,** *adj.*, lattice-ordered
структурногомоморфный, *adj.*, lattice-homomorphic
структурный, *adj.*, lattice, structural, parastrophic; **структурная матрица,** parastrophic matrix

струна, *f.*, string; **оттянутая струна,** plucked string
струя, *f.*, jet, spray, stream
студент, *m.*, student
ступенчатый, *adj.*, graduated, consecutive, step-; **ступенчатая функция,** step-function
ступень, *f.*, step, footstep, stage
стьюдентовый, *adj.*, Student's, Student; **стьюдентово отношение,** Student's ratio; **стьюдентовое отклонение,** Student's deviation
стюдентизированный, *adj.*, Student's; **стюдентизированное отклонение,** Student's deviation
стягиваемость, *f.*, contractibility, compressibility
стягиваемый, *adj.*, contractible, compressible, collapsible, subtended
стягивание, *n.*, tightening, contraction, retraction, compression, pinching
стягивать (стянуть), *v.*, tighten, pinch, tie, span, shrink, contract, subtend, retract
стягиваться, *v.*, shrink, contract
стягивающий, *adj.*, contracting, tending, subtending, spanning
стянуть (cf. **стягивать**), *v.*, contract, subtend, retract
субаддитивный, *adj.*, subadditive
суб-бигармонический, *adj.*, sub-biharmonic
субблок, *m.*, sub-unit, sub-block
субвалентный, *adj.*, subvalent
субгармонический, *adj.*, subharmonic
субгармоничность, *f.*, subharmonicity
субгеодезический, *adj.*, subgeodesic
субинвариантный, *adj.*, subinvariant, accessible
сублинейный, *adj.*, sublinear
субматрица, *f.*, submatrix
субметрический, *adj.*, submetric
субмодель, *f.*, submodel
субнормаль, *f.*, sub-normal
субнормальный, *adj.*, subnormal
субординация, *f.*, subordination
субплоский, *adj.*, subflat
субпроективный, *adj.*, subprojective
субрефлексивный, *adj.*, subreflexive
субстанциональный, *adj.*, substantive
субституция, *f.*, substitution
субституэнд, *m.*, substituend
субстрат, *m.*, substratum
субфинитный, *adj.*, sub-finite
субъект, *m.*, person, individual, subject
субъективизм, *m.*, subjectivism
субъективный, *adj.*, subjective
сугубо, *adv.*, doubly, twice, especially, particularly
судебный, *adj.*, legal, judicial
судить, *v.*, judge, predetermine
судно, *n.*, vessel, craft
судьба, *f.*, fate, fortune
судя, *adv. part.*, judging, if we judge; **судя по этому,** judging from this; **судя по тому, что,** judging from the fact that
суждение, *n.*, judgment, opinion, inference; **индуктивное суждение,** inductive inference
сужение, *n.*, contraction, constriction, narrowing, restriction
суженный, *adj.*, contracted, narrowed
суживать (сузить), *v.*, narrow down, contract, constrict
суметь, *v.*, be able, know, succeed (in)
сумма, *f.*, sum, union; **в сумме,** amounting to
суммарный, *adj.*, total, summary, summarized
сумматор, *m.*, adder, summator, integrator
суммация, *f.*, summation
суммирование, *n.*, summation, summing up; **суммирование распространяется на,** the summation is taken over
суммировать, *v.*, sum, sum up, add together
суммировка, *f.*, summation
суммируемость, *f.*, summability, integrability
суммируемый, *adj.*, summable, integrable
суммирующий, *adj.*, summing

суммируя, *adv. part.*, summing, by summing, if we sum; **суммируя по,** summing over

суммовой, *adj.*, sum, union

супер-аддитивный, *adj.*, super-additive

супергармонический, *adj.*, superharmonic

супергармоничность, *f.*, superharmonicity

супермультиплетный, *adj.*, super-multiplet

суперпозиция, *f.*, superposition, composition

суперпонироваться, *v.*, be superposed, be superimposed

суперфиниширование, *n.*, high finishing

суперэффективность, *f.*, supereffectiveness, superefficiency

суперэффективный, *adj.*, supereffective, superefficient

суппорт, *m.*, support, rest

супремум, *m.*, supremum

суррогат, *m.*, substitute; **топологический суррогат,** topological substitute

суспензия, *f.*, suspension

сутки, *pl.*, twenty-four hours, day

суток, *gen. pl.* of **сутки**

суточный, *adj.*, daily, diurnal

суть, *f.*, essence, substance

суть (from **быть**), (they) are

сухой, *adj.*, dry, arid

сушка, *f.*, drying

существенно, *adv.*, essentially, substantially; **существенно особая точка,** essential singularity

существенность, *f.*, importance, essence

существенный, *adj.*, essential

существо, *n.*, essence, being, entity; **по существу,** actually, essentially; **по существу дела,** essentially, fundamentally

существование, *n.*, existence; **доказательство существования,** existence proof; **квантор существования,** existential quantifier

существовать, *v.*, exist, be

сущность, *f.*, essence, main point, entity; **в сущности говоря,** generally speaking

сфера, *f.*, sphere

сферический, *adj.*, spherical

сферическисимметричный, *adj.*, spherically symmetric

сфероид, *m.*, spheroid

сфероидальный, *adj.*, spheroidal

сферо-конический, *adj.*, sphero-conal, sphero-conical

сформулированный, *adj.*, formulated, stated

сформулировать, *v.*, state, formulate

схема, *f.*, scheme, plan, diagram, circuit; **конечная схема,** finite scheme, finite circuit; **схема со многими устойчивыми состояниями,** multistable configuration, multistable circuit; **теория схем,** communication theory; **схема "и",** "and" circuit; **моделирующая схема,** analogous circuit; **схема антисовпаданий,** anti-coincidence circuit; **схема с импульсным возбуждением,** pulse-actuated circuit; **схема задержки импульсов,** pulse-delay circuit; **схема генерации импульсов,** pulse-generating circuit; **релейная схема,** relay circuit; **схема удвоения напряжения,** voltage-doubling circuit

схематизация, *f.*, schematization, planning

схематика, *f.*, circuitry, schematics

схематически, *adv.*, schematically, diagrammatically

схематический, *adj.*, schematic, diagrammatical

схемный, *adj.*, network, circuit, system

сходимость, *f.*, convergence; **топология простой сходимости,** simple convergence topology; **сходимость в среднем,** mean convergence

сходить, *v.*, descend, come down, get off

сходиться, *v.*, converge, come together, meet; **сходиться к,** converge to; **сходиться в среднем,** converge in mean

сходный, *adj.*, similar, compatible, consistent; **сходная черта,** similarity; **сходная секвенция,** cognate sequent

сходственный, *adj.*, similar, like, compatible

сходство, *n.*, resemblance, similarity, analogy

сходящийся, *adj.*, convergent, concurrent

схожий, *adj.*, like, similar

сцепление, *n.*, coupling, linking, cohesion, adhesion

сцепленный, *adj.*, geared, coupled, linked, chained, cohesive; **сцепленное множество,** enchained set; **сцепленные области,** overlapping domains

сцинтиллирующий, *adj.*, scintillating

сцинтилляция, *f.*, scintillation

счастье, *n.*, luck; **к счастью,** fortunately

счесть (cf. **считать**), *v.*, count

счет, *m.*, calculation, computation, count; **за счет,** at the expense of

счетно, *adv.*, denumerably, countably

счетноаддитивный, *adj.*, denumerably-additive, countably additive

счетно-компактный, *adj.*, countably compact, separable

счетно-кратный, *adj.*, countably-multiple

счетно-паракомпактный, *adj.*, countable-paracompact

счетноразложимый, *adj.*, denumerably decomposable

счетнорешающий, *adj.*, computing, calculating

счетность, *f.*, denumerability, countability; **вторая аксиома счетности,** second axiom of countability

счетный, *adj.*, denumerable, countable, counting, calculational; **счетная линейка,** slide rule; **счетная машина,** calculator; **счетное множество,** denumerable set; **не более чем счетный,** *adj.*, at most countable; **счетное реле,** counting relay (*comp.*)

счетчик, *m.*, counter, indicator, accumulator

счетчиксцинтиллятор, *m.*, scintillation counter

счеты, *pl.*, abacus

счисление, *n.*, calculus, calculation; **система счисления,** number system; **смешанная система счисления,** mixed-base notation

считать (счесть), *v.*, count, compute, reckon, consider, regard, assume; **считать доказанным,** *v.*, take for granted, assume

считаться, *v.*, consider, be considered, be regarded

считая, *adv. part.*, considering, regarding, if we regard

сшивка, *f.*, sewing together; **теорема о сшивке,** sewing theorem

съезд, *m.*, congress

съем, *m.*, removal, sampling; **момент съема,** sampling instant

съемка, *f.*, survey

съемочный, *adj.*, surveying, survey

сыграть, *v.*, play, perform

сыпучий, *adj.*, free-flowing, loose

сырой, *adj.*, untreated, crude, raw

сырье, *n.*, raw material

сэкономить (cf. **экономить**), *v.*, economize, save

сюда, *adv.*, here

Т

та (cf. **тот**), *pron.*, that

таблица, *f.*, table, list, array, plate; **прямоугольная таблица,** rectangular array, matrix; **таблица сопряженности признаков,** contingency table

табличный, *adj.*, table, tabular; *M*-**табличный,** *adj.*, *M*-table; *M*-**табличное представление,** *M*-table representability

табулирование, *n.*, tabulation

табулированный, *adj.*, tabulated

табулировать, *v.*, tabulate

табулятор, *n.*, tabulator

тавтологический, *adj.*, tautological

тавтология, *f.*, tautology

так, *adv.*, so, thus, like this; **точно так же,** in just the same way; **так как,** *conj.*, as, since; **так же как и выще,** as above; **так называемый,** *adj.*, so-called; **так что,** so that; **это не так,** it is not the case; **так же,** also

также, *adv.*, also, too, as well

таки, *part.*, after all; **опять-таки,** again; **так-таки,** really

таким (cf. **такой**), such; **таким образом,** thus

такнодальный, *adj.*, tacnodal; **такнодальная точка,** tacnode

таковой, *adj.*, such, the same; **как таков,** as such

такой, *pron.*, such, so, that; **таким образом,** thus; **такой же, как,** the same as; **такой же . . . как,** as . . . as; **в таком случае,** in that case

такт, *m.*, time

тактический, *adj.*, tactical

там, *adv.*, there; **там же,** in the same place

тангаж, *m.*, pitch, pitching; **угол тангажа,** pitch angle

тангенс, *m.*, tangent

тангенсгальванометр, *m.*, tangent galvanometer

тангенсоида, *f.*, tangent curve

тангенциальный, *adj.*, tangential

тасование, *n.*, shuffle, shuffling (of cards)

тасовать (стасовать), *v.*, shuffle; **тасовать карты,** shuffle cards

тасовка, *f.*, shuffle, shuffling

тауберовый, *adj.*, Tauberian

таутохрона, *f.*, tautochrone

твердость, *f.*, hardness, solidity, firmness, rigidity

твердый, *adj.*, rigid, hard, firm; **твердое тело,** rigid body

творческий, *adj.*, creative

те (cf. **тот**), those

т. е., *abbrev.* **(то есть),** that is, i.e.

тезис, *m.*, thesis

тейлоровский, *adj.*, Taylor

текст, *m.*, text

текстильный, *adj.*, textile

текстуально, *adv.*, according to text

текстуальный, *adj.*, textual

текучесть, *f.*, fluctuation, instability, fluidity, fluid, yield

текучий, *adj.*, fluid, fluctuating, instable

текущий, *adj.*, flowing, flow, current, present-day; **текущая координата,** moving coordinate

тел, *gen. pl.* of **тело**

телевидение, *n.*, television

телеграфный, *adj.*, telegraphic; **телеграфное уравнение,** telegraph equation

телекоммуникационный, *adj.*, telecommunicational

телепараллелизм, *m.*, teleparallelism

телепередача, *f.*, telecommunication, transmission

телескоп, *m.*, telescope

телескопический, *adj.*, telescopic

телесный, *adj.*, solid (angle), corporal, solid; **телесная зональная функция,** solid zonal harmonic

телетайп, *m.*, teletype, teleprinter; **код телетайпа,** teleprinter code

телетайпный, *adj.*, teletype
телеуправление, *n.*, remote control
телеуправляемый, *adj.*, operated by remote control, remote control
телефония, *f.*, telephony
телефонный, *adj.* telephone, telephonic
тело, *n.*, body, field, solid, skew field; **материальное тело,** mass; **проблема двух (трех) тел,** two- (three-) body problem; **излучение черного тела,** blackbody radiation; **альтернативное тело,** alternative field, alternative division ring, **жидкое тело,** liquid
телодвижение, *n.*, movement, motion
телоподобный, *adj.*, field-like; **телоподобная алгебра,** field-like algebra
тем (cf. **тот**), by that, to them; *adv.*, so much the; **чем . . ., тем . . .,** the . . ., the . . .; **тем более, что,** the more so, as; **тем не менее,** nevertheless; **тем самым,** by the same token
тема, *f.*, theme, subject, topic
тематика, *f.*, themes, subjects
тематический, *adj.*, subject, thematic
тембр, *m.*, timbre, characteristic, quality
теми (cf. **тот**), (by) those
темнота, *f.*, dark, darkness
темный, *adj.*, dark
темп, *m.*, rate, speed, frequency, tempo; **ускорять темп,** *v.*, accelerate
температура, *f.*, temperature
температурный, *adj.*, temperature
температуропроводность, *f.*, thermal conductivity
тенденциозность, *f.*, bias, tendentiousness
тенденциозный, *adj.*, biased
тенденция, *f.*, tendency, inclination, trend, bias
тензор, *m.*, tensor; **тензор деформации,** strain tensor, deformation tensor; **тензор напряжения,** stress tensor; **тензор скорости деформации,** strain velocity tensor; **тензор проводимости,** conductivity tensor
тензорный, *adj.*, tensor; **тензорное исчисление,** tensor calculus
тень, *f.*, shadow, shade, umbra
теорема, *f.*, theorem
теоретико-, *prefix*, -theoretic
теоретико-вероятностный, *adj.*, probability-theoretic
теоретико-групповой, *adj.*, group-theoretic
теоретико-игровой, *adj.*, game-theoretic
теоретико-множественный, *adj.*, set-theoretic
теоретико-структурный, *adj.*, lattice-theoretic
теоретико-функциональный, *adj.*, function-theoretic
теоретико-числовой, *adj.*, number-theoretic
теоретически, *adv.*, theoretically, in theory
теоретический, *adj.*, theoretical
теоретичный, *adj.*, abstract, theoretical
теория, *f.*, theory
теперешний, *adj.*, present, contemporary
теперь, *adv.*, now, present; **теперь же,** right now
тепло, *n.*, heat, warmth; *adj.* (short form of **теплый**), warm
тепловой, *adj.*, thermal, caloric, heat
теплоемкость, *f.*, heat capacity, thermal capacity; **удельная теплоемкость,** specific heat
теплоизлучение, *n.*, thermal radiation, thermal emission, heat radiation
теплоизоляционный, *adj.*, (thermally) insulated
теплоизоляция, *f.*, heat insulation, thermal insulation
теплообмен, *m.*, heat exchange, heat transfer
теплообменник, *m.*, heat exchanger
теплопередача, *f.*, heat transfer
теплопроводность, *f.*, heat conductivity, thermal conductivity, heat conduction
теплопроводящий, *adj.*, heat conducting
теплосодержание, *n.*, heat content, enthalpy
теплота, *f.*, heat, warmth
теплый, *adj.*, warm

терм, *m.*, therm
термин, *m.*, term; **в терминах,** in terms (of)
терминология, *f.*, terminology, nomenclature
термионный, *adj.*, thermionic
термический, *adj.*, thermal, thermic
термодинамика, *f.*, thermodynamics
термодинамический, *adj.*, thermodynamic
термодиффузионный, *adj.*, thermodiffusion
термодиффузия, *f.*, thermal diffusion
термомагнитный, *adj.*, thermomagnetic
термопара, *f.*, thermocouple
термостатика, *f.*, thermostatics
термоэлемент, *m.*, thermoelement, thermocouple
термоэлектричество, *n.*, thermoelectricity
термоэлектродвижущий, *adj.*, thermoelectromotive; **коэффициент термоэлектродвижущей силы,** absolute thermoelectric power
термоэффект, *m.*, thermo-effect
термоядерный, *adj.*, thermo-nuclear
тернарный, *adj.*, ternary
терпеть (потерпеть), *v.*, suffer, undergo, endure, tolerate, support; **терпят разрыв,** are discontinuous, have discontinuities
территориальный, *adj.*, territorial
территория, *f.*, territory
терциарный, *adj.*, tertiary
терять (потерять), *v.*, lose, give off, give up, shed
теряя, *adv. part.*, losing; **не теряя общности,** without losing generality
тесеральный (= **тессеральный**), *adj.*, tesseral; **тесеральная гармоника,** tesseral harmonic
тесно, *adv.*, closely
теснота, *f.*, tightness, closeness, crowd
тесность, *f.*, closeness, tightness
тесный, *adj.*, tight, close, narrow; **в тесной связи с,** closely connected to
тессеральный, *adj.*, tesseral; **тессеральная сферическая функция,** tesseral surface harmonic
тест, *m.*, test
тетрагедральный, *adj.*, tetrahedral
тетрагон, *m.*, tetragon, quadrilateral
тетрагональ, *m.*, quadrangle
тетрагональный, *adj.*, quadrangular, quadrilateral
тетрациклический, *adj.*, tetracyclic
тетраэдр, *m.*, tetrahedron; **группа тетраэдра,** tetrahedral group
тетраэдральный, *adj.*, tetrahedral
тетраэдрический, *adj.*, tetrahedral
тетрод, *m.*, tetrode
тех (cf. **тот**), those, of those
техник, *m.*, technician, engineer
техника, *f.*, technology, engineering, techniques
технический, *adj.*, technical, engineering
техникум, *m.*, technical school, vocational school
технологический, *adj.*, technological
технология, *f.*, technology
течение, *n.*, current, stream, flow, trend; **в течение,** in the course of, during; **безвихревое течение,** irrotational flow
течь, *v.*, flow, leak
тильда, *f.*, tilde, dash; **тильда-операция,** tilde-operation
тип, *m.*, type, model
типический, *adj.*, typical, characteristic
типично, *adv.*, typically
типично-вещественный, *adj.*, typically real
типичность, *f.*, typicalness
типичный, *adj.*, typical, characteristic
типовой, *adj.*, standard, typical
тире, *n.*, dash, hyphen
титан, *m.*, titanium, boiler, Titan
тихоновский, *adj.*, Tychonoff
тканевый, *adj.*, tissue, woven, web
ткань, *f.*, web, fabric, material, tissue
т. н., *abbrev.* **(так называемый),** so-called

то, *pron.*, it, that, *conj.*, then; **то есть,** that is, i.e.; **то же,** the same; **одно и то же,** one and the same; **не то,** otherwise; **не то . . . не то,** either . . . or; **то ли . . . то ли,** whether . . . or, either . . . or; **(да) и то,** even, even then
Т-образный, *adj.*, T-shaped, right-angled; **Т-образное сочленение,** right-angled junction
товар, *m.*, wares, commodity, goods
товарный, *adj.*, commodity; **товарная карта,** commodity map
тогда, *adv.*, then, at that time; **тогда и только тогда,** if and only if; **тогда, когда,** when
того (cf. **тот**), (of) this; **для того чтобы,** in order that; **и без того,** even without that, in any case; **по мере того как,** as; **не(т) того, чтобы,** instead of; **кроме того,** furthermore; **без того чтобы,** unless
тождественно, *adv.*, identically
тож(д)ественность, *f.*, identity
тож(д)ественный, *adj.*, identical, identical to, same, same as; **тождественное отображение,** identity mapping
тож(д)ество, *n.*, identity
тоже, *adv.*, also, too, as well
ток, *m.*, current, flow; **постоянный ток,** direct current; **переменный ток,** alternating current; **темновой ток,** leakage current; **функция тока,** stream function, flow function
токсический, *adj.*, toxic
токсичность, *f.*, toxicity
толерантность, *f.*, tolerance
толерантный, *adj.*, tolerance; **толерантные пределы,** tolerance limits
толкование, *n.*, interpretation
толковать, *v.*, interpret, explain
толпа, *f.*, mob
толстостенный, *adj.*, thick-walled, heavy-walled
толстый, *adj.*, thick, heavy
толчок, *m.*, push, shock
толщина, *f.*, thickness
только, *adv.*, only, solely, merely, but; **тогда и только тогда,** if and only if; **только что,** just, just now; **как только,** as soon as; **не только . . . но и,** not only . . . but also
том, *m.*, volume
тому, cf. **тот**; **к тому же,** furthermore; **и тому подобное,** etc., and so forth
тон, *m.*, tone, pitch
тонкий, *adj.*, thin, fine, subtle, refined
тонко, *adv.*, thinly, finely; *pref.*, thin-
тонкостенный, *adj.*, thin-shelled
тонкость, *f.*, thinness, subtlety, fineness; **тонкости,** *pl.*, details, refinements
тонна, *f.*, ton
тончайший (cf. **тонкий**), *adj.*, finest
топка, *f.*, heating, furnace, melting
топливный, *adj.*, fuel
топливо, *n.*, fuel, firing; **жидкое топливо,** (fuel) oil, liquid fuel
топографический, *adj.*, topographical
топография, *f.*, topography
топологизация, *f.*, topologization
топологизированный, *adj.*, topologized
топологизировать, *v.*, topologize
топологизироваться, *v.*, be topologized
топологизирующий, *adj.*, topologizing
топологически, *adv.*, topologically
топологический, *adj.*, topological
топология, *f.*, topology
тор, *m.*, torus, anchor ring
торг, *m.*, bargaining, market, auction; **торги,** *pl.*, bidding
торговец, *m.*, dealer, merchant
торговля, *f.*, trade, commerce, barter
торговый, *adj.*, commercial, trade; **средняя торговой активности,** average sales
торец, *m.*, end-wall, paving block, element of a covering
торический, *adj.*, torus, pertaining to torus
торможение, *n.*, damping, braking, retardation, drag, inhibition
тормоз, *m.*, brake, obstacle
тормозить, *v.*, retard, damp, brake

тормозящий, *adj.*, inhibiting, damping, braking
торовидный, *adj.*, torus, torus-shaped, toroidal
тороид, *m.*, toroid
тороидальный, *adj.*, toroidal
торообразный, *adj.*, torus-shaped, toroidal
торс, *m.*, developable surface, torse, trunk
торсообразующий, *adj.*, developable
торцовый, *adj.*, pavement, covering
тот (та, то), *pron.*, that, those; **тот же самый,** the same; **тот же,** the same
тотализация, *f.*, totalization
тотально, *adv.*, completely, totally
тотальный, *adj.*, total, complete
тотчас, *adv.*, immediately, instantly
точечно, *adv.*, pointwise
точечно-, *prefix*, point-, pointwise
точечно-конечный, *adj.*, pointwise finite, point-finite
точечно-контактный, *adj.*, point-contact
точечно-опорный, *adj.*, point-supported
точечно-пересекающийся, *adj.*, intersecting pointwise
точечнотранзитивный, *adj.*, pointwise transitive
точечный, *adj.*, point, pointwise, dot; **точечный источник,** point source; **точечная решетка,** point lattice; **точечное множество,** punctiform set, totally disconnected set
точка, *f.*, point, place, spot, dot; **точка зрения,** point of view; **точка сосредоточения массы,** discrete mass point
точно, *adv.*, accurately, exactly, precisely, just, directly; **точно так же,** in exactly the same way
точность, *f.*, exactness, accuracy, precision; **с точностью до,** to within; **повышенная точность,** multiple precision
точный, *adj.*, precise, exact, explicit, correct, strict, close, proximate; **точный порядок,** proximate order; **точная верхняя грань,** least upper bound; **точная нижняя грань,** greatest lower bound; **точное представление,** faithful representation
тощий, *adj.*, meager, thin; **тощее множество,** thin set, meager set
травящий, *adj.*, etching
традиционный, *adj.*, traditional, conventional
традиция, *f.*, tradition
траектория, *f.*, trajectory, path, track, locus
трактат, *m.*, treatise
трактовать, *v.*, treat, discuss, interpret
трактовка, *f.*, interpretation, treatment
трактриса, *f.*, tractrix
транзистор, *m.*, transistor
транзисторный, *adj.*, transistor
транзитивность, *f.*, transitivity
транзитивный, *adj.*, transitive
трансвариация, *f.*, transvariation
трансверсаль, *f.*, transversal
трансверсально, *adv.*, transversally
трансверсальность, *f.*, transversality
трансверсальный, *adj.*, transverse, transversal
трансгрессивный, *adj.*, overlapping, intersecting
трансгрессия, *f.*, overlapping, intersection, transgression
трансзвуковой, *adj.*, transonic
трансляционный, *adj.*, pertaining to translation, translational, transmission, broadcasting
трансляция, *f.*, translation, transmission, broadcast
трансмиссионный, *adj.*, transmission
трансмиссия, *f.*, transmission
транспарантный, *adj.*, transparent
трансплантация, *f.*, transplantation
транспозиция, *f.*, transposition
транспонирование, *n.*, transposition, conjugation, conjugating
транспонированный, *adj.*, transposed, conjugate, conjugated
транспонировать, *v.*, transpose, conjugate
транспортир, *m.*, protractor

транспортировка, *f.*, transport, transportation
транспортный, *adj.*, transport, transporting, supply
трансфинитный, *adj.*, transfinite
трансформатор, *m.*, transformer
трансформационный, *adj.*, transformation
трансформация, *f.*, transformation
трансформировать, *v.*, transform
трансцендентность, *f.*, transcendence
трансцендентный, *adj.*, transcendental, transcendence
трапециевидный, *adj.*, trapezoidal
трапеция, *f.*, trapezoid, trapezium
трапецоидальный, *adj.*, trapezoidal
трассировка, *f.*, tracing
трата, *f.*, expenditure; **пустая трата,** waste
трафарет, *m.*, stencil, pattern, groove, routine
траффик, *m.*, traffic
требование, *n.*, requirement, demand; **технические требования,** specifications
требовать (потребовать), *v.*, require, demand; **что и требовалось доказать,** Q.E.D.
требуемый, *adj.*, required, requirement, specification; **требуемый допуск,** specification tolerance
требуется (cf. **требовать**), is required
трезубец, *m.*, trident; **трезубец Ньютона,** trident of Newton
тренд, *m.*, trend
трение, *n.*, friction; **поверхностное трение,** skin friction
тренировочный, *adj.*, training, practice
третий, *adj.*, third
третичный, *adj.*, tertiary
треть, *f.*, (one) third; **две трети,** two thirds
третье, *n.*, third, middle, alternative; **исключенное третье,** excluded middle; **закон исключенного третьего,** law of the excluded middle
треугольник, *m.*, triangle; **аксиома треугольника,** triangle inequality
треугольный, *adj.*, triangular
трех, *prefix*, tri-, three-,
трехгранник, *m.*, trihedron
трехгранный, *adj.*, trihedral, three-edged
трехзначный, *adj.*, three-valued, three-digit
трехиндексный, *adj.*, three-index; **трехиндексные символы Кристоффеля,** Christoffel three-index symbols
трехкратный, *adj.*, triple
трехмерник, *m.*, three-manifold, three-variety
трехмерный, *adj.*, three-dimensional, trivariate; **трехмерное нормальное распределение,** trivariate normal distribution
трехосный, *adj.*, triaxial, pertaining to three axes
трехпараметрический, *adj.*, three-parameter
трехразрядный, *adj.*, triply-discharging, three-digit
трехсвязный, *adj.*, triply connected
трехсторонний, *adj.*, three-sided, three-way
трехчлен, *m.*, trinomial
трехчленный, *adj.*, trinomial
трещина, *f.*, crack, split, fissure
три, *num.*, three
триад, *m.*, triad
триада, *f.*, triad
триангулировать, *v.*, triangulate
триангулируемость, *f.*, triangulability
триангулируемый, *adj.*, triangulable
триангуляция, *f.*, triangulation
тривектор, *m.*, trivector, three-vector
тривиальность, *f.*, triviality
тривиальный, *adj.*, trivial
триггер, *m.*, trigger, flip-flop (*comp.*); **счетчик на триггерах,** flip-flop counter; **триггер переноса,** carry flip-flop
триггерный, *adj.*, trigger, flip-flop
тригональный, *adj.*, trigonal

тригонометрический, *adj.*, trigonometrical
тригонометрия, *f.*, trigonometry
трижды, *adv.*, thrice, three times, triply
трилинейный, *adj.*, trilinear
трилистник, *m.*, three-leaved figure, trifolium
тринадцать, *num.*, thirteen
триод, *m.*, triode, transistor, triod
триодический, *adj.*, triodic
триортогональный, *adj.*, triorthogonal, triply orthogonal
триплет, *m.*, triplet, set of three
триплетный, *adj.*, triplet
трипотенциальный, *adj.*, tripotential
трисектриса, *f.*, trisectrix
трисекция, *f.*, trisection
триста, *num.*, three hundred
триэдр, *m.*, trihedron
троекратно, *adv.*, three times
троичный, *adj.*, divided into three, tripartite, ternary
тройка, *f.*, the three, set of three, triple
тройничный, *adj.*, ternary; **тройничная квадратическая форма,** ternary quadratic form
тройной, *adj.*, triple, threefold
тройственный, *adj.*, triple
трос, *m.*, cable, rope, line
тротуар, *m.*, pavement
трохоида, *f.*, trochoid
троякий, *adj.*, triple, threefold
трояко, *adv.*, in three (different) ways
труба, *f.*, pipe, duct; **подзорная труба,** telescope; **аэродинамическая труба,** wind-tunnel
трубчатый, *adj.*, tubular, tube, duct
труд, *m.*, work, labor, trouble, difficulty; **без труда,** easily
трудность, *f.*, difficulty, obstacle
трудный, *adj.*, difficult, hard
трудоемкий, *adj.*, laborious, labor-consuming
труды (cf. **труд**), *pl.*, works, memoirs
труизм (= трюизм), *m.*, truism
трущийся, *adj.*, rubbing, friction
тряска, *f.*, shaking, jolting
туда, *adv.*, there; **туда и сюда,** back and forth; **туда и обратно,** there and back
туземный, *adj.*, native, indigenous
туман, *m.*, fog, mist
туманность, *f.*, nebula, vagueness
туманный, *adj.*, nebulous, vague, obscure
туннель, *m.*, tunnel, duct, conduit
туннельный, *adj.*, tunnel
тупик, *m.*, dead end, impasse
тупой, *adj.*, obtuse, blunt
тупоугольный, *adj.*, obtuse, obtuse-angled
турбоальтернатор, *m.*, turbo-alternator
турбореактивный, *adj.*, turboreactive, turbo-; **турбореактивный двигатель,** jet engine, turbojet
турбулентность, *f.*, turbulence
турбулентный, *adj.*, turbulent
тут, *adv.*, here
тщательно, *adv.*, thoroughly, carefully
тщательный, *adj.*, careful, thorough
тыл, *m.*, rear; **служба тылов,** logistics; **организация тыла,** logistics
тыловой, *adj.*, rear
тысяча, *num.*, thousand
Тьюринг, *m.*, Türing; **машина Тьюринга,** Türing machine
тэта-функция, *f.*, theta-function
тюк, *m.*, package, bale
тяга, *f.*, thrust, propulsion
тяготение, *n.*, gravity, gravitation
тяготеть, *v.*, gravitate, be attracted, be drawn
тягучесть, *f.*, viscosity
тягучий, *adj.*, viscous, ductile, tensile
тяжеловесный, *adj.*, heavy, unwieldy
тяжелый, *adj.*, heavy, severe
тяжение (cf. **притяжение**), *n.*, attraction
тяжесть, *f.*, weight, gravity; **центр тяжести,** center of gravity, centroid

У

у, *prep.*, by, near, at, on, to, of; **у него (есть),** he (it) has
убегать, *v.*, flee, run off
убедительный, *adj.*, convincing, conclusive, striking
убеждать (убедить), *v.*, convince, persuade
убеждаться (убедиться), *v.*, convince oneself, be convinced
убеждение, *n.*, conviction, belief
убежденно, *adv.*, convincingly, with conviction
убежденный, *adj.*, confirmed, convinced
убранный, *adj.*, removed
убывание, *n.*, decrease, diminution, descent
убывать (убыть), *v.*, decrease, diminish, take away
убывающий, *adj.*, decreasing; diminishing, descending; **условие обрыва убывающей цепочки,** descending chain condition
убыль, *f.*, decrease, diminution; **идет на убыль,** is decreasing; **пошло на убыль,** began to decrease
убыстрение, *n.*, acceleration
убыток, *m.*, loss, disadvantage
убыть, cf. **убывать**
увеличение, *n.*, increase, enlargement, magnification, extension, expansion
увеличенный, *adj.*, enlarged, augmented
увеличивать (увеличить), *v.*, increase, enlarge, extend
увеличивающий, *adj.*, increasing, enlarging, extending
увеличительный, *adj.*, magnifying, expanding
уверенность, *f.*, certainty, confidence
уверенный, *adj.*, convinced, certain
увертка, *f.*, evasion, subterfuge
увидеть (cf. **видеть**), *v.*, see
увлекать (увлечь), *v.*, carry away, carry along
увлечение, *n.*, dragging; **коэффициент увлечения Френеля,** Fresnel dragging coefficient
увлеченный, *adj.*, dragged
увязка, *f.*, interrelationship, co-ordination
увязывать (увязать), *v.*, link, tie up, connect
угадывить (угадать), *v.*, guess, conjecture
углерод, *m.*, carbon
углеродный, *adj.*, carbon; **углеродный цикл,** carbon cycle
угловатость, *f.*, angularity
угловатый, *adj.*, angular
угловой, *adj.*, angular, corner; **угловая точка,** corner point, corner, point of break; **условие в угловых точках,** corner condition; **угловой коэффициент,** slope
углубление, *n.*, deepening, extension
углублять (углубить), investigate, examine, deepen, extend
угодный, *adj.*, desired, arbitrary; **как угодно,** anyhow, arbitrarily; **сколь(ко) угодно,** any amount, as much as desired, arbitrarily; **что угодно,** anything
угол, *m.*, angle, corner; **под углом в,** at an angle (of); **под прямым углом,** at right angles
угроза, *f.*, danger, threat
уд. в., *abbrev.* **(удельный вес)**, specific gravity
удаваться (удаться), *v.*, succeed, turn out well
удаление, *n.*, receding, moving off, elimination, removal
удаленный, *adj.*, distant, far, remote, removed, apart; **бесконечно удаленный,** *adj.*, infinite, infinitely distant; **бесконечно удаленная точка,** *f.*, point at infinity; **одинаково удаленный,** *adj.*, equidistant
удаляемый, *adj.*, receding

удалять (удалить), *v.*, remove, move off, send away
удаляться (удалиться), *v.*, recede, withdraw
удаляющий, *adj.*, receding, moving off, removing, sending away
удар, *m.*, blow, stroke, shock, thrust
ударный, *adj.*, shock, pertaining to shock
ударять, *v.*, strike, collide (with)
удаться (cf. **удаваться**), *v.*, succeed
удача, *f.*, success, good luck
удачно, *adv.*, successfully, well
удачный, *adj.*, successful
удваивать (удвоить), *v.*, double, duplicate, redouble
удвоение, *n.*, doubling, redoubling, duplication; **формула удвоения,** duplication formula; **схема удвоения,** doubling circuit; **схема удвоения напряжения,** voltage-doubling circuit
удвоенный, *adj.*, doubled, duplicate, duplicated
удвоитель, *m.*, doubler; **удвоитель частоты,** frequency doubler
удельно, *adv.*, specifically
удельный, *adj.*, specific; **удельная работа деформации,** specific work of deformation; **молярная удельная теплоемкость,** molar specific heat; **удельная теплота,** specific heat
уделять (уделить), *v.*, give, spare
удержание, *n.*, retention, deduction, restraint, constraint
удерживать, *v.*, retain, hold, keep (from), deduct
удивительно, *adv.*, astonishingly, surprisingly; **не удивительно,** it is no wonder that
удивительный, *adj.*, astonishing, striking
удивление, *n.*, surprise, astonishment
удлинение, *n.*, lengthening, prolongation, continuation, extension; **относительное удлинение,** aspect ratio
удлиненный, *adj.*, oblong, elongated, extended; **удлиненный эллипсоид вращения,** prolate spheroid
удлинять (удлинить), *v.*, extend, expand, lengthen, prolong, elongate
удобнее, *adj.*, more convenient, more suitable
удобно, *adv.*, conveniently; *pred.*, it is convenient
удобность, *f.*, convenience
удобный, *adj.*, suitable, convenient, opportune
удобство, *n.*, convenience, ease
удовлетворение, *n.*, satisfaction, compliance
удовлетворенный, *adj.*, satisfied; **быть удовлетворен,** *v.*, be satisfied
удовлетворительно, *adv.*, satisfactorily
удовлетворительный, *adj.*, satisfactory
удовлетворять (удовлетворить), *v.*, satisfy, comply (with), meet
удовлетворяться (удовлетвориться), *v.*, be satisfied
удовлетворяющий, *adj.*, satisfying, complying (with), meeting
удовольствие, *n.*, pleasure
удовольствоваться (cf. **довольствоваться**), *v.*, be content, content oneself
удостоверять (удостоверить), *v.*, certify, verify, attest, prove
уединенный, *adj.*, isolated, solitary
уже (cf. **узкий**), *adj.*, narrower
уже, *adv.*, already, now, by this time; **уже не раз,** more than once
узел, *m.*, knot, node, group, assembly; **узел интерполяции,** point of interpolation; **тип узла,** knot-type; **узлы сети,** nodes (or vertices) of a network; **узел управления,** control assembly
узкий, *adj.*, restricted, narrow; **в узком смысле,** in the restricted sense; **задача с узким местом,** bottleneck problem
узкополосный, *adj.*, narrow-band
узловой, *adj.*, nodal, main; **узловая линия,** nodal curve; **узловая точка,** node
узнавать (узнать), *v.*, recognize, learn, find out

уйти (cf. **уходить**), *v.*, leave, go away
укажем (cf. **указать**), we shall indicate, we shall find
указание, *n.*, indication, instruction, designation
указанный, *adj.*, indicated, stated, mentioned
указатель, *m.*, indicator, index
указать (cf. **указывать**), *v.*, indicate, find, determine
указывать (указать), *v.*, indicate, show, find, determine
указывающий, *adj.*, pointing out, indicating, showing
укладка, *f.*, packing, laying, stacking
укладывать, *v.*, pack, stack
укладывающийся, *adj.*, being packed, being stacked
уклон, *m.*, slope, inclination
уклонение, *n.*, deviation, digression, variance
уклоняться, *v.*, deviate, avoid, digress, elude
уклоняющийся, *adj.*, deviating, eluding
укорачивание, *n.*, shortening, contraction
укорачивать (укоротить), *v.*, shorten, contract
укорочение, *n.*, contraction, shortening, truncation
укороченный, *adj.*, shortened, contracted, truncated, curtate
укрепление, *n.*, strengthening, consolidation
укреплять (укрепить), *v.*, strengthen, reinforce, consolidate
укрупнение, *n.*, enlargement, consolidation, grand total
укрупненный, *adj.*, enlarged, consolidated, total, grand total; **выборка из укрупленных партий,** grand-lot sample
укрупнять, *v.*, enlarge, extend, amplify
укрытый, *adj.*, covered, concealed
улавливать (уловить), *v.*, catch, detect, discern
улитка, *f.*, spiral, helix, limaçon
улиткообразный, *adj.*, spiral, helical
уложение, *n.*, packing, code
улучшать (улучшить), *v.*, improve
улучшение, *n.*, improvement, refinement, adaptation
улучшенный, *adj.*, improved
ультрагиперболический, *adj.*, ultrahyperbolic
ультразвуковой, *adj.*, ultrasonic
ультраидеал *m.*, ultra-ideal
ультракороткий, *adj.*, ultra-short
ультрапоказательный, *adj.*, ultraexponential
ультраразделитель, *m.*, ultradivisor
ультрарешетка, *f.*, ultra-lattice
ультраслабый, *adj.*, ultraweak
ультрастабильный, *adj.*, ultrastable
ультрасферический, *adj.*, ultraspherical
ультраустойчивость, *f.*, ultrastability
ультраустойчивый, *adj.*, ultrastable
ультрафильтр, *m.*, ultrafilter
ультрафиолетовый, *adj.*, ultra-violet
ултраэллиптический, *adj.*, ultra-elliptic
ум, *m.*, mind, intellect
умаляться (умалиться), *v.*, diminish, be disparaged
умение, *n.*, ability, knowledge
уменьшаемое, *n.*, minuend
уменьшать (уменьшить), *v.*, reduce, diminish, decrease
уменьшающий(ся), *adj.*, decreasing
уменьшение, *n.*, diminution, decrease, reduction, depreciation
уменьшенный, *adj.*, diminished, reduced
умеренно, *adv.*, moderately
умеренный, *adj.*, moderate, medium, temperate, mild
умерший, *adj.*, dead, deceased
уместность, *f.*, pertinence, relevency
уместный, *adj.*, proper, relevent, appropriate
уметь, *v.*, be able (to), know, know how (to)
умножать (умножить), *v.*, multiply, increase, augment
умножающий, *adj.*, multiplying; **умножающее устройство,** multiplier; **умножающая машина,** multiplier

умножение, *n.*, multiplication, product
умноженный, *adj.*, multiplied
умножитель, *m.*, multiplier, factor
умозаключать (умозаключить), *v.*, conclude, deduce
умозаключение, *n.*, conclusion, inference, deduction
умозрительный, *adj.*, theoretical, speculative
умственный, *adj.*, mental, intellectual
унивалентность, *f.*, univalence
универсально, *adv.*, universally
универсальность, *f.*, universality
универсальный, *adj.*, universal, general-purpose
университет, *m.*, university
университетский, *adj.*, university
универсум, *m.*, universe
уникальный, *adj.*, unique
уникогерентность, *f.*, unicoherence
уникогерентный, *adj.*, unicoherent
уникурзальный, *adj.*, unicursal
унимодальность, *f.*, unimodality
унимодальный, *adj.*, uni-modal
унимодулярный, *adj.*, unimodular
унипотентный, *adj.*, unipotent
унирациональность, *f.*, unirationality
унирациональный, *adj.*, unirational
унитальный, *adj.*, unital, unitary
унитарность, *f.*, property of being unitary; **унитарность матриц,** unitary matrices
унитарный, *adj.*, unitary
унификация, *f.*, unification
униформизация, *f.*, uniformization
униформизированный, *adj.*, uniformized
униформизировать, *v.*, uniformize
униформизироваться, *v.*, be uniformized
униформизирующий, *adj.*, uniformizing
униформный, *adj.*, uniform
уничтожаемый, *adj.*, annihilable, effaceable
уничтожать, *v.*, annihilate, destroy, obliterate, annul, suppress
уничтожение, *n.*, destruction, annihilation, suppression
упадок, *m.*, decline, decay
упаковка, *f.*, packing, wrapping
упаковочный, *adj.*, packing, wrapping; **упаковочный коэффициент,** packing coefficient, packing factor
упирать, *v.*, rest, set, lean on, base
уплачиваться (уплатиться), *v.*, be paid
уплотнение, *n.*, condensation, contraction; **скачок уплотнения,** shock wave
уплощение, *n.*, flattening
упоминаемый, *adj.*, mentioned
упоминание, *n.*, mention, reminder, mentioning
упоминать (упомянуть), *v.*, mention, refer (to)
упомянутый, *adj.*, mentioned
упорядочение, *n.*, ordering; **частичное упорядочение,** partial ordering; **полное упорядочение,** complete ordering, well-ordering
упорядоченность, *f.*, ranking, rank, ordering; **простая упорядоченность,** simple ordering; **коэффициент корреляции упорядоченности,** rank correlation coefficient; **ограниченный по упорядоченности,** *adj.*, order-bounded
упорядоченный, *adj.*, ordered, simply ordered; **частично упорядоченный,** partially ordered; **неполно упорядоченный,** partially ordered
упорядочивание, *n.*, ranking, ordering, regulation
упорядочивать, *v.*, regulate, put in order
упорядочивающий, *adj.*, regulating, ordering
употребительный, *adj.*, common, commonly used, customary
употребление, *n.*, use, usage, application; **выходить из употребления,** *v.*, go out of use; **вышедший из употребления,** *adj.*, out of use, obsolete
употреблять (употребить), *v.*, use, take, apply

управление, *n.*, control, direction, management, control circuit; **планирование управления,** management planning
управляемость, *f.*, controllability, control
управляемый, *adj.*, controlled, guided, directed
управлять, *v.*, manage, control, handle, run, operate, govern
управляющий, *adj.*, control, pilot, controlling, guided, directing
упражнение, *n.*, exercise
упрочение, *n.*, strengthening, hardening
упрощать (упростить), *v.*, simplify
упрощаться (упроститься), *v.*, be simplified
упрощающий, *adj.*, simplifying
упрощение, *n.*, simplification
упрощенный, *adj.*, simplified
упрощенство, *n.*, oversimplification
упругий, *adj.*, elastic, resilient
упруго, *adv.*, elastically
упруго-вязкий, *adj.*, viscoelastic
упругопластический, *adj.*, elastico-plastic
упруго-связанный, *adj.*, elastically attached
упругость, *f.*, elasticity, resiliency
упускать (упустить), *v.*, let go, neglect, miss, overlook
упущение, *n.*, neglect, omission
уравнение, *n.*, equation; **уравнение в частных производных,** partial differential equation; **разностное уравнение,** difference equation; **уравнение деления окружности,** cyclotomic equation; **уравнение в полных дифференциалах,** exact differential equation; **уравнение хода луча,** ray-tracing equation; **уравнение правдоподобия,** likelihood equation
уравнивать (уравнять), *v.*, equate, equalize, smooth, level
уравнительный, *adj.*, equalizing, equating, leveling
уравновешенный, *adj.*, balanced, steady, in equilibrium; **уравновешенная выборка,** balanced sample; **уравновешенный некомплектный блок,** balanced incomplete block
уравновешивать, *v.*, put in equilibrium, balance, equalize, neutralize
уравнять (cf. **уравнивать**), *v.*, equate
урезывание, *n.*, curtailment, reduction
урезывать (урезать), *v.*, reduce, curtail
урна, *f.*, urn
урновый, *adj.*, pertaining to urn
уровень, *m.*, level, standard; **уровень значимости,** significance level; **уровень энергии,** energy level; **линия уровня,** level curve, level line; **поверхность уровня,** level surface, equipotential surface
урожай, *m.*, yield, harvest
урысоновский, *adj.*, Urysohn
усваивание, *n.*, mastery, understanding
усваивать (усвоить), *v.*, assimilate, master, become familiar (with)
усваиваться, *v.*, be understood
усвоение, *n.*, understanding, mastery
усечение, *n.*, truncation
усеченный, *adj.*, truncated, cut off; **усеченное распределение,** truncated distribution; **усеченные данные,** censored data; **усеченная выборка,** truncated sample; **усеченный конус,** frustrum of a cone
усиление, *n.*, amplification, strengthening, intensification, extension, sharpening
усиленный, *adj.*, reinforced, fortified, amplified, strengthened, sharpened, strong; **усиленный закон больших чисел,** strong law of large numbers
усиливать, *v.*, reinforce, intensify, amplify, sharpen, strengthen
усиливающий, *adj.*, reinforcing, amplifying
усилие, *f.*, stress, intensification, effort
усилитель, *m.*, amplifier, intensifier; **усилитель мощности,** power amplifier

усилить (cf. **усиливать**), *v.*, amplify, intensify, sharpen, strengthen

ускользание, *n.*, escape, eluding; **игра на ускользание,** eluding game

ускользать (ускользнуть), *v.*, slip away, escape, elude

ускорение, *n.*, acceleration, speeding up; **ускорение силы тяжести,** acceleration of gravity

ускоритель, *m.*, accelerator, booster

ускоряемый, *adj.*, accelerated

ускорять (ускорить), *v.*, accelerate

ускоряющий, *adj.*, accelerating

уславливаться (условиться), *v.*, stipulate, agree (on a condition), arrange, settle

условие, *n.*, condition, term; **при условии,** provided that; **условие минимальности,** minimum condition, descending chain condition; **условие максимальности,** maximum condition, ascending chain condition

условимся (cf. **уславливаться**), let us agree (to)

условиться (cf. **уславливаться**), *v.*, agree (on a condition), stipulate

условленный, *adj.*, agreed, fixed, arranged, stipulated

условно, *adv.*, on condition (that), under condition, conditionally, conventionally, by convention

условность, *f.*, conditionality, convention

условный, *adj.*, conditional, conventional, prearranged; **условный союз,** conditional conjunction; **условная дисперсия,** conditional variance; **условное распределение,** conditional distribution; **условное среднее (значение),** conditional mean (value); **условная вероятность,** conditional probability; **условное математическое ожидание,** conditional expectation

усложнение, *n.*, complication

усложнять (усложнить), *v.*, complicate

услуга, *f.*, service

усматривать (усмотреть), *v.*, perceive, discern, discover, attend

усмотрение, *n.*, discretion, judgement; **на усмотрение,** to (one's) judgement; **по усмотрению,** according to (one's) judgement

усовершенствование, *n.*, improvement, refinement, advance

усовершенствованный, *adj.*, improved, perfected, adjusted

усовершенствовать, *v.*, improve, develop, perfect, refine

усомниться, *v.*, doubt

успевать (успеть), *v.*, manage, be able, make progress (in)

успех, *m.*, success, progress; **с успехом,** successfully; **с тем же успехом,** equally well, just as well

успешно, *adv.*, successfully

успешный, *adj.*, successful

усреднение, *n.*, average, averaging, neutralization; **усреднение по группе,** group averaging; **усреднение игры,** mixed extension, mixed extension of a game

усредненный, *adj.*, neutralized, averaged

усреднять, *v.*, neutralize, average

усредняющий, *adj.*, averaging

усталость, *f.*, fatigue, tiredness

устанавливаемый, *adj.*, established

устанавливать (установить), *v.*, establish, set, ascertain, determine, install

установив, *adv. part.*, having established, having determined; **установив это,** having established this

установившийся, *adj.*, established, stationary, terminal, steady-state

установить, cf. **устанавливать**

установка, *f.*, mounting, installation, arrangement, placing, aim, purpose

установление, *n.*, establishment, ascertainment

установленный, *adj.*, established, fixed

установочный, *adj.*, adjusting

устаревший, *adj.*, obsolete

устарелый, *adj.*, obsolete

устный, *adj.*, oral, verbal

устойчивость, *f.*, stability, steadiness, rigidity, resistance; **статистическая устойчивость,** statistical regularity
устойчивый, *adj.*, stable, steady; **устойчивое равновесие,** stable equilibrium
устраивать (устроить), *v.*, make, perform, arrange, carry out, organize, place
устраивая, *adv. part.*, carrying out, performing, arranging
устранение, *n.*, elimination, removal
устраненный, *adj.*, reduced, eliminated
устранимость, *f.*, elimination, eliminability, removability
устранимый, *adj.*, removable, eliminable; **устранимая особенность,** removable singularity
устранить, cf. **устранять**
устранять (устранить), *v.*, remove, eliminate, reduce
устремлять (устремить), *v.*, direct, turn (to)
устремляться (устремиться), *v.*, turn (to), be directed (to), converge to, tend to
устроить, cf. **устраивать**
устройство, *n.*, apparatus, arrangement, system, organization; **цифровое счетное устройство,** digital computer
уступать (уступить), *v.*, yield, concede
устье, *n.*, mouth
утвердившийся, *adj.*, firmly established, consolidated, accepted
утвердительно, *adv.*, affirmatively, positively
утвердительный, *adj.*, affirmative, positive
утверждать (утвердить), *v.*, state, assert, affirm, predicate
утверждаться, *v.*, be established, be firmly established
утверждающий, *adj.*, asserting, asserting that
утверждение, *n.*, statement, assertion, confirmation, affirmation
утвержденный, *adj.*, affirmed, asserted, approved
утомительный, *adj.*, tedious, tiresome
утомление, *n.*, fatigue
утончать, *v.*, make thinner, refine
утончение, *n.*, refinement, attenuation, thinning
утонченность, *f.*, refinement
уточнение, *n.*, more precise definition, sharpening, refinement, correction, revision
уточненный, *adj.*, refined, more precise, proximate, corrected
уточнять (уточнить), *v.*, make more precise, define more exactly, correct, revise
утраивать (утроить), *v.*, triple
утрата, *f.*, loss
утрачивание, *n.*, loss, losing
утрачивать (утратить), *v.*, lose
утроение, *n.*, tripling
утроенный, *adj.*, triple
утроить (cf. **утраивать**), *v.*, triple
уход, *m.*, leaving, departure, care, maintenance, drift; **уход частоты,** frequency drift
уходить, *v.*, leave, depart
уходящий, *adj.*, leaving, departing, going off, diverging
ухудшать (ухудшить), *v.*, make worse, worsen, deteriorate
ухудшение, *n.*, deterioration
участвовать, *v.*, participate, involve
участие, *n.*, participation, collaboration
участник, *m.*, contestant, player, participant, partner, competitor
участок, *m.*, part, section, region, locality, cell
учащать, *v.*, make more frequent, increase the frequency
учащийся, *m.*, student, pupil
учебник, *m.*, text-book, manual
учебный, *adj.*, educational, academic
учение, *n.*, studies, learning, doctrine, teaching
ученик, *m.*, pupil, disciple, learner
учено, *adv.*, scientifically, learnedly

ученость, *f.*, learning, erudition
ученый, *adj.*, learned, erudite
учесть (cf. **учитывать**), *v.*, consider
учет, *m.*, calculation, registration, accounting, discount; **норма учета,** discount rate; **с учетом,** with regard (for, to)
учетверенный, *adj.*, quadruplicate, quadruple
учетверять, *v.*, quadruple
учетный, *adj.*, registration, accounting, discount; **учетная цена,** *f.*, accounting price; **учетный процент,** *m.*, discount; **учетные издержки,** *pl.*, accountings
училище, *n.*, school, college
учитель, *m.*, teacher
учитывая, *adv. part.*, taking into account, granting; **учитывая это,** granting this, taking this into account
учитывать (учесть), *v.*, take into account, consider
учитывающий, *adj.*, taking into account, considering
учить, *v.*, teach, instruct
учиться, *v.*, learn, study
учреждать (учредить), *v.*, set up, found, establish
учреждение, *n.*, founding, establishment, institution
учтенный, *adj.*, accounted for, taken into account
ущерб, *m.*, damage, injury, detriment, harm; **без ущерба для общности,** without loss of generality
уязвимый, *adj.*, vulnerable
уяснение, *n.*, elucidation, clarification
уяснять (уяснить), *v.*, understand, clarify, explain

Ф

фаза, *f.*, phase, period; **угол сдвига фаз,** phase angle; **движение по фазе,** phase motion; **фаза оживления,** expansion phase; **фаза сжатия,** contraction phase; **разность фаз,** phase difference; **изменение фазы,** phase change
фазис, *m.*, phase
фазовый, *adj.*, phase; **фазовое колебание,** phase oscillation; **фазовое движение,** phase motion; **фазовое пространство,** phase space; **фазовый сдвиг,** phase change, phase shift
фазный, *adj.*, phase
факт, *m.*, fact, case
фактически, *adv.*, actually, practically, in fact
фактический, *adj.*, factual, actual, real, virtual
фактор, *m.*, factor, coefficient, cause; **факторы**, *pl.*, factors, elements
фактор-алгебра, *f.*, quotient algebra
факторгруппа, *f.*, factor group, quotient group
фактор-замкнутый, *adj.*, factor-closed, quotient-closed
факториал, *m.*, factorial
факториальный, *adj.*, factorial
факторизация, *f.*, factorization
факторизуемый, *adj.*, factored, factorable
фактор-кольцо, *n.*, quotient-ring
фактор-мера, *f.*, quotient measure
фактор-многообразие, *n.*, quotient, quotient manifold
фактормножество, *n.*, factor set, quotient set, quotient
фактор-модуль, *m.*, quotient module, difference module
факторный, *adj.*, factor, factorial
фактор-пространство, *n.*, factor space, coset space, quotient space

фактор-символ, *m.*, quotient symbol
факультет, *m.*, faculty, department
фальшивый, *adj.*, false
фантазия, *f.*, fantasy, fancy, imagination
фантастический, *adj.*, fantastic, imaginary
фарад, *m.*, farad
феллеровский, *adj.*, Feller
феномен, *m.*, phenomenon
феноменологический, *adj.*, phenomenological
фермиевский, *adj.*, Fermi
ферромагнетизм, *m.*, ferromagnetism
ферромагнитный, *adj.*, ferromagnetic
ферроэлектрический, *adj.*, ferroelectric
фиг., *abbrev.* (**фигура,** *f.*), figure, illustration
фигура, *f.*, figure, configuration
фигурировать, *v.*, appear, play part of, figure
фигурирующий, *adj.*, appearing
фигурный, *adj.*, figured, curly; **фигурные скобки,** braces, curly brackets (*sometimes* parentheses [cf. **скобка**])
физик, *m.*, physicist
физика, *f.*, physics
физиологический, *adj.*, physiological
физиология, *f.*, physiology
физический, *adj.*, physical
фиксаж, *m.*, fixative, fixing (agent)
фиксатор, *m.*, index, locator, latch, holder
фиксация, *f.*, fixing, setting
фиксирование, *n.*, fixing, settling
фиксированный, *adj.*, fixed, constant, settled, stipulated; **фиксированный объем выборки,** fixed sample-size
фиксировать, *v.*, fix, settle, state, hold fixed
фиксирующий, *adj.*, fixing, holding fixed; **фиксирующая схема,** hold circuit (*comp.*)
фиксируя, *adv. part.*, fixing, holding fixed, if we hold fixed
фиктивный, *adj.*, imaginary, fictitious
филиал, *m.*, branch (of an organization), subsidiary
философия, *f.*, philosophy
философский, *adj.*, philosophical
фильм, *m.*, film
фильтр, *m.*, filter, strainer
фильтрационный, *adj.*, filtrational, filtration
фильтрация, *f.*, filtration; **кольцо с фильтрацией,** filtered ring
фильтровать, *v.*, filter, filtrate
фильтростроение, *n.*, filter-composition, filter
фильтрующий, *adj.*, filtering
финальный, *adj.*, final
финансовый, *adj.*, finance, financial, fiscal
финансы, *pl.*, finances
финитарный, *adj.*, finite, finitary
финитный, *adj.*, finite, finitary
финслеровый, *adj.*, Finsler
фирма, *f.*, firm; **под фирмой,** under the guise of; **мощность фирмы,** firm capacity
фирменный, *adj.*, firm, company; **фирменное планирование,** company planning
флаттер, *m.*, flutter
флуктуационный, *adj.*, fluctuation, fluctuating
флуктуация, *f.*, fluctuation
флуктуирующий, *adj.*, fluctuating; **поле с флуктуирующей плотностью,** fluctuating density field
флуоресценция, *f.*, fluorescence
флуоресцирующий, *adj.*, fluorescent
флюктуация (= **флуктуация**), *f.*, fluctuation
флюоресценция (= **флуоресценция**), *f.*, fluorescence
фокальный, *adj.*, focal
фокус, *m.*, focus; **не в фокусе,** out of focus
фокусировать, *v.*, focus
фокусировка, *f.*, focussing
фокусирующий, *adj.*, focussing
фокусный, *adj.*, focal, focus
фольга, *f.*, foil
фон, *f.*, background; **фон шума,** background noise

фонд, *m.*, fund, stock; **фонды,** *pl.*, funds, capital stock
фонема, *f.*, phoneme
фонематический, *adj.*, phonemic
фонетика, *f.*, phonetics
фонетический, *adj.*, phonetic
фоновый, *adj.*, background; **фоновое рассеяние,** background scattering, nonresonance scattering
фонон, *m.*, phonon (a quantized lattice vibration)
форма, *f.*, form, shape, quantic
формализация, *f.*, formalization
формализировать, *v.*, shape, give form (to), formalize
формализм, *m.*, formalism
формализованный, *adj.*, formalized
формализуемость, *f.*, formalizability
формализуемый, *adj.*, formalizable
формалистический, *adj.*, formalistic
формалистичность, *f.*, formalism
формально, *adv.*, formally
формальность, *f.*, formality
формальный, *adj.*, formal
формула, *f.*, formula
формулирование, *n.*, formulation
формулировать, *v.*, formulate
формулировка, *f.*, formula, statement, formulation
форсированный, *adj.*, forced
фотограмметрический, *adj.*, photogrammetric
фотограмметрия, *f.*, photogrammetry, photographic survey
фотографический, *adj.*, photographic
фотоионизация, *f.*, photo-ionization
фотомагнитный, *adj.*, photomagnetic
фотон, *m.*, photon
фотонный, *adj.*, photon
фотопоглощение, *n.*, photoabsorption
фоторасщепление, *n.*, photodisintegration
фотосфера, *f.*, photosphere
фотоумножитель, *m.*, photomultiplier
фотоэлектрический, *adj.*, photoelectric
фотоэлемент, *m.*, photo-cell
фотоэффект, *m.*, photoeffect, photoelectric emission
фрагмент, *m.*, fragment
фрагментарный, *adj.*, fragmentary
фраза, *f.*, phrase, sentence
фракционный, *adj.*, fractional, differential; **фракционная перегонка,** fractional distillation; **уравнение Рэлея для фракционной перегонки,** Rayleigh's equation for differential distillation
фредгольмость, *f.*, Fredholm property
фрезеровать, *v.*, mill, cut, notch
фрикционный, *adj.*, frictional, friction
фробениусовый, *adj.*, Frobenius
фронт, *m.*, front, battle-front; **передний фронт,** leading edge
фронтальный, *adj.*, frontal, front
фуксовый, *adj.*, Fuchsian
фуксоидный, *adj.*, Fuchsoid
фундаментальный, *adj.*, fundamental, basic, solid, substantial
фундированный, *adj.*, grounded (on), based (on)
функтор, *m.*, functor
функционал, *m.*, functional
функционально, *adv.*, functionally; **функционально полный,** *adj.*, functionally complete
функционально-инвариантный, *adj.*, functionally invariant, invariant
функциональнополный, *adj.*, (functionally) complete
функционально-теоретический, *adj.*, function-theoretic
функциональный, *adj.*, functional; **функциональный определитель,** Jacobian, functional determinant
функционировать, *v.*, function, operate
функция, *f.*, function; **функция выгоды,** utility function; **функция выигрыша,** payoff, payoff function; **функция истинности,** truth function; **нуль-функция,** null function, zero function; **функция оборота,** return function; **обратная функция,** inverse function; **функция окончательных решений,** terminal-decision function;

функция-ответ, response-function; **неполная бэта (гамма) функция,** incomplete beta (gamma) function; **функция плотности,** density function, frequency function; **функция потерь,** loss function; **функция распределения,** distribution function, partition function; **функция риска,** risk function; **функция решения,** decision function; **решающая функция,** decision function; **функция скачков,** step function, jump function; **функция следования (за),** successor function (to); **функция стоимости,** cost function; **функция сумм,** totient function; **функция тока,** stream function

фут, *m.*, foot

Х

хамелевский, *adj.*, Hamel; **хамелевское тело,** Hamel body; **хамелевская база (база Хамеля),** Hamel basis

хаотический, *adj.*, random, chaotic

хаотичный, *adj.*, random, chaotic

хаотичность, *f.*, randomness, state of chaos

характер, *m.*, character, nature; **характер-функция,** characteristic function

характеризация, *f.*, characterization

характеризовать, *v.*, characterize, specify, define, describe

характеризоваться, *v.*, be characterized

характеризующий, *adj.*, characterizing

характеристика, *f.*, characteristic, property, index, character, measure, degree; **характеристика эксцесса,** measure of excess

характеристический, *adj.*, characteristic

характерно, *adv.*, characteristically; *pred.*, characteristic; **характерно, что,** it is characteristic that

характерный, *adj.*, typical, characteristic, distinctive

хаусдорфовость, *f.*, property of being a Hausdorff space

хаусдорфовый, *adj.*, Hausdorff

хватать (хватить), *v.*, suffice, be sufficient

хвост, *m.*, tail, remainder; **хвост распределения,** tail of the distribution, remainder of the distribution

хвостовой, *adj.*, pertaining to tail, tail, tailend, rear, remainder; **хвостовое отверстие,** tail pipe

хи-квадрат, *m.*, chi-square

химический, *adj.*, chemical

химия, *f.*, chemistry

хитрость, *f.*, trick

ход, *m.*, motion, run, speed, movement, course, entry, operation, progress, move; **случайный ход,** chance move; **личный ход,** personal move; **уравнение хода луча,** ray-tracing equation

ходить (cf. **идти, пойти**), *v.*, go, go (to), run, pass, move

хозяйственный, *adj.*, economic, business

хозяйство, *n.*, economy; **плановое хозяйство,** planned economy

холодный, *adj.*, cold, cool

холостой, *adj.*, dummy, blank, empty

хопфовский, *adj.*, Hopf, pertaining to Hopf

хорда, *f.*, chord; **хорда дуги,** span

хордовый, *adj.*, chord

хороший, *adj.*, good

хорошо, *adv.*, well

хотеть, *v.*, wish, want

хоть, *conj.*, although, at least, even, just, for example, if only; **хоть бы,** if only, I wish; **хоть и,** although

хотя, *conj.*, although; **хотя бы,** even if, if only; **хотя и,** although; **хотя бы и так,** even if it were so

хранение, *n.*, storage, conservation
хранить, *v.*, keep, store, preserve
хребет, *m.*, crest, ridge, spine
хроматический, *adj.*, chromatic
хронограф, *m.*, chronograph
хронологизирующий, *adj.*, timing, dating
хронологический, *adj.*, chronological
хронометр, *m.*, chronometer, timepiece
хронометраж, *m.*, time-keeping, time-study
хронометрия, *f.*, chronometry
хронометрирование, *n.*, exact timing
хронометрический, *adj.*, chronometric
худо, *adv.*, badly, poorly
художественный, *adj.*, artistic
худой, *adj.*, bad, lean, thin
худший, *adj.*, the worst, worse, inferior
хуже, *adv.*, worse

Ц

цапфа, *f.*, pin, trunnion, journal
цвет, *m.*, color, tint; **основные цвета,** primary colors
цветной, *adj.*, colored, chromatic, color
цевиан, *m.*, cevian; **цевиан треугольника,** cevian of a triangle
целевой, *adj.*, specific, purposeful; **целевая установка,** aim, purpose
целенаправленный, *adj.*, purposeful, single-minded
целесообразность, *f.*, appropriateness, advisability, expediency
целесообразный, *adj.*, appropriate, advisable, expedient
целеустремленный, *adj.*, goal-seeking, purposeful
целиком, *adv.*, entirely, wholly, as a whole; **целиком и полностью,** *adv.*, completely, entirely
целое, *n.*, integer; **единое целое,** unit
целозамкнутость, *f.*, complete closure
целозамкнутый, *adj.*, completely closed, integrally closed
целозамыкание, *n.*, complete closure
целостность, *f.*, completeness, entirety, integrity; **область целостности,** integral domain
целостный, *adj.*, integral
целость, *f.*, wholeness, entirety, safety
целочисленный, *adj.*, integral; **статистика целочисленных величин,** enumerative statistics
целый, *adj.*, whole, entire, integral; **в целом,** in the large, on the whole; **целое число,** integer; **целая функция,** entire function, integral function
цель, *f.*, aim, purpose, target; **с этой целью,** to this end; **в целях,** with a view (to)
цельный, *adj.*, whole, unified, total, entire
цена, *f.*, value, price; **анализ цен,** cost analysis; **вектор цен,** price vector; **бюджет рациональных цен,** ration-point budget; **нижняя чистая цена,** lower pure value; **верхняя чистая цена,** upper pure value
цензурирование, *n.*, censoring
цензурированный, *adj.*, censored; **цензурированная выборка,** censored sample
ценить, *v.*, value, estimate
ценность, *f.*, value
ценный, *adj.*, valuable
центр, *m.*, center, midpoint; **центр тяжести,** centroid, center of gravity
централизатор, *m.*, centralizer
централизация, *f.*, centralization
центрально, *adv.*, centrally

центрально-разностный, *adj.*, central-difference
центрально-симметрический, *adj.*, centrally symmetric
центральный, *adj.*, central; **центральная предельная теорема,** central limit theorem
центрирование, *n.*, centering
центрированность, *f.*, property of being centered, centrality
центрированный, *adj.*, centered, central, centralized
центрировать, *v.*, center, centralize
центрирующий, *adj.*, centering
центрифуга, *f.*, centrifuge
центрифугирование, *n.*, centrifuging
центроаффинность, *f.*, centroaffineness
центроаффинный, *adj.*, centroaffine
центробежный, *adj.*, centrifugal
центроид, *m.*, centroid
центростремительный, *adj.*, centripetal
цепкий, *adj.*, tenacious, cohesive, prehensile
цепной, *adj.*, chain; **цепная дробь,** continued fraction; **цепная линия,** catenary; **цепное правило,** chain rule; **цепная эквивалентность,** chainwise equivalence
цепочечный, *adj.*, chain; **цепочечный индекс,** chain index
цепочка, *f.*, chain, sequence, circuit; **условие обрыва возрастающей (убывающей) цепочки,** ascending (descending) chain condition
цепь, *f.*, chain, circuit; **цепь маркова,** Markov chain; **условие обрыва цепей,** chain condition; **∇-цепь,** cochain; **цепь сизигий,** chain syzygies
цефеида, *f.*, variable star, cepheid
цикл, *m.*, cycle, series, loop; **малый цикл,** minor cycle, word time; **цикл итерации,** iterative loop
циклический, *adj.*, cyclic, cyclotomic
цикличность, *f.*, cyclicity
циклоид, *m.* (**циклоида** *f.*), cycloid
циклоидальный, *adj.*, cycloidal, cycloid
циклоидный, *adj.*, cycloidal, cycloid
циклонический, *adj.*, cyclonic
циклотрон, *m.*, cyclotron
циклотронный, *adj.*, cyclotron
цилиндр, *m.*, cylinder, drum
цилиндрический, *adj.*, cylindrical, cylinder, tube, tubular; **цилиндрическая область,** tube domain
цилиндроид, *m.*, cylindroid
циркулировать, *v.*, circulate
циркулирующий, *adj.*, circulating
циркуль, *m.*, compasses, dividers
циркулянтный, *adj.*, circulant; **циркулянтная матрица,** circulant matrix
циркуляр, *m.*, circular
циркулярный, *adj.*, circular, circulation, rotational
циркуляция, *f.*, circulation, gyration
циссоида, *f.*, cissoid
циссоидальный, *adj.*, cissoidal
цитата, *f.*, quotation, citation
цитирование, *n.*, citing, quoting
цитированный, *adj.*, cited
цитировать, *v.*, cite, quote
цифра, *f.*, figure, number, digit, cipher
цифровой, *adj.*, digital, numerical
цоколь, *m.*, base, basis, foundation, socle

Ч

ч., *abbrev.*, **час, часть, что; ч. и т. д. (что и требовалось доказать),** Q.E.D.

час, *m.*, hour

часовой, *adj.*, clock, watch, pertaining to clock; **часовая стрелка,** hourhand, hand of a clock; **по часовой стрелке,** clockwise; **против часовой стрелки,** counterclockwise

частица, *f.*, particle, part, fraction, grain

частично, *adv.*, partially, partly

частично-рекурсивный, *adj.*, partially recursive, partial recursive

частичный, *adj.*, partial

частно, *adv.*, partially

частно-дифференциальный, *adj.*, partial differential; **частно-дифференциальное поле,** partial differential field

частное, *n.*, quotient

частность, *f.*, detail, particularity; **в частности,** in particular, specifically

частный, *adj.*, partial, particular, special, private; **частная производная,** partial derivative; **уравнение в частных производных,** partial differential equation; **частное решение,** particular solution; **частный случай,** special case; **частное значение,** particular value; **уастное распределение,** marginal distribution

часто, *adv.*, often, frequently

частота, *f.*, frequency, frequency ratio

частотноизбирательный, *adj.*, frequency selective; **частотноизбирательная схема,** frequency selective network

частотный, *adj.*, frequency; **частотная интерпретация,** frequency interpretation; **частотная область,** frequency domain

частотограмма, *f.*, periodogram

частый, *adj.*, frequent, rapid

часть, *f.*, part, side (of an equation or inequality), share, portion; **правая часть,** right (hand) side; **левая часть,** left (hand) side; **по частям,** partially, by parts, in parts; **интегрировать по частям,** *v.*, integrate by parts; **большей частью,** usually, for the most part, most of the time; **по большей части,** mostly, for the most part

частью, *adv.*, partly; cf. also **часть**

частям, cf. **часть; интегрировать по частям,** integrate by parts

часы, *pl.*, clock, watch

чаша, *f.*, cup, bowl

чаще, *adv.*, more often; *comp.*, *sup.* of **часто, частый,** more frequently, more rapidly

чебышевский, *adj.*, Tchebyshev, Chebyshev

чего (*gen.* of **что**), (of) which, (of) what; **после чего,** after which

чезаровский, *adj.*, Cesàro

чей, *pron.*, whose, of which

чеканить, *v.*, stamp, hammer, mint

человеческий, *adj.*, human

чем, *conj.*, than, rather than, instead; *pron.*, cf. **что; чем . . ., тем,** the . . . the

чередование, *n.*, alternation, interchange, rotation

чередовать, *v.*, alternate

чередоваться, *v.*, alternate

чередующийся, *adj.*, alternating

через, *prep.*, across, over, through, by, by means of

черепаха, *f.*, scoop, shell, tortoise

чересчур, *adv.*, too, excessively

чернота, *f.*, blackness, dark

черный, *adj.*, black; **черное тело,** black body; **излучение черного тела,** blackbody radiation

черт., *abbrev.* **(чертеж),** figure, fig.

черта, *f.*, line, stroke, hyphen, streak, feature; **в основных чертах,** mainly, in the main; **в общих чертах,** roughly, generally, in a general way; **проводить черту (между),** *v.*, distinguish (between); **операция с чертой,** stroke-operation

чертеж, *m.*, drawing, figure, diagram, draft

чертежный, *adj.*, drawing; **чертежная доска,** drawing board

чертить, *v.*, draw, sketch, trace, describe

черточка, *f.*, little line, dash, hyphen

черчение, *n.*, drawing, designing

чет, *m.*, even number, even; **чет и нечет,** odd and even

четверка, *f.*, four (set of four), quadruple

четверной, *adj.*, fourfold; **четверная группа Клейна,** Klein's four-group

четвертичный, *adj.*, quaternary

четвертной, *adj.*, one fourth, quarter

четвертый, *adj.*, fourth; **четвертая группа,** four-group

четверть, *f.*, one fourth, a quarter, phase (of the moon); **четверть круга,** quadrant

четверть-конец, *m.*, quarter-end

четкий, *adj.*, clear, precise, accurate

четкость, *f.*, clearness, accuracy

четный, *adj.*, even

четность, *f.*, parity, prop. of being even, evenness; **внутренняя четность,** intrinsic parity

четыре, *num.*, four

четырежды, *adv.*, four times, fourfold

четырех-, *prefix*, four-, tetra-, quadri-

четырехадресный, *adj.*, four-address

четырехгранник, *m.*, tetrahedron

четырехгранный, *adj.*, tetrahedral

четырехлепестковый, *adj.*, four-leaved, four-leafed; **четырехлепестковая роза,** four-leaved rose

четырехлистный, *adj.*, four-sheeted

четырехмерный, *adj.*, four-dimensional

четырехполюсник, *m.*, quadripole, four-terminal network, four-pole network

четырехрядный, *adj.*, four-row

четырехсторонник, *m.*, quadrilateral

четырехсторонний, *adj.*, quadrilateral, four-sided

четырехугольник, *m.*, quadrangle

четырехугольный, *adj.*, quadrangular

чечевица, *f.*, lens, lentil

числа-близнецы, *pl.*, number-twins, prime twins

численно, *adv.*, numerically

численность, *f.*, number, quantity, strength, size, count

численный, *adj.*, numerical

числитель, *m.*, numerator

числительное, *n.*, numeral, number; **количественное числительное,** cardinal (number); **порядковое числительное,** ordinal (number)

числить, *v.*, count

число, *n.*, number, quantity, integer, date; **натуральное число,** positive integer, natural number; **без числа,** countless, innumerable; **число Бетти,** Betti number; **число измерения,** dimension; **число степеней свободы,** number of degrees of freedom; **в том числе,** among them, including; **группа чисел,** word, message; **часть числа,** syllable; **десятичное число,** decimal; **число разрядов,** register length

числовой, *adj.*, numerical, number; **числовая прямая,** number line, number axis, real axis; **числовая шина,** number bus, number transfer bus

чисто, *adv.*, purely, clearly; **чисто мнимый,** *adj.*, pure imaginary; **чисто коренная квадратичная форма,** primitive quadratic form, properly primitive quadratic form

чистый, *adj.*, pure, proper, clear, clean; **нижняя чистая цена,** lower pure value; **верхняя чистая цена,** upper pure value; **чистая стратегия,** pure strategy; **чистый вес,** net weight

читатель, *m.*, reader

читать (прочесть), *v.*, read, scan

член, *m.*, member, term; **член пропорции,** proportional, term of a proportion; **средний член,** mean (proportional)
членить, *v.*, divide into parts, articulate
членство, *n.*, membership
чрезвычайно, *adv.*, especially, exceedingly, very, extraordinarily
чрезвычайный, *adj.*, extraordinary, extreme
чрезмерный, *adj.*, extreme, excessive
чтение, *n.*, reading, scanning; **частота чтения,** scan frequency
что, *pron.*, what, that, who, anything; *conj.*, that, how, why; **так, что,** so that; **для того, что,** in order that, in order to, so that; **что не** lest, in order not (to); **вот что,** the following; **с чего бы,** why; **что-то,** something; **что-нибудь,** something; **что . . . что,** whether . . . or; **что касается,** concerning, as to; **что и требовалось доказать (ч. и т. д.),** Q.E.D.
чтобы, *conj.*, that, in order that, in order to; **вместо того чтобы,** instead of
чувствительность, *f.*, sensitivity, perceptibility, quick response
чувствительный, *adj.*, sensitive, quick-response
чувство, *n.*, sense, feeling
чувствовать, *v.*, feel, experience
чуждый, *adj.*, alien, strange, extraneous
чужой, *adj.*, strange, another's
чуть, *adv.*, scarcely, hardly; **чуть не,** almost, nearly; **чуть только,** as soon as; **чуть-чуть,** *adv.*, almost, hardly
чью (from **чей**), whose, of which
чья (from **чей**), whose, of which

Ш

шабер, *m.*, scraper
шаблон, *m.*, mould, pattern, model
шаг, *m.*, pitch, step, pace; **шаг винта,** pitch of a screw; **шаг за шагом,** step by step
шаговый, *adj.*, step, step-type
шайба, *f.*, washer
шанс, *m.*, chance
шапка, *f.*, cap
шапочка, *f.*, cap, cap of a surface
шар, *m.*, sphere, ball; **земной шар,** terrestial globe; **воздушный шар,** balloon
шарик, *m.*, small ball, bead, globule
шарикоподшипник, *m.*, ball-bearing
шарнир, *m.*, hinge, joint
шаровидность, *f.*, sphericity
шаровидный, *adj.*, spherical
шаровой, *adj.*, spherical, globular; **шаровая функция,** solid spherical harmonic; **шаровая точка,** umbilical point
шарообразный, *adj.*, sphere-shaped, spherical
шасси, *n.*, chassis, under-carriage
шатун, *m.*, connecting-rod
шейка, *f.*, neck, collar, pin, pivot
шенноновский, *adj.*, Shannon, pertaining to Shannon
шероховатость, *f.*, roughness, coarseness
шероховатый, *adj.*, rough, coarse
шерсть, *f.*, wool
шестеренка, *f.*, gear, pinion, drive gear
шестерка, *f.*, the six
шестерня, *f.*, gear, pinion; **ведущая шестерня,** drive gear; **коническая шестерня,** bevel gear
шестеро, *n.*, six, group of six
шести, *prefix*, six-, hex-
шестигранник, *m.*, hexahedron
шестигранный, *adj.*, hexahedral
шестидесятиричность, *f.*, counting by 60's

шестидесятиричный, *adj.*, sexagesimal, to the base 60
шестикратный, *adj.*, sextuple
шестимерный, *adj.*, six-dimensional
шестисторонний, *adj.*, having six sides, six-sided
шестиугольник, *m.*, hexagon
шестиугольный, *adj.*, hexagonal
шестнадцатиричный, *adj.*, sextodecimo, sexadecimal (*comp.*)
шестой, *adj.*, sixth
шесть, *num.*, six
шина, *f.*, bus (*comp.*); **шина передачи чисел,** number transfer bus
шире (cf. **широкий**), *adj.*, wider, broader
ширина, *f.*, width, breadth, range; **ширина связи,** band width
широкий, *adj.*, wide, broad, extensive; **в широком смысле слова,** in the broad sense of the word
широко, *adv.*, widely, in a broad fashion
широкополосный, *adj.*, wide-band, broad-band; **широкополосный квадратичный усилитель,** wide-band square-law amplifier
широта, *f.*, width, breadth, latitude, range; **семи-интерквартильная широта,** semi-interquartile range; **широта распределения,** range of a distribution; **широта выборки,** range, range of the sample
ширь, *f.*, extent, expanse, open space; **во всю ширь,** to its full extent
шифр, *f.*, cipher, code
шкала, *f.*, scale, unit
шкальный, *adj.*, scale
шкаф, *m.*, cabinet, case
шкив, *m.*, pulley, sheave
шлифовка, *f.*, polishing, grinding
шнур, *m.*, cord, fuse
шов, *m.*, seam, joint, junction
шпунт, *m.*, groove, slot, channel
шпур, *m.*, spur, trace
шрейеровый, *adj.*, Schreier
шрифт, *m.*, print, type; **курсивный шрифт,** italics, italic type
штамп, *m.*, stamp, punch, die, plate
штамповка, *f.*, stamping, punching
штарковский, *adj.*, Stark; **штарковская энергия,** Stark energy; **штарковский эффект, эффект Штарка,** Stark effect
штат, *m.*, state, staff, establishment
штепсель, *m.*, plug, switch
штепсельный, *adj.*, plug, switch
штрих, *m.*, prime, accent, stroke
штриховать, *v.*, shade, hatch
штука, *f.*, piece, thing
штучный, *adj.*, piece; **штучная работа,** piece-work
штырь, *m.*, pin, dowel
штырька, *f.*, pin, nail, dowel
шум, *m.*, noise; **тепловой шум,** shot noise
шунт, *m.*, shunt, by-pass
шунтировать, *v.*, by-pass, shunt
шунтирующий, *adj.*, shunt; **шунтирующая емкость,** shunt capacitance

Щ

щель, *f.*, aperture, gap
щетка, *f.*, brush; **считывающая щетка,** reading brush
щеточный, *adj.*, brush
щит, *m.*, board, shield, guard; **центральный щит приборов,** central control board; **распределительный щит,** distributing board
щуп, *m.*, feeler, probe, test rod
щупать, *v.*, feel, touch, probe

Э

э. в., *abbrev.* **(электрон-вольт)**, *m.*, electron-volt
эвклидовый, *adj.*, euclidean
эвольвента, *f.*, evolvent, evolute
эвольвентный, *adj.*, evolvent, evolute
эволюта, *f.*, evolute
эволюционный, *adj.*, evolutionary
эволюция, *f.*, evolution
эвристически, *adv.*, heuristically
эвристический, *adj.*, heuristic
эвтектический, *adj.*, eutectic; **эвтектическая температура**, eutectic temperature
эйконал, *m.*, eikonal
эйлеровый, *adj.*, Euler, pertaining to Euler
эйнстейновский, *adj.*, Einstein, Einsteinian
эйнштейновый, *adj.*, Einstein, Einsteinian
экватор, *m.*, equator
экваториальный, *adj.*, equatorial
эквационально, *adv.*, equationally
эквациональный, *adj.*, equational
эквиангармонический, *adj.*, equianharmonic
эквиангармоничность, *f.*, equianharmonicity
эквиареальный, *adj.*, equiareal
эквиаффинный, *adj.*, equiaffine
эквивалент, *m.*, equivalent
эквивалентность, *f.*, equivalence; **отношение эквивалентности**, equivalence relation
эквивалентный, *adj.*, equivalent
эквивариантный, *adj.*, equivariant
эквидистанта, *f.*, equidistant curve
эквидистантность, *f.*, equidistance
эквидистантный, *adj.*, equidistant
эквипартиция, *f.*, equipartition
эквиполлентность, *f.*, equipollency
эквиполлентный, *adj.*, equipollent
эквипотенциальный, *adj.*, equipotential
эквипроективный, *adj.*, equiprojective
эквиустойчивость, *f.*, equistability
эквихордальный, *adj.*, equichordal
эквицентроаффинный, *adj.*, equicentroaffine
экзамен, *m.*, examination
экзаменационный, *adj.*, examination
экземпляр, *m.*, copy, specimen, sample
экзистенциализм, *m.*, existentialism
экзистенциальный, *adj.*, existential
экзоэнергетический, *adj.*, exoenergy
экзоэргический, *adj.*, exoergic
экипаж, *m.*, vehicle, crew
эклиптика, *f.*, ecliptic
эклиптический, *adj.*, ecliptic
экология, *f.*, ecology
эконометрика, *f.*, econometrics
эконометрический, *adj.*, econometric
экономика, *f.*, economics
экономить, *v.*, economize
экономический, *adj.*, economic
экономия, *f.*, economy
экран, *m.*, screen, shield, barrier
экранирование, *n.*, screening, shielding, insulation, screening effect
экранировать, *v.*, shield, screen
экранировка, *f.*, shielding, screening
эксковариантный, *adj.*, excovariant
эксконтравариантный, *adj.*, excontravariant
экскурс, *m.*, excursus, digression
эксперимент, *m.*, experiment, test, trial
экспериментально, *adv.*, experimentally
экспериментальный, *adj.*, experimental
экспериментатор, *m.*, experimenter, experimentalist
экспериментирование, *n.*, experimentation
экспериментировать, *v.*, experiment
эксперт, *m.*, expert
экспертиза, *f.*, expert opinion, consultation, examination
эксплуатация, *f.*, exploitation, operation
экспозиция, *f.*, exposure, exposition
экспонент, *m.*, exponent, index

экспонента, *f.*, exponential curve
экспоненциал, *m.*, exponential
экспоненциально, *adv.*, exponentially
экспоненциальный, *adj.*, exponential
экспонирование, *n.*, exposure
экспорт, *m.*, export, exportation
экспортация, *f.*, exportation
экстензор, *m.*, extensor
экстенсивно, *adv.*, extensionally, extensively
экстенсивный, *adj.*, extensive, extensional
экстенсиональность, *f.*, extensionality
экстенсиональный, *adj.*, extensional
экстенсия, *f.*, extension
экстинкция, *f.*, extinction
экстраполирование, *n.*, extrapolation
экстраполированный, *adj.*, extrapolated
экстраполировать, *v.*, extrapolate
экстраполирующий, *adj.*, extrapolating
экстраполяционный, *adj.*, extrapolational
экстраполяция, *f.*, extrapolation
экстрема, *f.*, extreme, extremal, extremum
экстремаль, *f.*, extremal, extremum
экстремальный, *adj.*, extreme, extremal
экстремизация, *f.*, extremalization
экстремум, *m.*, extremum
эксцентрицитет, *m.*, eccentricity
эксцентрический, *adj.*, eccentric, off center
эксцентричность, *f.*, eccentricity
эксцентричный, *adj.*, eccentric, eccentricity
эксцесс, *m.*, kurtosis, excess, flatness
эл, *num.*, eleven (in a proposed duodecimal system)
эластичность, *f.*, elasticity
эластичный, *adj.*, elastic, flexible
элегантность, *f.*, elegance
элегантный, *adj.*, elegant
электрический, *adj.*, electric
электричество, *n.*, electricity
электроакустический, *adj.*, electroacoustical
электровакуумный, *adj.*, electrovacuum
электрогидродинамический, *adj.*, electro-hydrodynamical
электрогравитационный, *adj.*, electrogravitational
электрод, *m.*, electrode
электродвижущий, *adj.*, electromotive
электродинамика, *f.*, electrodynamics
электрокалорический, *adj.*, electrocaloric, electrothermal
электролит, *m.*, electrolyte
электролитический, *adj.*, electrolytic
электромагнит, *m.*, electromagnet
электромагнитный, *adj.*, electromagnetic
электрон, *m.*, electron
электронвольт, *m.*, volt, electron volt
электроника, *f.*, electronics
электронно-лучевой, *adj.*, electron-emitting, electron; **электронно-лучевая трубка,** electron tube, Williams tube
электронно-оптический, *adj.*, electron-optical
электронно-позитронный, *adj.*, electron-positron
электронный, *adj.*, electronic, electron; **электронная оптика,** electron optics
электрооптика, *f.*, electro-optics
электрооптический, *adj.*, electro-optic, electro-optical
электропередача, *f.*, transmission, electrotransmission
электропроводность, *f.*, electric conductivity, conductivity, electrical conduction
электроскоп, *m.*, electroscope
электросопротивление, *n.*, resistivity, electrical resistivity
электростатика, *f.*, electrostatics
электростатический, *adj.*, electrostatic
электротехника, *f.*, electrical engineering
элемент, *m.*, element, cell, unit; **элемент запрета,** inhibit circuit
элементарно-геометрический, *adj.*, elementary geometric

элементарность, *f.*, elementary character, simplicity
элементарный, *adj.*, elementary, primary
элементный, *adj.*, element, pertaining to element
элерон, *m.*, aileron, flap
элиминация, *f.*, elimination
элиминирование, *n.*, elimination
элиминированный, *adj.*, eliminated
элиминировать, *v.*, eliminate
элиминируемость, *f.*, eliminability
элиминируемый, *adj.*, eliminable, removable
элиминирующий, *adj.*, eliminating
эллипс, *m.*, ellipse; **эллипс рассеяния,** ellipse of concentration, concentration ellipse
эллипсоид, *m.*, ellipsoid; **эллипсоид рассеяния,** ellipsoid of concentration
эллипсоидальный, *adj.*, ellipsoidal
эллиптико-гиперболический, *adj.*, elliptic-hyperbolic
эллиптический, *adj.*, elliptic
эмбрион, *m.*, embryo
эмбриональный, *adj.*, embyronic; **эмбриональное развитие,** embyronic growth
эмиссионный, *adj.*, emissive, emission
эмиссия, *f.*, emission
эмиттер, *m.*, emitter, sender
эмиттерный, *adj.*, emitter, emitting
эмпиризм, *m.*, empiricism
эмпирический, *adj.*, empirical
эмульсия, *f.*, emulsion
эндоергический, *adj.*, endoergic
эндоморфизм, *m.*, endomorphism
эндоморфоз, *m.*, endomorphism
эндоморфозный, *adj.*, endomorphic
эндоморфный, *adj.*, endomorphic
эндотермический, *adj.*, endothermal, endothermic
эндоэнергетический, *adj.*, endoenergy
эндоэргический, *adj.*, endoergic
энергетический, *adj.*, power, energy, energetic
энергичный, *adj.*, energetic
энергия, *f.*, energy
энтальпия, *f.*, enthalpy
энтропийный, *adj.*, entropy
энтропический, *adj.*, entropic, entropy
энтропия, *f.*, entropy
энцефалографический, *adj.*, encephalographic
энциклопедический, *adj.*, encyclopedic
энэдр, *m.*, *n*-hedral, *n*-hedron
эпидемия, *f.*, epidemic
эпидерма, *f.*, epidermis, skin, hull
эпиморфизм, *m.*, epimorphism
эпиморфный, *adj.*, epimorphic, surjective
эпицентр, *m.*, epicenter
эпицентрический, *adj.*, epicentric
эпицикл, *m.*, epicycle
эпициклический, *adj.*, epicyclic
эпициклоида, *f.*, epicycloid
эпициклоидальный, *adj.*, epicycloidal
эпоха, *f.*, epoch, age, era
эпсилон-энтропия, *f.*, epsilon entropy
эпюра, *f.* (**эпюр,** *m.*), diagram, curve
эра, *f.*, era
эрг, *m.*, erg
эргодический, *adj.*, ergodic
эргодичность, *f.*, ergodicity
эрмитово-, *prefix*, Hermitian-
эрмитово-кососимметрический, *adj.*, skew-Hermitian
эрмитово-симметрический, *adj.*, Hermitian-symmetric
эрмитовый, *adj.*, Hermite, Hermitian
эрстед, *m.*, oersted (magnetic unit)
эскалаторный, *adj.*, escalator; **эскалаторный метод,** escalator method
эскиз, *m.*, sketch, outline, study
эскизный, *adj.*, sketch, sketchy
эта, *pron. f.*, this, that
эталон, *m.*, standard (of measure)
эталонировать, *v.*, standardize
эталонный, *adj.*, standard
этап, *m.*, stage, step
эти (cf. **этот**), *pl.*, these
этим (cf. **этот**), by this, to these; **с этим,** with this
этими (cf. **этот**), by these; **с этими,** with these
этих (cf. **этот**), these, of these

это (cf. **этот**), *pron. n.*, this, that
этот (**эта,** *f.*, **это,** *n.*), *pron. m.*, this, that; **с этой целью,** to this end; **по этому поводу,** in this connection
этюд, *m.*, study, sketch, exercise
эфемерида, *f.*, ephemeris
эфемеридный, *adj.*, ephemeris, ephemeral
эфемерный, *adj.*, ephemeral
эффект, *m.*, effect, result
эффективно, *adv.*, effectively, efficiently
эффективно-открытый, *adj.*, effectively open
эффективность, *f.*, effectiveness, efficiency
эффективный, *adj.*, effective, efficient, efficiency
эффектор, *m.*, effector
эфферентный, *adj.*, efferent; **проводимость эфферентной части,** conduction on the efferent side
эшелон, *m.*, echelon, echelon grating; **пропускающий эшелон,** transmission echelon; **отражательный эшелон,** reflection echelon

Ю

юбка, *f.*, skirt, shell, cup
юг, *m.*, south; **юго-восток,** *m.*, southeast; **юго-запад,** *m.*, southwest
южнее, *adv.*, to the south, southward
южный, *adj.*, south, southern
юпитер, *m.*, Jupiter (planet)
юрисдикция, *f.*, jurisdiction
юрист, *m.*, lawyer, jurist

Я

я, *pron.*, I, myself
явиться (cf. **являться**), *v.*, emerge, appear
явление, *n.*, appearance, occurrence, phenomenon, emergence; **явление Гиббса,** Gibbs phenomenon
является (from **являться**), is (*with pred. in instr. case*)
являть, *v.*, show, be
являться (явиться), *v.*, be; appear, emerge, be revealed
являются (from **являться**), are (*with pred. in instr. case*)
являющийся, *adj.*, being, which is, appearing, emerging
явно, *adv.*, explicitly, evidently, obviously; **явно,** short form of **явный,** it is evident, it is clear
явный, *adj.*, explicit, evident, clear
явствовать, *v.*, appear, follow, be clear, be obvious
ядерный, *adj.*, nuclear, kernel
ядро, *n.*, kernel, nucleus, main body, core; **открытое ядро,** interior (of a set); **групповое ядро,** group germ
язык, *m.*, language, tongue, setting
языковедение, *n.*, linguistics
языкознание, *n.*, linguistics
язычок, *m.*, small clapper, reel, bolt (of a lock)
яйцеобразный, *adj.*, egg-shaped, oviform, oval
якобиан, *m.*, Jacobian
якобиевый, *adj.*, Jacobian
якобы, *particle*, as though, as if
якорь, *m.*, anchor
яма, *f.*, hole, depression; **воздушная яма,** air pocket

янтарный, *adj.*, amber
янтарь, *m.*, amber
ярд, *m.*, yard
яркий, *adj.*, bright, intense
ярко, *adv.*, brightly, brilliantly
яркость, *f.*, brightness, brilliance, luminosity, intensity
ярлык, *m.*, tag, label; **приклеивание ярлыков,** tagging
ярлычок, *m.*, label, tag
ясно, *adv.*, clearly, distinctly, explicitly; short form of **ясный; ясно, что,** it is clear that; **как это заранее ясно,** as is already clear
ясность, *f.*, clearness, lucidity, explicitness
ясный, *adj.*, clear, distinct, explicit
ячеечный, *adj.*, cell-like, cell, cellular, tesseral
ячеистый, *adj.*, pertaining to cell, cellular, cell
ячейка, *f.*, nucleus, cell, tessera
ячейкообразный, *adj.*, cellular, cellulated, tesseral
ящик, *m.*, box